PHYSICS AND MICROPHYSICS

PRINCE LOUIS VICTOR de BROGLIE

Dr. ès-Sc., 1924; Prof. of Theoretical Physics, Paris Univ. (Inst. Henri Poincaré) 1928; Nobel Prizeman for Physics. 1929; Permanent Sec.. Acad. des Sciences, 1942; Mem. Acad. Française, 1944.

AUTHOR OF

Current Interpretation of Wave Mechanics
Introduction to the Vigier Theory of Elementary Particles
Matter and Light, The New Physics
New Perspectives in Physics
Non-Linear Wave Mechanics
Revolution in Physics: A Non-Mathematical Survey of Quanta

PHYSICS
and
MICROPHYSICS

by
LOUIS DE BROGLIE

Translated by
MARTIN DAVIDSON

With a Foreword by
ALBERT EINSTEIN

The Universal Library
GROSSET & DUNLAP
NEW YORK

CONTENTS

FOREWORD

THIS is a unique book. It was de Broglie who first recognized the close physical and formal relationship between the quantum states of matter and the phenomena of resonance, at a time when the wave nature of matter had not yet been discovered experimentally.

The presentation of molecular physics of the last decades with its startling experimental results and creative theories should broaden and deepen the scope of every reader.

What impressed me most, however, is the sincere presentation of the struggle for a logical concept of the basis of physics which finally led de Broglie to the firm conviction that all elementary processes are of a statistical nature. I found the consideration of Bergson's and Zeno's philosophy from the point of view of the newly acquired concepts highly fascinating.

The author combines his creative talents with clear critical and philosophical thinking.

ALBERT EINSTEIN.

TRANSLATOR'S NOTE

THROUGHOUT the translation the original has been adhered to closely except for a few places where free renderings have been necessary to make the presentation more suitable for non-French readers. Inevitably with a book on such a subject some of the matter has required modification since the original publication, but notes at the ends of the chapters indicate such cases. These translator's notes are indicated by numbers in the text, and are collected correspondingly numbered at the end of each chapter. Notes at the foot of the text pages are by the original author.

With the approval of the author Chapter XII, "Un Glorieux Moment de la Pensée Scientifique Française" has been omitted, and Chapters IX, XIII, XIV and XV have been summarized. The last three of these chapters deal mainly with the practical application of science to technology and in this respect differ essentially from most of the others which are chiefly concerned with pure science.

Soon after the translation was started additional matter was sent by the author to be inserted at the end of Chapter VIII. It was felt, however, that the second part of this, "On the Statistics of the Pure Cases in Wave Mechanics and the Interference of Probabilities", was more suitable for an Appendix. While most readers will find it both interesting and useful, others may find it rather difficult and in such cases it can be ignored as it is not absolutely essential for understanding the other additional matter of Chapter VIII.

I am greatly indebted to Mr. P. J. Melotte for his most valuable assistance in reading the typescript, galley proofs and page proofs, in which he made a considerable number of suggestions and amendments. I am also indebted to Mr. A. J. Pomerans, who read the galley proofs and suggested a number of alterations which clarified the translation. Lastly, I must acknowledge the kindness of Dr. J. Wishart, Statistical Laboratory, Cambridge, for reading the galley proof of the Appendix and for a number of suggestions.

January 1955.   M.D.

AUTHOR'S PREFACE

THE present volume combines a series of expositions or lectures on the subject of physics, scientific philosophy or of the history of the sciences.

The title of this work *Physics and Microphysics*, was chosen with the intention of stressing the formal opposition between two kinds of physics. First, there is the physics of phenomena on the large scale where the classical ideas of localization in space and time, of determinism, and of the individual object, are fully valid. Then there is the physics of the atomic and corpuscular scale where, as a sequel to the necessary intervention of the quantum of action, these ideas are obscured and subject to revision. In a prior work a number of points have been discussed amongst which the following are worthy of notice:

It has been shown in what way the leading ideas of physics and microphysics are contradictory to one another, and how it is that the picture which microphysics uses to describe the phenomena directly perceptible to our senses, constitutes only the statistical aspect of an immense number of elementary processes for which these pictures are not valid. A new general résumé of these questions is to be found in the chapter of the present book entitled *Revelations of Microphysics*, and certain special points are reconsidered in other chapters contained in the work.

A branch of physics that has developed with lightning rapidity during about the last fifteen years is the physics of the nucleus. After some wonderful discoveries this new science has made possible the utilization of atomic energy in conditions known to all. In this volume there is no account of the sequel to the remarkable investigations, of which a large number were carried out in France, which have rendered possible the manufacture of the atomic bomb. For some months much has been written on the subject and other savants should be more competent than the present writer to deal with it in detail. On the other hand, I have attempted, especially in the first two

11

chapters of the book, to draw a picture of the new conceptions to which the developments of the physics of the nucleus have led scientists in these last years—conceptions still being developed but already of great interest. At the end of the book will also be found some views on the consequences which the conquest of atomic energy may have for the future progress of science and for the future of human civilization. The prodigious increase of power which nuclear physics is going to place at the disposal of men raises, in the moral as well as in the material realm, problems which are grave and even distressing, and which no one at the present time can afford to disregard.

The author of this book, although he has worked in laboratories at certain periods of his life, is a theorist. The researches which led him in past years to propose the first bases of wave mechanics were of an essentially speculative nature. So it is not without a certain amount of surprise that he has seen, within a few years, the conception of wave mechanics lead to some techniques of the highest practical importance, such as electronic optics and the analysis of small structures by the diffraction of electrons, techniques which are outlined in Chapter VI. The establishing of these unforeseen repercussions of the new concepts of wave mechanics has led attention to the close relationship which exists between the discoveries of pure science and the progress of applied sciences and of technology. The reflection of this prepossession will be found in various parts of the work.

Certain studies of an historical nature also figure in this exposition; those which bear on the contemporary period are partly based on personal recollections. The history of the sciences has always seemed to me to be of great importance for a full understanding of their present state. Many of the scientific ideas today would be different from what they are if the paths followed by the human mind to reach them had been different.

The history of science is, moreover, one of the most enthralling branches of general history, for it gives us a balanced view of that great and perilous adventure which, by continually enlarging the perspective of our thought, and by completely transforming the conditions of our life, hurries us with ever-increasing tempo towards a mysterious future.

FIRST PART
SCIENCE

CHAPTER I

THE ELEMENTARY PARTICLES OF MATTER AND THE NEW THEORIES OF THE NUCLEUS OF THE ATOM

I PROPOSE to explain the present state of our knowledge of the elementary particles of matter and also to express some views on contemporary theories of the atomic nucleus. Before coming to the core of my subject, however, it is essential to present an outline, necessarily very brief, of the successive discoveries which have enabled physics to reach its present position.

The Atomic Hypothesis

We know that the atomic hypothesis, previously adopted in a somewhat vague form by the ancient philosophers, has been restated in a more precise form by the chemists and physicists of the nineteenth century, and that it has received an ever-increasing number of verifications.

It was the chemists who first introduced in a systematic form the conception of the atom into modern science. The study of chemically well-defined bodies led to their division into two quite distinct classes; the "compound bodies" which could be broken up into simpler bodies by appropriate chemical reactions, and the "simple substances" or "chemical elements" which resist every effort to decompose them by chemical means. The study of the quantitative laws (the law of constant proportions, the law of multiple proportions, etc.) according to which elements unite to form compounds, gradually led the chemists to adopt the following hypothesis: "An element is formed of small particles which are all identical, and which are, by definition, the atoms of that element. Compounds are formed by molecules constituted by the union, in a constant proportion, of the atoms of the constituent elements." This hypothesis was supplemented by another one suggested almost simultaneously—about 1815—by Ampère and Avogadro, and which is stated as follows:

15

"A gramme-molecule of any pure body (which occupies in the gaseous state, according to Gay-Lussac's Law, 22·3 litres under normal conditions of temperature and pressure) always contains the same number of molecules, whatever the body may be." This number, which is of primary importance for atomic physics, is called "Avogadro's number" or "Loschmidt's number".

We know that after many contentions, often very animated, the atomic hypothesis ended in a triumph and was accepted by all chemists. Today it serves as a basis for all our interpretations of chemical reactions and of the use of formulae explaining the constitution of molecules and their transformations in the course of chemical reactions.

The atomic hypothesis very soon entered the domain of physics where it provided explanations of an ever-increasing number of the properties of matter. The kinetic theory of gases, in assuming that a gas is composed of an enormous number of atoms or molecules endowed with rapid and random movements, has succeeded in interpreting the ideas of pressure, temperature, specific heat, etc., and also has led to the rediscovery of the fundamental laws which connect these quantities. Generalizing the results of the kinetic theory of gases, statistical mechanics has been able to provide a general interpretation of the idea of entropy and to interpret many properties of matter. Finally, it was the physicists who succeeded in providing direct proofs of the real existence of atoms. They arrived at this in studying especially the phenomena of flux, of Brownian and other movements which clearly show the discrete nature of matter, and also by accurately measuring Avogadro's number, by various methods. The agreement thus obtained of the values of this fundamental number, in particular in the noted experiments of Jean Perrin, has led to a conclusive proof of the existence of atoms.

I shall here recall that the hydrogen atom is the lightest of all, and as the Avogadro number is approximately 6.10^{23}, it is deduced that the hydrogen atom has a mass of about $1·66 \times 10^{-24}$ gramme. It is known at present that there are ninety-two elements[1] which can be arranged in a series—Mendéléef's periodic series—in which the sequence of the elements corresponds almost exactly with the order of the increasing atomic weights. Throughout Mendéléef's series the physical and chemical properties of the elements reveal periodic variations which have been explained by the quantum theory of the atom, to which reference will be made later on. The radius of the atom is of the order 10^{-8} cm., so that we may, as a first and very rough approximation, consider it as a sphere having this diameter.

The Electron

Whilst the proofs of the discrete structure of matter were accumulating, the discrete structure of electricity equally began to be established. The manner in which the existence of electrons was discovered half a century ago is too well known to call for a detailed account here. The laws of electrolysis, established by Faraday, had already given rise to the suspicion of the existence of discrete elements in the structure of electricity. Little by little this idea was formulated as follows:

"Negative electricity consists of small corpuscles—the *electrons*—all identical one with the other and possessing an extremely small mass and an electric charge. It has been possible to study the electrons which emanated from matter under various circumstances and which then moved independently in space (cathode rays and β-rays of radio-active substances). By collecting them in electrometers it was possible to verify first of all that their charge was negative; then, by subjecting them to electric and magnetic fields, it was possible to establish that the electrons, at least under the conditions when they could be studied, always move like small charged particles obeying the classical laws of mechanics, and this has made it possible to measure with precision their charge and mass. The mass of the electron is equal to 0.9×10^{-27} gm. and its charge $-e$ is 4×10^{-10} electrostatic units."[2]

The theory of electric phenomena was then remodelled by taking into consideration the existence of electrons. Negative electricity, consisting of electrons of very small mass, had appeared as the mobile part of electricity. Positive electricity, on the other hand, is usually carried by atomic ions which have a much greater mass than that of the electrons, and in consequence is much less mobile then negative electricity. Thus was revealed between the two electricities, which in many ways play symmetrical parts, a characteristic dissymetry, the positive appearing as much more closely linked to inert matter than the negative. This dissymetry is fundamental and we shall frequently find it throughout this treatise.

The Bohr Atom

After having recognized the corpuscular character of electricity, physicists wished to avail themselves of this knowledge to explain the structure of the atom. In point of fact, if the outstanding scientists who had developed the atomic hypothesis in modern times had, perhaps in imitation of the ancient atomists, conceived the atoms as simple and indivisible units, such a conception could not have been maintained. On the contrary, many facts indicated that the atoms must be complicated structures, were it only the extreme complexity of the bright spectra which they are capable of emitting. Since the electrons, which were observed to be ejected by matter under many conditions, must ultimately emanate from atoms, the idea that the atomic structure contained electric particles naturally suggested itself.

Thus, starting from the year 1900, attempts were made to construct "models" of atoms, which would represent them as structures formed by electric particles and which must be able to explain their physical and chemical properties. After many attempts the necessity for adopting a planetary model was recognized; the atom which occupies the position N in Mendéléef's series (or, as we would now describe it, the atom of atomic number N) would be formed by a central nucleus carrying a charge $+Ne$, this nucleus being the seat of practically all the atomic mass, and surrounded by N electrons each of charge $-e$, which revolve around it as the planets revolve around the sun, so that the whole atomic structure in its normal state is electrically neutral. The simplest atom is thus the first in Mendéléef's series, for which $N=1$, and is the hydrogen atom formed by one electron revolving around a nucleus with charge $+e=4\cdot8 \times 10^{-10}$ electrostatic units. This nucleus—the simplest of all atomic nuclei—is called the *proton*.

It was the famous experiments of Rutherford on the deflections of the α-rays of radioactive bodies during their passage through matter that led to the conclusion that practically all the mass of the atom is located in the central nucleus where it is united to positive charges of electricity. And here is revealed a new tendency of positive electricity to be associated with matter.

The planetary model of the atom would undoubtedly have remained a somewhat vague conception if Bohr had not formulated a remarkable general theory of the atom in 1913. This theory, which has been submitted to many quantitative verifications, has opened up a new epoch in the history of physics. For utilizing in this way the planetary model Bohr found it necessary to perfect it by introducing the general ideas of the quantum theory. The origin of this theory, which has demolished some of the best established physical theories, need not be retraced. It will suffice to say that Max Planck in 1900, in an intuition of genius during his studies on black body radiation, introduced the idea that there exists in nature a universal constant, Planck's Constant h, performing the role of an elementary unit of action in the mechanical sense of the term. According to Planck the existence of this quantum of action must always have as a consequence the fact that only certain movements predicted by the classical mechanics—the quantified movements—can exist in nature. As the quantum h has the extremely small value $6 \cdot 54 \times 10^{-27}$ erg-second, the restriction of movements due to its existence does not play any appreciable part in phenomena on the large scale, but in the atomic scale it intervenes in an important manner.[3] Bohr has taken it into consideration in his theory of the atom, and the planetary model which he has thus been able to develop has met with great success because it immediately explained the very peculiar and, up till then, very mysterious form of the spectral laws, of the periodicity of the physical and chemical properties for the elements in Mendéléef's series, and of a large number of other atomic properties.

After the realization of Bohr's theory the central nucleus remained the greatest mystery in the structure of the atom (ignoring the further mystery of the significance of the quanta). Within the nucleus is concentrated practically all the mass of the atom, and this is assembled in a space of which the dimensions are 100,000 times smaller than those of the atom, i.e. of the order 10^{-13} cm. in diameter. But though the nucleus was so small it was known at that time that it was undoubtedly complex. The phenomena of natural radioactivity, discovered well before that time by Henri Becquerel and by Pierre and Marie Curie, proved in fact that the nuclei of certain heavy atoms are liable to disintegrate spontaneously, producing a lighter nucleus, and that this disintegration could be accompanied by the emission of electrons or β-rays, of helium nuclei or α-rays, and of very penetrating radiations or γ-rays. But these phenomena of transmutation, all providing evidence of the internal complexity of the nuclei, hardly gave any information on their structure, the more so that, being beyond the range of our investigation, they take place at such speeds and under such conditions that these could not be modified at all. The situation was slightly improved in 1919 when Rutherford bombarded the light atoms of nitrogen with fast-moving α-particles, thus producing a transmutation by liberating the nuclei of hydrogen (protons) with the transformation of the nitrogen atoms into atoms of oxygen. In this way there was established the possibility of transmutation—the dream of the alchemists of the Middle Ages; and so a method was evolved which would allow physicists to explore the structure of the atomic nuclei by bringing about their disintegration. Nevertheless this method required a long time to yield all the results that were expected from it.

The discovery of isotopes, that is, atoms having practically the same physical and chemical properties with different atomic weights, came soon afterwards to draw the attention of physicists to the fact that the two then known characteristics of the nuclei—their positive electric charge and their mass—were not associated with each other in an unequivocal manner. Bohr's theory of the atom had shown that if we except certain phenomena not easily observed, the totality of the physical and chemical properties of an atom is determined by the positive charge of its nucleus, hence by its atomic number N, and is independent of the mass of the said nucleus. In practice there can thus exist nuclei with the same charge but with different masses, their physical and chemical properties being almost identical.

We know that the excellent experiments of Thomson and Aston and their successors have proved the existence and abundance of isotopes and have shown that most bodies believed up till then to be simple were actually mixtures of isotopes in a fixed proportion. This has been responsible for complicating very especially the classification of chemical elements since, as an instance, up to ten atoms of tin of different masses are known. At present it is necessary to distinguish between the isotope nuclei which have the same electric charge and different masses and the isobar nuclei which have the same mass with different charges. Amongst the most recently discovered artificial radioelements are frequently found "isomeric" nuclei having the same charge and the same mass, and differing only in their radioactive properties (their average life, for example).[4]

Earlier Conception of the Nucleus

Let us now consider the picture that could be made of the elementary particles and of the structure of the nuclei about the year 1925. We shall thus be in a better position to judge the progress that has been made since then. At that period two kinds of particles which might be worthy of the name of elementary particles were known; these were the electron which was prominent for a long time through its role as a mobile element of electricity, and the proton or nucleus of hydrogen, the lightest of all nuclei, of which the charge is equal to and the sign contrary to that of the electron, and which was naturally regarded as the unit of positive electricity. It was then naturally accepted that these were the two fundamental elementary particles through the agency of which all nuclei must be built up. The fact that the mass of the proton is 1,840 times greater than that of the electron (although the two particles have the same electric charge in absolute units) explained the tendency already mentioned for the positive electricity to attach itself more easily to matter than the negative. It is easy to see the consequences which resulted from the hypothesis that all nuclei would be formed of protons and electrons.

Let us consider the nucleus of an atom occupying the position N in Mendéléef's series, having thus the atomic number N. Its electric charge is Ne and it should contain a number of n_p of protons and a number n_E of electrons such that

$n_p - n_E = N$. Further, as the electrons have a mass which is almost negligible compared with that of the proton, the mass of this nucleus should be practically equal to n_p that of the proton. The atomic weights of all atoms should thus be practically equal to integral multiples of that of the hydrogen atom. At first sight this proposition seems to be contradicted by experiment, because the atomic weights of the elements with respect to hydrogen are usually far from integers. The discovery of isotopes, however, has enabled this difficulty to be overcome, for it is now known that every atomic nucleus has actually a mass which is very close to an integral multiple of that of hydrogen. If the apparent atomic weights of the usual elements are often far from being integral multiples of that of hydrogen, this is because the usual elements are really mixtures of isotopes in constant proportion and their apparent atomic weight is merely the mean of the atomic weights of the isotopes taking part in the mixture.

Nevertheless, there are small discrepancies between the mass of different nuclei, having due regard to the isotope, and the integral multiples of the mass of the proton, but these deviations, which are known as the "mass defect", can be explained by the energy liberated at the moment of the formation of the nucleus, if we take account of the principle of the inertia of energy which the theory of relativity has taught us. There are, then, no longer any serious difficulties against the hypothesis that the proton and the electron are the only two fundamental particles by which all nuclei, and in consequence all the atoms of matter, should be constructed. Nevertheless, we shall see that this hypothesis must be modified; new elementary particles have been discovered and our ideas on the structure of the nucleus have been perceptibly transformed.

Before we are able to arrive at an explanation of these questions it is necessary to recall how our ideas on particles in general have been profoundly modified by the introduction of wave mechanics and by the discovery of spin.

Wave Mechanics, the Spin and Energy of Exchange

First of all I shall recall very briefly how the development of our knowledge on light has led during about forty years

to a certain return to the old corpuscular ideas, without, however the abandonment of the undulatory theory and the
interpretation that it alone is capable of giving for the phenomena of physical optics. The existence of certain phenomena,
such as the photoelectric effect or the Compton effect, which
enable one, so to speak, to make a direct observation
of the elementary action of light on material particles, has
forced physicists to introduce the idea of *photon* or "corpuscle
of light" which, in a monochromatic wave of frequency ν
carries the energy $h\nu$. The necessity for maintaining the essential
results of the undulatory theory, while utilizing the idea of the
photon, has led to the development of a synthetic theory in
which the conceptions of wave corpuscle are in some measure
juxtaposed and related to each other in a somewhat subtle
manner by relations of probability. This new dualistic representation of light has in consequence served as a model for a
new conception of material particles which developed rapidly
between 1923 and 1927, i.e. wave mechanics.

In wave mechanics the idea of the propagation of waves is
associated with that of a material corpuscle in the same way
as in the theory of light, it has been necessary to associate the
photon with the luminous wave. This then leads us to interpret
the quantized states of the electron in the Bohr atom as states
where the wave associated with the electron is a stationary
wave, and to predict the possibility of obtaining with beams of
electrons phenomena analogous to the interference of light.
This prediction, in such flagrant opposition to the strictly
corpuscular conception of electrons and of material particles,
was completely confirmed in 1927 by the discovery of the
phenomenon of diffraction of electrons by crystals. It is now
certain that the wave-corpuscle-duality, discovered at first for
light, applies equally to matter; all material particles have
their associated waves just like the photons, and the totality
of their properties can be exactly described only by the processes of wave mechanics. Thus a "field" of waves is attached
to every particle, and this remark is essential for what
follows.

In 1925, at the very time when there was taking place the
great transformation of our conceptions regarding material
particles, physicists were further led to attribute to these a

new characteristic by introducing the *spin*. It was impossible by quantal theories to give an exact explanation of the details, the fine structure, as it was named, of the light and X-ray spectra and also certain complex magnetic phenomena, such as the anomalous Zeeman effect. This led to the view that outside its charge and mass, the electron would have another characteristic—the spin—in which there would be a kind of internal rotation and which would endow it with an intrinsic angular momentum and also with an intrinsic magnetic moment.

This idea had been developed by Uhlenbeck and Goudsmith who had endowed the electron with its own angular momentum equal to $\frac{1}{2}h/2\pi$, or half the quantal unit $h/2\pi$ of the angular momentum, and its own magnetic moment equal to Bohr's magneton $eh/4\pi mc$ or the quantal unit of magnetic moment. By means of these hypotheses it was possible to explain the spectroscopic and magnetic anomalies which previous theories could not interpret. It was certain from that time that for every material particle the spin was a characteristic as important as the mass or the electric charge, and there are now reasons for believing that the angular momentum of every particle, elementary or otherwise, is always, provided it is not zero, an integral multiple of the angular momentum $h/4\pi$ of the electron.

Dirac has defined the theory of electron spin within the framework of wave mechanics. As it is impossible here to deal with this beautiful theory which plays a role of the first rank in the contemporary development of our ideas on material particles, I shall content myself by stressing the fact that it has led to a remarkable prevision which has been verified by experiment: it predicted the existence of positive electrons. The equations of Dirac's theory present certain peculiarities (the existence of states of negative energy) which at first seemed to constitute a great difficulty for this theory. Dirac has interpreted these peculiarities as indicating the possibility of finding in nature *positive electrons* or *positrons*, which should be exactly the electric converse of electrons, that is, they should have the same mass with an equal charge but of contrary sign. A positive electron can only appear at the same time as a negative electron, as the principle of the conservation of electricity requires. There should then be the creation of an electron-positron pair and the energy required for this creation would be borrowed from an external agent, such as a photon of high frequency, which would be capable of supplying this energy. The positive electrons thus predicted would have a marked tendency, when they pass through matter, to unite with negative electrons and to annihilate themselves with the latter, their total energy escaping under the form of radiation.

This process of the annihilation of an electron-positron pair would thus be the exact opposite of the process of the creation of such a pair. In this way of looking at the matter, it must be assumed that at any instant there must be a great excess of negative electrons in nature. In consequence of this excess, the positive electrons which are created by the appearance of pairs would tend to disappear quickly by the annihilation of pairs, the universe thus incessantly tending to a return to a kind of normal condition in which it would have nothing but negative electrons. In these processes of appearance or disappearance of electron-positron pairs with the accompanying absorption or emission of radiant energy, we can say that there is a materialization of radiant energy in the first case and dematerialization of electronic energy in the second case. Such are the predictions to which Dirac's theory of the electron spin leads, and these predictions have been verified since then in a remarkable manner.

Before leaving these generalizations on the theories associated with wave mechanics, something will have to be said about the new concept of the energy of exchange. In wave mechanics, if we consider two particles of like nature exercising an interaction on each other (for example, two electrons acting on each other by their Coulombian electrostatic field) there exist between them two kinds of mutual energy. First is that which results from the classical ideas of the existence of the Coulombian interaction. Then there is another of a new type—the mutual exchange energy—which also is due to the interaction but which is bound up with the identity of the nature of the two particles. This exchange energy, of which no representation can be made with our old ideas, plays a very important part in nature indeed. It is due to it, especially, that we are able to explain the very particular character of the forces of valency in chemistry. Suppose we bring two atoms of hydrogen close together; between these two atoms there will be a mutual energy as a result of which they will have a tendency to unite with the formation of a stable molecule. But once the molecule is formed, it will have no tendency to capture a third atom to form a triatomic molecule; the valency of each atom H has been "saturated" by its union with the other atom H.

Within the framework of classical ideas on forces and mutual energies, it is impossible to explain in any way this saturation of interactions giving place to chemical combinations. On the contrary, by the conception of the exchange energy, wave mechanics explains the mechanism of chemical combinations and the nature of the saturability of valencies. We shall shortly see how, on the basis of this conception, we came to recognize the exact nature of the mutual energies that assure the stability of molecular structures, and also, once transposed to a still much smaller scale, to discover the reasons which assure the stability of the atomic nuclei.

Discovery of the Neutron and Positron

Since 1930 the physics of the nucleus entered into a period of very rapid development. It is impossible here to do more than give a very short account of the amazing scope of our knowledge; nothing will be said about the enormous development in artificially produced disintegrations, or about the discovery of artificial radioelements, which has brought renown to the name of M. and Mme Joliot-Curie. To keep within the limits of my discourse I only wish to retain that which treats of the existence of elemental particles until then unknown. From this point of view considerable progress has been made by the successive discovery in the years 1931-2 of the *neutron* by Chadwick and M. and Mme Joliot, and of the positive electron or *positron* by Anderson and by Blackett and Occhialini.

The neutron is a particle relatively heavy like the proton; it appears to have nearly the same mass as the proton but it has no electric charge, and in a way is a neutral proton. Devoid of charge, it has no ionization effect and for this reason it is much more difficult to detect and study than a charged particle. It is only by the mechanical effects that it causes by collisions with other particles that we have succeeded in proving its existence. As it has been verified that the disintegration of certain atomic nuclei is accompanied by the expulsion of neutrons (observed for the first time during the disintegration of beryllium submitted to α-rays bombardment), it may be considered that the neutron must play an essential part in the constitution of the nuclei, and it will be seen later what an important influence this idea has had on the evolution of our theories of the nuclei of atoms (see page 43 *et seq.*).

As for the positive electron or positron, this is a light particle having the same mass as the electron with an equal electric charge but of opposite sign. The properties of this new elemental corpuscle have been found to conform in their main lines to what had been predicted by Dirac's theory, especially in the matter of the creation and annihilation of pairs. The creation of an electron-positron pair requires the action of a quantum of radiation carrying at least the energy necessary for the creation of the two particles, that is to say, at least the sum of the internal energies of the two particles when they are at rest, a sum equal to $2mc^2$ in accordance with the principle of the inertia of energy. Inversely, the disappearance of a positron by its annihilation with an electron must cause the emission by radiation of an amount of energy equal to at least $2mc^2$, or 1,000,000 electron-volts. This can take place either by the emission of a single photon of at least 1,000,000 electron-volts or of two photons of at least 500,000 electron-volts each, according to whether the process is responsible for the appearance or otherwise of a nucleus.

All these predictions have been fully verified by the experiments of Jean Thibaud and Frédéric Joliot on the annihilation of positive electrons in matter. By means of a remarkable experimental method—the method of the trochoid—which has rendered the greatest services in this kind of research, Jean Thibaud[4] was able to show that the specific charge of the positron is, within the limits of experimental error, equal to that of the electron with opposite sign, which established satisfactorily the symmetry of the two light particles of electricity. The positive electron, first discovered in the cosmic rays, can now be obtained either by processes of materialization of pairs from radiations or as the product of the disintegration of certain artificial radio-elements. The natural radio elements never emit positrons but only β-rays formed of negative electrons. It is not the same for the artificial radio-elements amongst which certain ones emit negative β-rays formed of electrons, and others emit positive β-rays formed of positrons.

New Conception of the Nucleus

The discovery of the neutron and the positron, by doubling the number of elementary material particles, has greatly extended the field of possibilities of the structure of atomic nuclei. It has been pointed out that prior to the discovery of the neutron, our knowledge has led us, by utilizing the two kinds of elementary particles at our disposition, to consider the nucleus as a collection, generally very stable, of protons and electrons. This opinion appeared to be confirmed by various facts and especially by the readiness of certain naturally radioactive bodies (the only such known at that time) to disintegrate by emitting electrons in the form of β-rays. Nevertheless, the hypothesis that the nuclei of atoms were formed of protons and electrons raised a certain number of difficulties of which the following is one of the most important.

Wave mechanics showed that there was a relation between the alterations of intensity which is established in the rays of the spectral bands emitted by biatomic molecules of an element, and the number of constituents composing the nucleus of the element. On applying these conclusions to the molecule of nitrogen it was inferred that this should contain an even number of constituents. The nitrogen atom, however, has atomic number 7 and atomic weight 14. It is easy to conclude from this that, if the nucleus of nitrogen is composed of electrons and protons, it should contain 14 protons and 7 electrons, a total of 21 constituents—an odd number and so contradicting the preceding prediction.

Following the discovery of the neutron, Heisenberg proposed a new conception of the constitution of the nucleus, and this is generally adopted now. It postulates that the nucleus of the atom is composed of protons and neutrons, that is, of the aggregates of two kinds of heavy particles. If this is so, the nucleus with atomic number N and atomic weight P (integral) should contain N protons and P-N neutrons, as is easily seen. With these hypotheses we avoid the objections which gave rise to the older picture of the nuclei as formed of protons and electrons. For instance, the nitrogen nucleus of atomic number 7 and atomic weight 14 ought now to be considered as composed of 7 protons and 7 neutrons, which makes a total of 14 constituents—an even number in agreement with the prediction of wave mechanics.

With Heisenberg's hypothesis, however, how can we explain the fact that natural radio elements and certain artificial radio elements emit negative electrons at the time of their disintegration, whereas, on the contrary, other artificial radio-elements emit positrons? Today the following reply is given to this question.

Neutrons can be transformed into protons by the emission of a negative electron and protons can be transformed into neutrons with the emission of a positive electron. These are the kinds of transformations that are operative in the nuclei of radioelements when they eject negative β-rays or positive β^+-rays. Hence the proton and the neutron now appear as two different states of the same heavy particle which today is called the "nucleon", one of the states being positively charged and the other being neutral. The characteristic dissymetry which links positive electricity to the mass is seen reappearing here. We can easily imagine the existence of a negative proton having the same mass as the ordinary proton with a charge of equal and opposite sign. It would be the inverse particle of the ordinary proton as the positive electron is the inverse particle of the ordinary electron. But this negative proton never seems to exist, or if it does exist, its appearance must be exceptional because one has never been made evident. Furthermore, in the interactions which usually take place in the interior of atomic nuclei, the positive proton is closely associated with the neutron and not with the hypothetical negative proton. Thus, with the heavy particles it is the positive electricity alone that performs any role whilst, for the light particles, negative electricity has, on the contrary, a predominant role, the negative electron being stable and the positive electron having merely a transitory existence.

These new conceptions of the relations between the proton

and the neutron lead to a consequence which it is important to note. In the quantal theory of the emission and absorption of radiation we already knew, since Bohr's theory, that a light electric particle, such as the electron, can emit or absorb a quantum of radiation—a photon—when undergoing sudden changes of state. This is the reason why we can now state the following:

"Just as a light particle in changing its state can emit or absorb this ultra-light particle which is the photon, so the heavy particle which is the nucleon should be able, in changing its state, to emit or absorb the light particles which are the electrons and positrons." This conception, so interesting in its very form, was soon, as we shall see, to play a very important role in our theories of the nucleus.

Interactions between the Constituents of the Nucleus

Whilst these new conceptions were being developed, the necessity for developing a theory of the interactions between protons and neutrons capable of giving an account of the structure and stability of nuclear systems was felt. In 1932 Heisenberg suggested that there exists between the proton and the neutron a mutual energy belonging to the general type of exchange energies and corresponding to the fact that, by an exchange of charge, the proton can transform itself into the neutron and simultaneously the neutron can transform itself into the proton. He showed that we can thus explain both the stability of nuclear structures as also the fundamental fact that the atomic weights, after being double or practically double that of the atomic number for the lighter elements, starting with helium, tend to increase more and more above the double of the atomic number for the heavy elements as we ascend in Mendéléef's series. (For instance, in the case of nitrogen $N=7$, $A=14$, and of uranium $N=92$, $A=238$.) Heisenberg's theory, by completely modifying our ideas on the nature of the constituents of the nucleus and on the kind of mutual energy which holds them together, has marked a considerable progress for nuclear physics.

But when we speak of the mutual exchange energy between two particles this is equivalent to speaking of the existence of an interaction between these two particles. If then a mutual exchange energy exists between a proton and a neutron, it should have as its origin an interaction between the particles. This interaction however, cannot be of an electric nature since the neutron is electrically neutral and, if the hypothesis of actions at a distance be rejected, it must correspond to a presence of a "field" different from the electromagnetic field and belonging to a new type, a conclusion which we shall see is of the greatest interest.

For a proper understanding of the role played by the field in the transmission of interactions between particles, it is interesting to return to the theory of the interactions between particles charged by means of the electromagnetic field. Suppose that there are two particles in proximity; each exerts on the other a Coulombian electrostatic action and, moreover, if they are in motion and in consequence equivalent to convection currents, they also give rise to interactions of Laplace's electromagnetic type. If we reject the view of actions at a distance operating simultaneously between particles, we are led to believe that these Coulombian and Laplacian interactions take place through the medium of an electromagnetic field surrounding the particles. Recent quantal theories of the electromagnetic field, which take into account the existence of photons, have made it possible to define the mechanism of this transmission of interactions. Each of the two particles supposed to be in proximity is in direct interaction with the surrounding electromagnetic field, and in consequence is able to emit a photon associated with the electromagnetic field, a photon which the other particle is then able to absorb.

By the analysis of possible energy exchanges and of the momentum between two particles by means of photons linked with the surrounding electromagnetic field, present radiation theories show that these energies are equivalent to the existence between the two particles of classical forces of the Coulomb and Laplace types (to which are further added the interactions between the magnetic moments of the two particles if they have a spin). Thus the classical interactions between two electrified particles lead to possible emissions and absorptions of photons by the two particles.

How then can we attempt to represent the interaction

between a photon and a neutron which Heisenberg's nuclear theory requires? By analogy, we shall suppose that they take place through the medium of a field; but this will not be the electromagnetic, and must be a new type of field. In the same way in which the electromagnetic field is associated with the photon, we shall postulate our new field to be associated with light particles; it is in the exchange of these light particles that the neutron and the proton will interact. In other words, this exchange of light particles will need to be equivalent to the exchange energy foreseen by Heisenberg as necessary to exist between the proton and the neutron. We have seen that a proton should be able to transform itself into a neutron with the emission of a positive electron (or the absorption of a negative electron) and conversely, a neutron should be able to transform itself into a proton by the emission of a negative electron (or the absorption of a positive electron). It was, therefore, natural to think (although, as will be seen, this idea was shown to be fallacious) that the positive and negative electrons should perform an essential role in the new field which we try to visualize. But at this point I must first digress to show the difficulties which were presented in the interpretation of the spectra of the β-rays of radioactive bodies, which allows me to introduce the *neutrino*.

Continuous Spectra of β-rays and the Neutrino

In radioactive transformations where there is emission of negative electrons as a result of the disintegration of the nucleus, these electrons are emitted with variable energies so that the radioactive body which disintegrates emits in its totality a continuous spectrum of β-rays. Since the state of the radioactive atom before disintegration and that of the atom produced by the disintegration are well defined, the fact that the electrons emitted at the moment of disintegration have different energies, seems to contradict the principle of the conservation of energy. Moreover, it is definitely known that the proton and the neutron have, just as has the electron, each its own angular momentum (or spin) equal to $\frac{1}{2}$, the unit of spin being $h/2\pi$. Hence in the change of state which causes the proton to pass over to the state of the neutron, or vice versa, the variation of the spin can be only 0 or 1 in absolute value. Now the electron, having itself a spin equal to $\frac{1}{2}$, emission of an electron at the time of the change of state of a heavy particle could not take place with conservation of angular momentum. Thus, the original picture of the β-disintegration would contradict two of the great principles of conservation which today form the solid supports on which our physics is based.

To avoid this disastrous conclusion, physicists, whose ingenuity is never wanting, have imagined that the emission of β-rays in radioactive disintegrations must be accompanied by the emission of a very light and uncharged particle. Due to its electrically neutral character and its lightness, it would never leave any trace of its passage through matter and would thus escape observation. The liberated energy available at the time of disintegration would be shared in a variable way between the electron and the *neutrino* (this is the name that has been given to this hypothetical particle), and since the energy carried off by the neutrino escapes observation, an impression of a defect in the conservation of energy would be given.

This daring hypothesis is strongly supported by the fact that the maximum energy of β-rays, that is, the upper limit of the energy of their continuous spectrum, appears to agree with the difference of energy between the radioactive nucleus before the transmutation and the nucleus resulting from this. It is indeed easily understood that in the limiting case where the neutrino takes no energy, the β-electron must take away all the energy made available by the transmutation of the nucleus and that would be its maximum energy. On the other hand, in attributing to the neutrino the same spin $\frac{1}{2}$ as to the electron, it is easily seen that the conservation of the angular momentum can be satisfied. Physicists have been very pleased thus to be able to preserve the two great principles of conservation which had been threatened, and although the neutrino has obstinately refused to divulge its existence to experimenters, they have none the less generally admitted its existence.

Fermi's Field

The interpretation of β-emissions with the intervention of neutrinos had, then, led to the assumption that the transformation of 'a proton into a neutron and the inverse transformation are accompanied by the emission of a *pair* of particles, namely, a positive or negative electron and a neutrino. It seems natural to think that the field through the medium of which the exchange interaction imagined by Heisenberg operates between proton and neutron, is associated with these pairs of electron-neutrino particles, just as the usual electromagnetic interactions between charged particles take place through the medium of the electromagnetic field associated with the photons. Fermi tried to put this very interesting idea into practice to explain the interactions of Heisenberg. He has done this by letting a field of a new kind—the Fermi nuclear field—correspond to the electron-neutrino couple, Fermi's field being analogous to the electromagnetic field but carrying positive or negative electric charges. Let us then apply to the aggregate formed by a proton, a neutron and the nuclear field in question, the same kind of argument that was able to refer the Coulombian and Laplacian actions between two electric charges to exchanges of energy and momentum operating by means of the photons of the surrounding electromagnetic field; then these operations performed between the proton and the neutron in the interior of the nucleus can be explained as due to exchanges of energy and of momentum through the medium of Fermi's nuclear field. In consequence the exchange energies which, according to Heisenberg, assure the stability of the nuclei can be calculated. Such is the conception—very original and of great interest—developed some years ago by Fermi.

Unfortunately, the development of this theory of Fermi's nuclear field has not led to the success that had been hoped from it. In the first place, the theory of the emission of the β-spectra, to which we are thus naturally led, does not agree well with experiment, and if certain new hypotheses (due especially to Uhlenbeck and Konopinski) allow the partial elimination of the discordance, these hypotheses have a somewhat artificial character and are not at all satisfactory. Then—and this is yet more serious—the calculation of the forces of interaction between proton and neutron by Fermi's method leads to bond energies which are much smaller than those that are actually necessary to assure the stability of the nuclei. The reason for this is that the value of certain *a priori* arbitrary constants, which, according to Fermi, figure in the formulae of interaction between the heavy particles and the nuclear field, must be selected in a manner which takes into account the intensity of the β-emissions of radioactive bodies. As these emission have a relatively small probability, the values in question must be chosen to be very small, in which case the interactions between the proton and the neutron, which cause the interaction between a heavy particle and the nuclear field to interpose twice, would be much smaller than the stability of the nuclei requires. In other words, the very way by which Fermi's theory seeks to relate the proton-neutron reactions to the β-emissions through the nuclear electron-neutrino field leads to an inaccurate order of magnitude. The brilliant attempt of Fermi thus appeared to meet with a check, but we shall see that the fundamental idea of the nuclear field has been taken up by Yukawa in a new form which has led to his remarkable prediction of the *heavy electron* or the *meson*.

Yukawa's Field and the Meson

Confronted by the check to Fermi's theory, Yukawa, a Japanese physicist, put forward in 1935 the suggestion that the interaction between heavy particles operated, not through the medium of a nuclear field of Fermi's type, associated with pairs of particles of spin $\frac{1}{2}$ (electron-neutrino couples) but through the medium of another field—Yukawa's nuclear field—which was supposed to be associated with particles having the same charge as the electrons, but with a spin equal to 1 (the unit being $2\pi/h$). These new particles would be capable of being emitted one by one, and not in pairs as in the case of the particles of Fermi's field. Developing his calculations, the Japanese scientist announced in his first memoir in 1935 that in attributing to these then unknown particles a mass equal to about 200 times that of the electron, there would be obtained, for the proton-neutron exchange energies, satisfactory values corresponding to the actual stability of the nuclei.

At the time of its appearance Yukawa's hypothesis appeared too daring and devoid of any serious foundation. But two years later the thorough study of those particles which made their presence known in cosmic rays succeeded in revealing the existence of particles hitherto unknown, in which the electric charge, positive or negative, appears practically equal to that of electrons of the same sign, but of which the mass was decidedly much greater than the electron mass. These particles are known as "heavy electrons" or "mesotons" or again as "mesons". Their mass is not yet known with certainty, but the most reliable experiments seem to agree on a value between 130 and 300 times that of the electron. A recent measurement of this mass made by Leprince-Ringuet and his collaborators has given a value equal to 240 ± 20 times the mass of the electron. We see how remarkably the prophetic views of Yukawa have been confirmed by experiment. Now if it is admitted that the new particle discovered in the cosmic rays is actually that which should occur in the nuclear fields, we are immediately led to the following conclusions.

In the case of transformation of a neutron into a proton, the meson emitted must have the charge $-e$ of the electron to assure the conservation of the electricity; this is, therefore, a heavy negative electron. In the case of the inverse transformation of the proton into a neutron, the emitted meson must, on the contrary, have the charge $+e$ of the positive electron and in consequence be analogous to a heavy positive electron. But if, from the point of view of their electric charges, these charged mesons really deserve the title of heavy electrons, on the other hand, from the point of view of their spin, rather are they heavy photons, since they have, like the photons, a spin equal to 1. The wave equations which represent their place in the framework of wave mechanics have, besides, a form very analogous to that of Maxwell's equations. At present the theory of the interactions between the proton and the neutron through the medium of the nuclear field associated with the mesons seems to be established on sufficiently solid bases and to furnish satisfactory results so far as the prediction of nuclear phenomena is concerned. We see, then, from this point of view as well, that the discovery of the meson was of considerable importance.

There is more besides. The developments of experimental researches on the forces which are exercised between heavy particles have shown that the proton-proton and neutron-neutron interactions must be of the same order of magnitude as the proton-neutron interactions. To explain this fact in the theory of the nuclear field it has become necessary to suppose that besides the charged mesons, positive or negative, there exist *neutral mesons*, also called *neutrettos*, which would have the same spin and probably the same mass and which would be without an electric charge. These new neutral particles would also be of the nature of "heavy photons". The interaction between two protons or between two neutrons would operate through the medium of the field associated with these neutrettos without being accompanied by any exchange of charges. Up to the present there is no direct experimental proof of the existence of the neutral meson, but its introduction into the theory of nuclear fields has established a symmetry which is very satisfying to the mind and leads us to think that the neutral mesons actually exist. The difficulty of detecting them can be precisely explained by their electric neutrality which would cause the observable effects of their passage through matter to be very feeble.

As will have been gathered, the theory of Yukawa's nuclear field is very superior on a number of points to the theory of Fermi's field. Nevertheless, whilst Fermi's theory established a direct connexion between the nuclear field and the β-rays (or more correctly in this interpretation, of electron-neutrino pairs) by the radioactive bodies, such a direct connexion no longer exists in Yukawa's theory. But there are reasons of an experimental nature which have suggested the idea of an instability of charged mesons which are apparently capable of disappearing after pursuing a certain course in matter. This is interpreted by assuming that mesons are capable of decomposing into an electron-neutrino pair. The emission of a meson by a radioactive nucleus, followed by the decomposition of this meson into an electron-neutrino pair, would then be equivalent to the emission of a β-ray. It is in this way that we interpret the origin of continuous β-spectra in the theory of Yukawa's nuclear field, in a more indirect way than in Fermi's theory, but nevertheless also satisfactory.

Summarizing: although the properties of mesons are still rather imperfectly known, nevertheless their existence does not appear to be any longer in doubt, and their introduction in the theory of the nuclear field, so remarkably foreseen by

Yukawa before their discovery, has been responsible for considerable progress in this theory. This progress has consisted essentially in replacing Fermi's nuclear field associated with pairs of particles of spin $\frac{1}{2}$, capable of appearing and disappearing in pairs, by Yukawa's field associated with particles of spin 1, capable of appearing or disappearing singly.

Recapitulation

In conclusion we shall recapitulate the knowledge that we have today on the elementary particles of matter (ignoring the photon without charge and mass, or of infinitesimal amount, and spin 1, which appertains to light) by drawing up the following table[5]:

	Electric charge	Mass at rest	Spin in units of $h/2\pi$
Proton	$+e = +4\cdot8 \times 10^{-10}$ e.s.u.	$M = 1\cdot66 \times 10^{-24}$ gm.	$\frac{1}{2}$
Negative electron	$-e = -4\cdot8 \times 10^{-10}$ e.s.u.	$m = 0\cdot90 \times 10^{-27}$ gm. $= M/1,840$	$\frac{1}{2}$
Postive electron	$+e$	m	$\frac{1}{2}$
Neutron	0	$1\cdot6627 \times 10^{-24}$ gm.	$\frac{1}{2}$
Positive meson	$+e$	about $250m$	1
Negative meson	$-e$	,,	1
Neutral meson?	0	,,	1
Neutrino?	0	?	$\frac{1}{2}$
Negative proton?	$-e$	M	$\frac{1}{2}$

The first two particles in this table have been known for a long time; the existence of the next two is certain today and that of the two charged mesons also appears to be well established. There are strong theoretical reasons which, as has been shown, argue in favour of the existence of the neutrino and the neutretto, but up to the present their existence has not been confirmed by experiment—an explanation of which might be the electric neutrality of these corpuscles. As to the negative proton, which reasons of symmetry alone have led us to conceive, its existence is still very problematic.

It may also be added that the particular magnetic moment of the electron and positron is the equivalent of Bohr's magneton; that of the proton, which *a priori* seems as though it should also be equal to a small Bohr magneton, has the abnormal value of 2·9 small Bohr magnetons. Finally, that of the neutron would be of opposite sign and should have a value of about 2 small magnetons. I shall not here stress the possible sources of these values which are a little unexpected. The individual magnetic moments of the other particles in the table are not known, though the small Bohr magneton has a value 1/1,850 that of the electronic magneton.

Summing up, it can be seen from the outline that has been given how our knowledge of the elementary particles of matter has been extended and how the progress has transformed our theoretical conceptions on the constitution of the nuclei and on the fields that assure their stability. Many of these new theoretical ideas undoubtedly must be revised and perhaps discarded, but it is nevertheless certain that, thanks to the admirable development in nuclear physics during the last ten years, a vast field of research, both experimental and theoretical, opens before us today in a realm of which the interest from every point of view is of fundamental importance, seeing that we are now probing the most intimate secrets of matter.

[1]Within recent years some other elements have been discovered, such as americium, curium, berkelium and californium. Their atomic numbers are 95, 96, 97 and 98 and their atomic weights 241, 242, 243 and 244, respectively. Berkelium was produced when americium was bombarded with α-particles at the University of California and californium was produced when the nuclei of curium were struck by α-particles. Comparatively recently it was announced that another element, atomic number 99 and atomic weight 247 has been made sometime ago in the University of California cyclotron at Berkeley and other laboratories in America. It was provisionally named ekaholium and was produced by adding nuclear particles to uranium. It was stated to be radioactive and short-lived, changing into berkelium in a few minutes, and showed analogies with holium. Another element with atomic number 100 was produced early this year (1954) and showed analogies with erbium. It has been suggested that at least two more chemical elements will be produced in time.

[2]A more recent evaluation of the charge on an electron is 4.802×10^{-10} e.s.u.

[3]The value of Planck's Constant is given by Beardson and Watts, 1951, as 6.62363×10^{-27}.

[4]Various radioactive substances show very great differences in their speeds of transmutation, some being very short-lived while others show no appreciable diminution in their radioactivity over immensely long periods. The same percentage of the number of atoms which still remain at any period will decay per unit time and hence the probability of their radioactive decay can be expressed numerically. The *reciprocal* of this probability is the *average life* of the substance.

Very often the *half-life* period is used instead of the average life, and denotes the times during which half the original number of atoms decays. The half-life is slightly less than the average life.

[5]Data relating to the fundamental particles are subject to constant revision and refinement. The 1954 revision of the table on p. 38 is as follows:

	Mass	Spin
Proton	$M = 1.65 \times 10^{-24}$ gm.	
Electron	$m = M/1,836$	
Neutron	1.655×10^{-24} gm.	
Positive π-meson	$276m.$	o
Negative π-meson	$276m.$	o
Neutral π-meson	$266m.$	o
Neutrino	o	

CHAPTER II

ATOMIC PHYSICS AND NUCLEAR PHYSICS

DURING sixty years the investigations of physicists have progressively penetrated more and more deeply into the study of material structures. Since the beginning of the nineteenth century certain physicists, in succession to Dalton, Prout, Ampère and Avogadro, agreed that the elements are composed of atoms of which different combinations give rise to a whole variety of compounds which are studied by mineral and organic chemistry. It is by the characteristic simplicity and indestructibility of atoms that these scientists explained the role that the elements played through these simple bodies in all chemical combinations. This conception, which for a long time was disputed by the physicists and chemists who were adverse to hypotheses without direct experimental foundation, received in the last years of the nineteenth and the earlier years of the twentieth centuries a striking confirmation; this was due to the experiments which proved the discrete structure of matter. Many and different experiments, in the front rank of which are those of Jean Perrin, have supplied a precise value—always the same—for the number of molecules contained in the gram molecule (Avogadro's or Loschmidt's number). In addition, other experiments have revealed the phenomena of fluctuations in density and energy which the discrete structure of matter alone can explain; again, others have shown the existence of the properties of thin laminæ in matter, which can only be interpreted by comparing them to stratified layers of molecules. Finally, it is fitting to recall that the experiments of Dunoyer on molecular jets have provided a proof—perhaps even more direct—of the existence of molecules. In short, the atomic hypothesis, for a long time disputed, has now come to be accepted by everyone.

But scientific investigation is never finished, for as soon as questions concerning one stage of reality are slightly clarified, others arise at a lower or higher stage. This is what took place in the case of the question we are now considering. Once the existence of the atom was proved, it was obvious that the atom was not the simple and indivisible particle which the ancient philosophers had thought, and no doubt also the first promoters of the atomic hypothesis in modern science. The multitude of spectral rays emitted by atoms, the possibility of making electrified corpuscles emanate from atoms, for example by photoelectric effects, and that of acting on the emission of spectral rays by submitting a luminous source to a magnetic or electric field and many other facts emerged little by little, proving that the atom is a complicated system in which electricity plays an essential role. From that moment was presented the question of imagining the internal structure of the atom, of deducing from it the laws of spectral emissions and of associating with it the totality of the physical and chemical properties of matter. We were thus confronted by an immense new branch of physics, which was to be created in its entirety, but the study of which seemed bound to be most fruitful. The name "atomic physics" has been given to this new science.

To approach the study of atomic physics it was necessary to know the properties of electricity on a very small scale, because electricity seemed to play a fundamental role in the atom. Now at this time experiments had established the existence of a discrete structure of negative electricity, owing to the discovery of the electron—that grain of negative electricity which had been found in cathode rays, in β-radiation of radioactive bodies, and in the stream of negative electricity escaping from metals submitted to certain irradiations or raised to high temperatures. The theorists had made use of this new idea of the discontinuous structure of electricity, and Lorentz, extending to the very small scales the properties of electricity observed in our own scale, had constructed his theory of electrons, which had explained a great many phenomena and the success of which, particularly in relation to the prediction of the Zeeman effect, showed the existence of electrons in the interior of atoms.

Free scope was then given to the imagination of the constructors of "atomic models". J. J. Thomson conceived of it as a sphere filled with positive electricity in which negative electrons floated. Perrin, on the contrary, preferred (and he was right) to compare it to a small solar system in miniature where the central sun carried a positive charge while the planetary electrons revolved around it. But all these atom builders accepted the same fundamental postulate, viz. that it should be possible to apply the mechanical and electromagnetic laws which had been proved on the larger scale to the interior of the atoms themselves. More generally, that it should be possible to extend into the inconceivably small domains—the interiors of the atoms—the conceptions and pictures drawn from the usual macroscopic observation and up till then used with success by all the physical theories. On this point, as we shall see, they were all mistaken.

The beautiful and conclusive experiments of Rutherford and his students on the deviations suffered by α-particles during their passage through matter, supplied the proof about 1910 that in the atom all the positive electricity and almost all the mass are concentrated at the centre of the system in an extremely small space. Taking up again Perrin's ideas, Rutherford then conceived that the atom contains at its centre a "nucleus" carrying a positive charge $+Ne$ and practically all the mass of the atom, around which gravitated N electrons very much lighter, each with a charge—e. Each type of atom is characterized by a value of an integer N and it was quickly seen that this "atomic number" is equal to a number in the position of the corresponding element in Mendéléef's periodic series. Rutherford's planetary model is, moreover, entirely of the classical type; it is a reduction of the planetary systems of astronomy to the atomic scale, with the simple substitution of electric forces for gravitational forces. But this planetary model has not been able to lead to a satisfactory theory of atoms, taking into consideration the totality of their properties and in particular of their spectroscopic properties, except by the introduction, due to Bohr, of the laws of the quantum theory, into the framework of this planetary model.

It is impossible to give even a rapid résumé in this brief exposition of the different stages of the theory of the atom— first of all under the old quantal form of Bohr and Sommerfeld, then under the new form of quantal and wave mechanics. Let us try, however, to state precisely in a few lines the essential characteristics of the very rapid development of the theories of atomic physics (about 1913-30). The materials which were then used by theorists for constructing atoms were solely the electrons, corpuscles of negative electricity with already well-known properties, and the nuclei. The latter were envisaged as units, the intimate structure of which they did not seek to scrutinize, and which almost entirely played the role of Coulombian centres of force. The only forces allowed to act on the electrons of the atom were those derived from the electrostatic field created by the nucleus (and eventually those arising from electromagnetic fields applied from the exterior, as in the Zeeman or Stark effects). All these foundations of the atomic theory were simple and well known. The difficulty here was to know which mechanics should be used to predict and describe the states of movement of atomic systems. The first idea was to consider them as systems governed by the classical mechanical laws, which would lead us to regard them as simple reductions, on an extremely small scale, of mechanical systems described on our scale by classical mechanics. This first hypothesis having failed to explain the stability of atoms and the existence of their energy levels, it became necessary to introduce quanta.

In the hands of Bohr, Sommerfeld and others, the old theory of the quanta then intervened in the atom of the theorists, to limit by restrictive conditions—in which Planck's constant figured—those electronic movements which were foreseen by the old mechanics. Then came the new quantal and wave mechanics which rediscovered and reinterpreted the results of the first quantal theory of the atom, after amending them in more than one place. But wave mechanics has not only opened up a new way of calculating the phenomena of atomic physics; it has also brought conceptions which have radically transformed the picture on which, up till then, were based all the physical theories. In addition, it has shown that the certainties and the determinism of classical physics should, in this new domain, give way to quantal uncertainties and to probabilities.

Thus, we do not today find in the atomic scale the characteristics which classical physics had been led to attribute to macroscopic systems. Contrary to an opinion often expressed, and in particular to a stimulating idea of Pascal, the infinitely small no longer appears as an analogous reduction of the infinitely great. A kind of dissolution of continuity appears when, in descending the scale of magnitudes, we reach the atomic world; this is due to the existence of the quantum of action—Planck's constant—which measures its magnitude and which, in comparison with our usual units, is numerically very small though, nevertheless, finite. It is practically impossible to form a clear picture of the real nature of the essential physical discontinuity which today we call the quantum of action. This is because it combines, in a way totally contrary to our intuition and our habits of thought, the configuration of mechanical systems in space and their dynamical evolution in the course of time, but of its fundamental importance in nature there is no doubt. From the point of view of general concepts, it is certainly the progressive introduction in two stages (the old and the new theory of quanta) of quantal conceptions of the new mechanics which has been the essential factor in the development of physics between 1900 and 1930.

But this development has equally brought forward other new concepts of which the importance, already great in the theory of the atom, has been affirmed perhaps even more in the physics of the nucleus; I propose to speak about the idea of spin, the exclusion principle and exchange interactions.

The spin was first revealed as a new and up till then unknown property of electrons. In developing the quantal theory of the atom it was seen that, if the electron was nothing but a corpuscle endowed with a very small mass and a very small negative electric charge, a large number of phenomena of atomic physics, notably the fine structure of the optical spectra or the spectra of X-rays and the Zeeman effects, would be much simpler than they really are. Uhlenbeck and Goudsmit correctly concluded that the electron must be something much more complicated than had been thought up till then. They proposed to attribute to it, in addition to its charge and mass, an intrinsic angular momentum and magnetic moment, closely united with each other, both determined by the existence of the quantum of action and expressed with the aid of the constant h. Physically this comes to endowing the electron with a sort of intrinsic quantized rotation and it is this new characteristic of the electron that has been named the "spin". Its importance has not ceased to increase daily; in fact it is not only the electron which would be endowed with spin; all the particles of microscopic physics appear to have one and it is impossible nowadays to construct a general theory of these particles without constantly speaking of spin.

Dirac's theory of the electron has, for the first time, given a precise mathematical form to the properties of the electron when we take account of its spin. More recent theories, generalizing the formalism of Dirac, have been able to represent the properties of spin of different kinds of particles, actually known in atomic and nuclear physics, and even—so great is the directive force of mathematical analogies—of those which have not been discovered. In atomic physics, strictly speaking, the role played by spin has been incessantly increasing, and it is in combining the existence of spin with the exclusion principle that it has been possible to construct in all its generality the theory of the exchange interactions.

The exclusion principle, due to Pauli, expresses one of the laws—the most surprising and the least capable of interpretation with the aid of the classical ideas—which has been encountered in the development of the new mechanics. It affirms that for certain categories of particles (and specially, it seems, for all those which can pretend to the title of elementary corpuscles), two particles can never be found at the same instant in the same quantal state, at least if we are careful in defining quantal states by taking into consideration the orientation of the spin. Certain other categories of particles, on the contrary, escape the application of Pauli's principle. From this point of view, then, there exist two different sorts of particles—those which obey the exclusion principle and those which do not. Their respective properties are very different; the first follow the statistics of Fermi-Dirac, the second that of Bose-Einstein. A formalism of great range explains these fundamental facts; to describe from the point of view of wave mechanics the *state* of the particles, it utilizes the systematic employment of wave functions—symmetrical or unsymmetrical. If it is admitted in conformity with the present indications of experiments, that all elementary corpuscles obey the exclusion principle and have the same spin, $h/4\pi$, as the electron, then it can be shown that a complex particle formed by an *even* number of elementary corpuscles and having in consequence an *integral* spin (in units of $h/2\pi$), never obeys the exclusion principle, but follows *Bose's* statistics, whilst a complex particle formed by an *odd* number of corpuscles and possessing in consequence a *half integral* spin (in units of $h/2\pi$) obeys the exclusion principle and follows Fermi's statistics. The demonstration of this remarkable theorem is of capital importance for the theory of the nuclei.

The application of the principle of wave mechanics has led to a new idea—that of the exchange energy. This idea makes its appearance when we study, by the method of successive approximations, the energy of interaction existing between two particles of the same nature, and proceeding from the existence of a mutual potential of interaction, such, for example, as Coulomb's potential. In this calculation we find, besides the terms of mutual energy which correspond, in the classical sense, to the admitted potential of interaction, other terms which have no interpretation in classical physics, and which are connected with the possibility of exchanging the roles played in a system by two particles of the same nature without any change in the state of the system as a whole. These new terms explain the exchange interaction which is wholly characteristic of the new mechanics.

Applied to simple cases such as that of the molecule of hydrogen H_2 (where two electrons are displaced in the field by two protons—centres of Coulombian forces) it is seen that these exchange interactions have properties altogether different from those of classical interactions and give rise in particular to phenomena of "saturation", thus providing the means for obtaining the explanation—for a long time impossible—of the saturation of valency forces in chemical combinations. The exchange interactions change sign when we pass from a state represented by a function of a symmetrical wave with reference to the variables of space, to a state represented by a function of an unsymmetrical wave with reference to these variables. Now for a particle obeying the exclusion principle, a symmetrical state with reference to the variables of space must be unsymmetrical with regard to spins, and vice versa. From this it follows that the interactions between two particles vary according to whether their spins are parallel or non-parallel. All these remarks, already of the utmost importance in the physics of the atom, have been transposed, as we shall see, into the physics of the nucleus, where they also play an essential role. It may be added that the elegant theory of the helium atom, due to Heisenberg, has provided a very fine illustration of these new theoretical conceptions.

Obviously we could not have remained satisfied indefinitely to consider the nucleus of atoms as a simple centre of force the structure of which is utterly incapable of analysis; we should have endeavoured to figure these nuclei as complex particles formed from more elementary constituents, and there were many good reasons for this. As stated on page 16 it was known that there are ninety-two elements, hence at least ninety-two kinds of different nuclei, and this number had been further considerably increased by the discovery of isotopes. It is scarcely possible to admit the existence of such a large number of unreducible physical units. Furthermore, for more than forty years the discovery of natural radioactive bodies has shown that the nuclei of heavy elements are susceptible of breaking up in giving birth to a less heavy nucleus and to light particles (α-particles), to very light particles (β-particles or electrons) to say nothing about very high frequency rays (γ-rays). The experiments of Rutherford (1919) which led to the disintegration of nitrogen nuclei by bombardment with α-particles, had then shown that even the nuclei of the light elements are complex, and had opened the road to operations artificially producing nuclear disintegrations. The developments of these processes have had as a climax the discovery of artificial radio-elements by M. and Mme Joliot and the recent realization of the atomic bomb.

Thus all the nuclei were appearing as complex structures except the simplest of all, the hydrogen nucleus or *proton*, which assumed the role of unit of positive electricity. The proton, with the same spin as the electron, whose charge is equal and opposite to the electronic charge, conforms to Fermi's statistics and obeys the exclusion principle. All this seems to indicate that the proton has the right, just as has the electron, to the title of elementary corpuscle. The electron and the proton were therefore the two elementary corpuscles which physicists had at their disposal when, between 1920 and 1930, the physics of the nucleus, stimulated by Rutherford's experiments on artificial disintegration, later by those of Aston on isotopes, started to take its first step.

Thus the first theory of the nucleus was, in this way, a proton-electron theory. In conformity with the old ideas of the English physicist Prout, it attributed to all the elements (taking the isotopes into consideration) atomic weights which were integral multiples of that of hydrogen; then, establishing the existence of small differences between these integral multiples and the atomic weights (or more exactly the nuclear weights) of actual isotopes, it came to explain them by invoking the relativity principle of the inertia of energy. According to this, when electrons and protons united in the course of an exothermic process to form a stable nucleus, the nucleus so formed must have a mass slightly less than the sum of the masses of its constituents, the difference representing the mass associated with the energy radiated at the moment of the formation of the nucleus. Introducing in conjunction with the atomic number which defines the charge of a nucleus, the mass of that nucleus, it is found that this mass, expressed by taking as the unit either the mass of the proton or the sixteenth part of that of the oxygen atom, is not exactly an integer. The mass number of a nucleus was then defined as the nearest integer (in the system of units used) of the exact nuclear mass. The difference between the mass number and the nuclear mass, known as the "mass defect", is very simply related to the binding energy of the nucleus, and similarly in the case of the quantity called "packing fraction" by Aston. The study of the variation of these characteristics of the nuclei, when we consider in succession the different elements of Mendéléef's series and the whole of the isotopes, is fundamental; in particular, the variation of the mass defect or of the packing fraction as a function of the atomic number, represented by Aston's famous curve, is very important to know and to interpret.

From about 1930 a new phase was opened in the history of nuclear physics. On the one hand new particles were discovered, the intervention of which in nuclear phenomena is certain and enhances very considerably the theoretical possibilities. On the other hand, by making use of the discovery of *neutrons*—at that period very recent—Heisenberg in 1932 substituted for the old proton-electron conception of the nucleus a proton-neutron conception, the success of which has been considerable, and which has renewed the whole theory of the nucleus. From that time it seemed certain that nuclei are formed from protons and neutrons and that the laws of wave mechanics are applicable to these systems. The essential difficulty encountered by the theory of the nucleus no longer lies either in the choice of constituents of the nucleus or in the nature of the mechanical laws which it is necessary to apply to them; rather does it bear on the determination of the types of interactions which must be recognized amongst the constituents. The situation, then, in this dawn of nuclear physics is totally different, from the point of view of the theorist, to that which existed at the dawn of atomic physics. In atomic physics we knew the constituents of the atom and that all the interactions should emanate from the Coulombian potential; but we did not know what mechanics to apply to the movement of these constituents, classical mechanics clearly showing itself inadequate.

It has been necessary to introduce the quanta, and later a new mechanics entailing the greatest conceptual revolutions, to make the physics of the atom progress. In the physics of the nucleus, at least up to the present, it does not seem that there is any need to introduce new mechanical laws different from those which had succeeded in the atomic realm. But the difficulty here affected first the nature of the constituents, then the form of the interactions. The discovery of the *neutron*, followed by the famous memoir of Heisenberg, has been responsible for regarding the nucleus as composed of protons and neutrons; but besides these, there intervene in nuclear phenomena not only negative electrons, well known for a long time, and their associates, *postive electrons*, discovered a little after the neutrons, but probably also *heavy electrons* or *mesons*, charged or neutral. The former were recently discovered in cosmic rays, and the latter are still hypothetical, the existence of which, foreseen by Yukawa, appeared to be closely associated with the nature of nuclear forces. Another corpuscle, of which we have as yet no direct experimental information, the *neutrino*, appears equally to take part in the β-disintegrations. As to the types of interactions existing between the constituents of the nucleus, it has been necessary to think of them in such a way as to give an account of the facts, and this work—of great difficulty—has already led to some remarkable results which we propose to summarize on completing this picture of the whole.

An entirely new idea arising from Heisenberg's theoretical attempt on the nucleus is as follows: The proton and the neutron should be regarded, not as two distinct corpuscles, but as the same heavy corpuscle in two different states, one, the proton state, positively charged, the other, the neutron state, electrically neutral. This heavy corpuscle with its two aspects would be the fundamental unit of the nucleus; it has been proposed to name it the "nucleon" and this title seems a fortunate one. The first question which then arises in the theory of the nucleus is the determination of the mode of interactions of the nucleons amongst themselves, so as to obtain an exact forecast of the properties of the nuclei. A fact which appears to be established with certainty is that these interactions only take place at very small distances of the order 2×10^{-13} cm., a distance very much smaller than the dimensions of the heavy nuclei, which are of the order 9×10^{-13} cm. (in diameter). Moreover, these reactions appear to possess properties of saturability which bring them nearer to the valency interactions, ensuring the stability of the molecules.

Reflecting on these facts, Heisenberg came to the conclusion that the interaction between two nucleons, one in the proton state and the other in the neutron state, must have the characteristics of an exchange interaction of a particular nature implying an exchange of charge between the two nucleons, the neutron becoming a proton and the proton a neutron. Heisenberg showed that we could thus explain certain important characteristics of the nuclei, and in particular, the fact that the light nuclei contained as many neutrons as protons (the mass number being equal to double the atomic number), whilst, because of the Coulombian repulsion between protons, heavier nuclei contain an increasing proportion of neutrons (mass number greater than double the atomic number). To represent the new reactions which he conceived, Heisenberg introduced a new and very curious formalism, that of the "isotopic spin", which established a sort of analogy, probably of a purely formal nature, between the spin and the electric charge.

If the introduction of the interaction imagined by Heisenberg had brought about a decisive progress to the theory of nuclei, it was soon discovered that of itself alone it was insufficient. In fact, if Heisenberg's interaction alone existed amongst the nucleons (with, it goes without saying, the Coulombian repulsion between protons), the nucleus of heavy hydrogen, the deuteron, $_1^2H_0$, should be more stable than the α-particle, the helion $_4^2He$ which is the nucleus of helium. Now actually it is not at all like this; on the contrary, helium is, about fourteen times more stable than the deuteron. A young Italian scientist, Majorana, a student of Heisenberg, concluded from this that in addition to Heisenberg's interaction, it was necessary to introduce another sort of interaction permitting not only an exchange of charge, but also an exchange of spin between proton and neutron. It is Majorana's interaction which affords an explanation of the great stability of helium. Nevertheless it does not replace Heisenberg's interaction which must co-exist with it, and without which we should not be able to explain the great difference of stability existing between the states of 3S and 1S of the deuteron.

When two nucleons are one in the proton state and the other in the neutron state, there exist between them the interactions of the Heisenberg and Majorana types. But do interactions also exist between two nucleons which are both in the proton state or both in the neutron state? At the beginning of the development of the present nuclear theories it was said: "If proton-proton and neutron-neutron interactions exist they are necessarily much more feeble than proton-neutron interactions." But experiment has decided otherwise. In observing the deviation of protons by protons it was concluded that proton-proton interactions were of the same order as, and even in certain cases undoubtedly rigorously equal to, proton-neutron interactions.

Relying on these results, three American authors, Breit, Condon and Présent, put forward a hypothesis which has had a great success because it is really very attractive. They supposed that the total interaction between two nucleons is independent of their state of charge, an exception being naturally made for the Coulombian repulsion. The interactions—truly nuclear—between two nucleons would be independent of the fact that they are in the proton state or the neutron state. It is *the hypothesis of independence with regard to the charge* which has played an important role in nuclear theories of these last years. Although this hypothesis cannot be regarded as established in all its generality, it appears probable that interactions between nucleons are, at least, little sensitive to the state of the charge of these nucleons. But as soon as this idea is accepted important consequences develop.

First of all it is obvious that interactions between proton and proton or between neutron and neutron, if they exist, cannot be of either the Heisenberg of the Majorana type, because interactions of these two types imply a change of state of charge by the exchange of charge, which is only possible for a proton and a neutron. It is necessary, therefore, to introduce still other types of nuclear interactions, either by returning to interactions of the classical type, not allowing any "exchange" between the nucleons (interactions of the Wigner type), or by considering interactions permitting exchange of spin without exchange of charge (interactions of the Bartlett type). We shall thus obtain altogether four types of nuclear interactions, the Wigner, Bartlett, Heisenberg, and Majorana types, capable of superposing themselves in variable proportions.

Moreover, the introduction of proton-proton and neutron-neutron interactions renders necessary an important extension of the exclusion principle. In fact, as long as the non-existence or the very small importance of these interactions was admitted, we understood why a nucleus formed entirely of neutrons could not be stable and we also explained why the neutrons and protons are equal in number in the light stable nuclei. But when we attribute the same importance to proton-proton and neutron-neutron actions on the one hand, and to proton-neutron actions on the other hand, we do not know why there is a tendency in the light nuclei to equality in the number of protons and of neutrons, and yet this fundamental fact calls for an interpretation. This can be obtained by an extension of the Pauli principle to the electric charge. This is how this extension will be stated analytically:

Let us consider two nucleons having the same wave function in what concerns their spatial co-ordinates (we then often say that they have the same orbital state); if they have also the same state of spin (parallel spins) the exclusion principle generalized for the charge will affirm that their electric charges should be different, that is to say, that one should be a proton and the other a neutron. There will then be a tendency for the formation of proton-neutron pairs of which the two constituents will have the same orbital state and the same state of spin. Thus, in the simplest state, that of the deuteron in its normal state 3S, we must give parallel spins to the proton and the neutron. Two neutrons and two protons will be able to have the same orbital state if the two neutrons on the one hand, and the two protons on the other hand, have antiparallel spins. We should then obtain an especially simple and stable nuclear combination which corresponds exactly to the helium nucleus— the α-particle—the great stability of which has already been noticed. Thus the general theory of nuclear interactions can be established with perfect symmetry and great elegance of expression.

The general theory about which we have just spoken is, in a certain way, phenomenal; it admits the existence of the interactions suggested by experimental results and it explains this existence by an appropriate formalism, without seeking to delve into the nature and origin of the interactions which it invokes. We are able to go further and to seek to connect the nuclear interactions to the exchanges of light particles amongst the nucleons, these exchanges being effected through the medium of a field of a new type—the nuclear field. This amounts to giving the nuclear reactions an interpretation analogous to that proposed by the quantal theory of fields for the electromagnetic interactions. The quantal theory of fields considers, in fact, the electromagnetic interactions between two electrically charged particles, as due to the exchange of photons operating between the two particles through the medium of the Maxwellian electromagnetic field. If we accept this argument, by analogy we should then consider the exchanges of charge and spin which accompany the nuclear interactions as operating through the agency of particles connected with the "nuclear field" in the same way in which the photons are connected with the electromagnetic field. What are these particles which are responsible for this union between the nucleons as the photons are for the union between the electrified particles? Two different answers have been successively given to this question.

The first was given by Fermi who was then studying the difficult problem of continuous β-spectra. The solution envisaged by Fermi consists in supposing that the nuclear interactions took place by means of pairs formed by a positive or negative electron and a neutrino, the latter a light corpuscle with no electric charge and whose intervention in the phenomenon of the β-ray emission from radioactive bodies is necessary to assure the conservation of energy and that of angular momentum (see page 24). The nuclear field would thus be connected with electron-neutrino pairs, and this interesting conception has led to a formula representing the distribution of energies in the continuous β-spectra of radioactive bodies. This formula, which at first had not seemed to represent the facts very accurately, seems today on the contrary, in the light of more precise experiments, better verified than had been thought at first. Nevertheless, Fermi's theory, taken as a whole, encounters a very grave difficulty. If we determine the arbitrary constant which figures in Fermi's formulae in such a way as to make them correspond to the experimental values relative to the β-spectra, we are led to forecast for the nuclear interactions intensities which are much too feeble and totally insufficient to assure the stability of nuclei. The final conclusions to draw from Fermi's attempt are as follows:

The fundamental conception according to which the nuclear interactions take place through the agency of light corpuscles connected with a "nuclear field" appears very profound and should be retained. Fermi's formula for the distribution of the energies between the electrons of the continuous β-spectra seems to represent the facts with a good approximation; but the hypothesis that nuclear fields are connected with electron-neutrino pairs does not appear satisfactory.

Fermi's fundamental conception was taken up again in 1935 by the Japanese physicist, Yukawa, under a somewhat different form which has led to a remarkable success—the prediction of the existence of heavy electrons or *mesons*. Yukawa started off with the idea that the nuclear field should decidedly not be associated with pairs of corpuscles, as Fermi had imagined, but with simple particles. This hypothesis seems to us to be more natural than that of Fermi and better in accord with the way in which it has been possible to develop the wave mechanics of the photon to interpret the electromagnetic field and its quantified aspects. From this theory Yukawa was able to deduce the form of the potential from which the nuclear interactions must proceed. He finds:

$$V(r) = C \frac{e^{-\frac{r}{r_0}}}{r}$$

r being the distance between the two nucleons. The constant r_0 must then give a measure of the "radius of action" of the nuclear forces—a radius of action which, we know from the results of experiment, is of the order 2×10^{-10} cm. Yukawa's theory further shows that we must have

$$r_0 = \frac{h}{2\pi\mu_0 c}$$

h being Planck's constant, c the speed of light *in vacuo*, and μ_0 the appropriate mass for the particles associated with the nuclear field. It has been deduced from this that μ_0 is equal to about 200 times the mass of the electron. Yukawa then daringly supposed the existence of semi-light particles whose mass would be of the order of 200 times that of the electron. The discovery in 1938–9 in cosmic rays of particles up till then unknown, which had in effect a mass of this order, supplied a remarkable confirmation to Yukawa's thesis, although up to the present there has been no direct experimental proof showing that these "heavy electrons" or "mesons" found in cosmic rays, actually play an essential role in internuclear phenomena. If, nevertheless, admitting Yukawa's views, we suppose that the mesons are the carriers of nuclear fields, we shall have to seek to base the whole theory of nuclear interactions on the existence and properties of "mesonic fields".

The mesons actually revealed by experiment in cosmic rays are charged, some positively, others negatively, their charges, moreover, appearing numerically equal to those of the two kinds of electrons. One conceives, therefore, that the exchange of a charged meson between two nucleons, one in the proton state and the other in the neutron state, should be able to explain the interactions of the Heisenberg and Majorana types where there is an exchange of charge. To explain the interactions of the Bartlett and Wigner types (and in particular the proton-proton and neutron-neutron interactions which do not involve any exchange of charge) it is necessary to assume in addition the existence of "neutral mesons" or "neutrettos". Theorists have not shrunk from this conclusion although experiment has not, up till now, supplied the proof of the existence of neutral mesons. Moreover, neutral mesons only being able to act very feebly on matter, by the very reason of their electric neutrality, we imagine that their detection would be very difficult.

Yukawa's theory of the "mesonic" nuclear field has been able to develop and especially to succeed in rediscovering Fermi's formula for the continuous β-spectra, by considering β-radio-activity as a secondary phenomenon due to the decomposition of the mesons emitted by the radioactive nuclei into an electron and a neutrino. The possibility of such a decomposition of mesons has as a result a certain instability of these particles—an instability which today appears to be demonstrated. The theory of mesonic fields has, moreover, encountered certain difficulties, especially in that which concerns the exact theoretical prediction of the duration of the life of the mesons. These difficulties, however, appear capable of being overcome with the assistance of appropriate hypotheses which we cannot here dwell on.

Be that as it may, we can foresee after what has been said, how interesting are these theories of the nuclear field and what horizons they have opened to theoretical research in the domain—so fundamental—of the atomic nucleus. Assuredly they are much bolder than the theories about which we have spoken at the commencement, and concerning which aspiration limits itself to defining the nuclear interactions in conformity with experimental indications, and to classifying them; in fact they seek to penetrate deeply into the nature of these interactions. Being more daring they are also less sound, and it is still difficult to say what their future will be. They constitute, nonetheless, the extreme point of that magnificent branch of general physics, namely, the quite young "Physics of the Nucleus" and it is this which gives their study the greatest interest.

CHAPTER III

LIGHT IN THE PHYSICAL WORLD

In the physical world light plays an essential and peculiar role. From time immemorial physicists, intent on the study of observable phenomena, have reserved for it a place apart in the whole of natural agents. They have always been intrigued by its subtle nature and by its incredible speed of propagation in space. One might believe that this exceptional place held by light in our scientific knowledge proceeds simply from the fact—in some way accidental—that one of our five senses— sight—is specialized in the perception of luminous phenomena. This is not so, as can be easily seen from what follows. In the first place we see clearly that another physical phenomenon, like sound, the perception of which is also the attribute of one of our senses, is, from the general point of view of the physicist, far from possessing the importance of light. A simple periodic movement of media—solid, liquid, or gaseous —sound is not a specialized entity in the physical world, and its study, however interesting it can be in different ways, cannot teach us anything essential on the structure of the universe. On the other hand, we know today that luminous phenomena are but a small fraction of a much more extensive class of phenomena—the phenomena of radiation.

There exist, in fact, innumerable radiations of which the luminous radiations are but a very small part; we can classify these radiations in order of decreasing wave lengths in the following way:

Electromagnetic radiations (Hertzian waves of wireless transmission);
Infra-red radiations;
Visible radiations (light in the usual meaning of the word);
Ultra-violet radiations;
X-ray radiations (Röntgen-rays);
γ-radiations.

In this immense gamut of radiations, that which includes visible light—hardly an octave—is perceived by our eye. It is by the aid of indirect means (electric effects, raising of temperature, photographic impressions, etc.) that we succeed in disclosing the existence of non-visible radiations, but this existence is certain and we know without any doubt that all these radiations have the same essential properties as visible light and play the same privileged role in nature. We see, therefore, how this privileged role is independent of the fact that one of our senses is adapted to the perception of visible light, seeing that a multitude of other radiations, to which our eye is insensible, shares with visible light the peculiarity of holding a primordial place in nature.

What, then, for the physicist, are the reasons which assure to light, and more generally, to radiations, so singular an importance in the vast totality of agents which observation and experiment show us at work in natural phenomena? These reasons are very different from those which the poet or merely the man of the street could invoke. To the poet, light is the adorable fairy which adorns nature with a thousand graces, ornamenting with brilliant colours the clouds at the setting of the sun and giving to the deep sea the shades of precious stones imitating in turn emerald or amethyst. The more prosaic man in the street will say that light is indispensable for his activity and his work, whilst acknowledging how a warm sunshine adds to the pleasure of his leisure hours; he will aver how much artificial light—electric light in particular—repelling the shades of the night, has added to the pleasure of our life and to the length of that part of the day which we can use for our work and recreations. If, by chance, he finds himself suddenly plunged into darkness through the severe restrictions imposed by a period of privation, he will be able to measure to what degree light is indispensable for all our occupations.

But the physicist does not allow himself to be misled either by emotions of aesthetic sensibility or by the emphatic but restricted remarks of the common view; it is in the data of experiment and of observation, it is in the general conception of the physical universe to which these data lead him that he demands the reason for his judgements, the solid bases of his affirmations. For him, then, if light—or more generally radiation—deserve to receive a place of honour amongst the natural entities, it is because the properties which they manifest in observable phenomena are peculiar, it is because physical theory, summing up the whole of our knowledge, is led to attribute to it a capital importance in the universe. Let us then examine in detail for what reasons, both concrete and theoretical, the physicist is led to proclaim the primacy of light.

First of all, *light is the fastest of messengers*. For a long time men have had an intuition of this remarkable property of light. Lucretius in his *De Natura Rerum* had already attributed an inexpressible speed to those pellicles detached from the surface of material bodies which, according to him, constituted light. For a long time it was believed that it was propagated instantaneously with an infinite speed; attempts made to measure its speed, especially in the middle of the seventeenth century, had not given any result. It was the Danish astronomer, Roemer, working at the Observatory of Paris, who first succeeded in 1676, in attributing to light, a finite speed of propagation. The observation of the occultations by Jupiter of the satellites of this planet enabled him to calculate the time taken by light to travel over the diameter of the orbit described by the earth around the sun; he thus found for the speed of light a value, which, expressed in our present system of units, is about 313,000 kilometres per second—undoubtedly an excessive, but nevertheless finite, value.

A considerable number of experiments, which we cannot here recall in detail, have enabled us for the past century to measure the speed of propagation of light in empty space with much greater precision and have led to values very close to, but less than, 300,000 kilometres a second.[1] High as this speed may be, it is nevertheless limited and light takes time, often very considerable, to traverse the immense distances which separate the stellar systems. If it requires only about eight minutes to come from the sun which is relatively very near us, it yet requires four years to travel to us from the nearest star, and contemporary astronomers know that it takes millions of years to come from the distant nebulae to our little earth. It is not, therefore, the high value of the speed of light which is the essential fact; it is because this speed cannot be attained by any material body in motion, that it cannot be exceeded by any signal; it is a *limiting speed.*

It is the development and the verifications of the relativity theory which have led us to recognize this character of the *limiting speed* of the velocity of light *in vacuo.* The relativity theory has, in fact, shown us that the mass of bodies, practically constant when they are impelled with the moderate speeds which we usually observe on our scale, increases rapidly when their speed approaches that of light *in vacuo*, and would become infinite if it could attain this limiting speed. To impart to a material body the speed of light *in vacuo*, it would, therefore, be necessary to provide it with an infinite energy, which is impossible; every material body, therefore, moves less quickly than light. Only light, or, if we prefer to use the modern corpuscular language, the "photons" which compose it, are able, because of their evanescent mass, to attain this limiting speed. This remarkable property gives to light an exceptional place in the total of entities which constitutes the physical world. If we wish to signal the occurrence of an event to another rational being we cannot send him a signal which would travel to him more quickly than a light signal (the word being taken in its most general sense, which includes the electromagnetic radiations of wireless, as well as X-rays and γ-rays. And here is one of the reasons for the primacy of light in physics; we repeat, it is the fastest of messengers.

This rapid propagation of luminous perturbations possesses another remarkable characteristic; *light has no need of any support for its propagation.* To understand this point clearly it is necessary to give a rapid summary of the two rival conceptions of light which men of science have given in the course of the centuries. Sometimes they compared a beam of light to a collection of very many small projectiles describing trajectories in close proximity, and conceived a source of light as projecting luminous corpuscles in all directions. Sometimes they preferred to represent light as a wave spreading out into space like the ripples which spread on the surface of a sheet of water, the luminous source being then a centre of agitation where the waves originate, which then proceed to spread out all around. The first conception was that of Lucretius, without doubt of

Descartes, then of Newton, Laplace, Biot, etc. The second, brilliantly supported by Huygens towards the end of the seventeenth century was to experience a triumph—apparently complete—thanks to research effected between 1815 and 1820 by the great Frenchman, Augustin Fresnel. The phenomena of interference and diffractions, suspected in the seventeenth century by Grimaldi and observed later by Newton, had just been studied with greater precision by Young. Malus had just discovered the phenomena of polarization. Augustin Fresnel, in an imposing work, admirable both in its theoretical and experimental parts, showed that the wave conception of light alone is capable of explaining the phenomena of interference and diffraction, and when we introduce into it the hypothesis of the transversality of the waves, of explaining the effects of polarization. We cannot here analyse the immense work accomplished in a few years by a young scientist who died of consumption at the age of thirty-nine. Let us merely say that after his (Fresnel's) labours the undulatory nature of light appeared to be proved and that it was accepted as certain during the whole of the latter end of the nineteenth century.

But if light is formed by waves which are spread about in space, must we not imagine that it has for support a medium which vibrates? Is not the existence of this medium necessary to give (to use the expression of Lord Salisbury) a subject to the verb undulate? Fresnel, in agreement with Huygens's ideas on this, did not doubt it. Just as mechanical disturbances and sound constitute the vibrations of media, solid, liquid, or gaseous, propagated through these media, in the same manner, in his view, light must be the vibration of some medium which serves as its support. As light is transmitted in regions devoid of ponderable matter, he was obliged, therefore, to imagine that what we call empty space is in reality filled with a subtle medium, imponderable and escaping our perception, a medium the vibrations of which constitute light.

This medium had received the name "ether" and for a long time the attempt was made to define the elastic properties of this ether as a means of finding the laws of the propagation of light. The task did not prove easy to accomplish; it was necessary to endow the ether with properties altogether paradoxical, to suppose it was harder than steel although it escapes our senses and that the stars move through it without any difficulty and without undergoing any appreciable friction! When after 1860 we had become accustomed—following on Maxwell, as will be recalled later—to consider light as having an electromagnetic nature, we continued to speak of the ether as a kind of medium of reference for the electromagnetic quantities constituting light, but this idea of the ether became more and more artificial and less and less concrete; one felt it becoming outworn. In the first years of the twentieth century the theory of relativity was destined to give it the fatal blow. Supported by the experimental fact, proved by the celebrated experiments of Michelson, that it is impossible to know whether we are in motion or at rest with reference to the ether, Albert Einstein supposed that natural phenomena, and in particular electromagnetic and luminous phenomena, are the same in all systems of reference moving in a straight line and with uniform velocity with reference to the fixed stars, an hypothesis which involves the abandonment of the idea of the ether.

The success of Einstein's hypotheses, the confirmation of their consequences by experiment, have led physicists to give up the idea of a medium serving as a support for the luminous waves with almost complete unanimity. The classical conception of luminous undulations, held by Huygens and Fresnel necessarily implied the existence of a medium sustaining the waves. The corpuscular conception, on the contrary, had no need for such a medium. We shall see further on that there is today a partial return to the corpuscular conception of light, since the existence of corpuscles of light—the photons—is admitted. It appears that with photons, there should be no further need for the ether and that the difficulty should be removed. But the new theory of light, also, has the need to take account of waves, and the denial of the existence of the ether compels us in itself, even if for no other reasons to give to these waves a much less concrete significance than Fresnel and his successors had done. One thing which is certain remains today; while mechanical disturbances and sound have need of a material support, of a vibrating medium which transmits them, light, more independent of matter, can be propagated without any support, and this in spite of the undulatory aspect which it often presents to us.

We have earlier referred to Maxwell and his electro-magnetic theory of light; what Maxwell has taught us is that *light is the purest form of the electromagnetic field*. In fact, electro-magnetic fields are generally associated with the presence and movement of electricity, that is to say, in the final analysis to the presence and movement of electrified particles which enter into the constitution of matter. Charged bodies are surrounded by an electrostatic field, conducting bodies traversed by an electric current are surrounded by a magnetic field. On the other hand, the discovery of induction in 1831 by Faraday, then the introduction by Maxwell of the displacement current into the general theory of electricity, have taught us that every variation of a magnetic field gives rise to an electric field, and every variation of an electric field gives rise to a magnetic field.

The enormous number of electrified particles which consti-tute matter and which are in constant movement are, therefore, surrounded by electric and magnetic fields the variations of which mutually generate one another; the total of these very complicated electromagnetic fields give rise to the mean effects of charges and electric currents observable on our scale, effects of which the nature is, therefore, essentially statistical. The precise study of the consequences of Maxwell's electromagnetic theory, especially when we take into consideration the existence of corpuscles of electricity, as H. A. Lorentz has systematic-ally done in his theory of electrons, leads then, to the proof that if an electric charge is endowed with an accelerated motion, it radiates electromagnetic energy whilst its motion pro-gressively dies down. This electromagnetic energy assumes at a great distance from its source the form of an electromagnetic wave which is propagated indefinitely. According to the frequency of the waves thus emitted, they will belong variously to the category of Hertzian waves, to that of ultra-violet, visible or infra-red radiations, or again to X-rays or γ-rays. Thus all forms of light, in the general sense of the word which includes all radiations, would be constituted by electro-magnetic fields which, being in some way freed from their connexions with electrified matter, move freely in space.

To be sure the picture which is thus provided for us by

the classical electromagnetic theory of radiation is not, as we know well today, wholly exact, because it ignores the existence of quanta and discontinuities resulting therefrom; but we also know from Bohr's correspondence principle that the classical picture retains a certain value. Moreover, the discontinuous and quantal conception of light leads us to affirm that all forms of light in free propagation are formed by "photons" freed from all connexion with electrified particles of matter (these photons being, of course, accompanied by their electromagnetic field, which brings us back to the same conclusion but expressed differently). And that is why we can say that light is the purest form of the electromagnetic field.

Let us now come to a vital point which, from the intellectual point of view, would suffice of itself to hold light in high regard. *Light has revealed to us the duality of waves and corpuscles* thus enabling us to penetrate deeply into the secrets of the physical world. We have already previously recalled that light had been conceived in turn as a stream of corpuscles and a propagation of waves and we have seen that Augustin Fresnel made the undulatory conception triumph in a manner which, for a long time, appeared to be conclusive. But the beginning of our century was to bring the surprise of the renewal of the corpuscular conception of light. The study of the photoelectric phenomenon, where we see a metal submitted to an irradiation, expelling electrons, led to the recognition that this phenomenon follows laws totally incompatible with the undulatory conception of radiations. As Einstein has shown since 1905, all this takes place as if a ray of light of frequency v were formed from grains of energy of value hv, h being Planck's constant of quanta. There was thus a revival—though in new form—adapted to the conceptions of the theory of the quanta, of the old hypothesis that light is formed by corpuscles to which the name "photons" was soon given.

Einstein's idea proved to be very fruitful; it has led to an explanation of a great many facts which the undulatory theory could not interpret, such as the existence of an upper limit of frequencies in the spectra of X-rays, the existence of the Compton and Raman effects, etc. Was it necessary to conclude that Newton was right as opposed to Fresnel? No indeed, because the phenomena of interferences and diffraction are there to show us the necessity to maintain, at least in part, the undulatory picture of light, and the very definition of photons requires the participation of the frequency, which is an undulatory conception. We must then of necessity seek to find a kind of compromise between the granular and the undulatory views of light. That this is a difficult task is easily seen if we reflect on it, for it is clear that it will be necessary for this difficult synthesis to be effected, to discard many of the ideas held by all the classical theories, to correlate the ideas of determinism and individuality, to introduce systematically probabilities into elementary phenomena, and to account in the description of phenomena for certain complementary aspects which are carried out while opposing each other.

The necessity for reconciling the granular and undulatory aspects of light suggests the idea of extending this duality of waves and corpuscles to all the elements of matter, in particular to electrons. We thus come to a general theory, known today under the name "wave mechanics", all the developments and successes of which it is impossible for us to recall here. Not only has this theory completely transformed atomic physics, but it has extended to all matter the conceptions of probability, of uncertainty, of non-individuality, of complementary aspects which the study of light had already suggested, thus opening new horizons to the philosophy of nature.

We thus perceive the fundamental service which light has rendered us in revealing the duality of waves and corpuscles; it has illuminated our minds as it has illuminated our bodies.

Up till now we have often opposed light and matter, the latter being associated with mass and often with electricity, while the former always appears free from inertia and charge. But if these two fundamental entities of the physical world appear to oppose one another, they are none the less related because they are both special forms of energy. In principle, therefore, there is nothing against the view that energy, while always conserving itself, can pass from the material to the luminous form and vice versa. We know today that it is actually so; this fact breaks down the barrier which seemed to separate light and matter and, to complete the enumeration of the fundamental properties which assure light a privileged place amongst the physical entities, we can now add that *light is, in short, the most refined form of matter.*

This final union of the conceptions of light and of matter in the unity of this protoform entity which is energy, has been completely proved by the progress of contemporary physics on the day it discovered that material particles are capable of disappearing while giving rise to radiation, whilst radiation is capable of condensing into matter and of creating new particles. It is thus that two electrons of opposite sign (the ordinary negative electron and the positive electron or the positron) can mutually annihilate each other; this dematerialization of a pair of electrons, which observes the conservation of electricity (since two charges equal and of opposite signs disappear at the same time) is accompanied by the emission of two photons of radiation, so that the energy of the two electrons is found entirely in the form of radiation energy. In this phenomenon energy changes its form while conserving itself; from matter it becomes light, and conversely, in favourable circumstances, a photon can give birth to a pair of electrons of contrary sign. In this case once again there is conservation of energy and of electricity, but here the energy of light has become matter.

All these facts clearly prove that light and matter are only different aspects of energy which can take in succession one or the other of these two appearances. But what characterizes light in the whole of the manifestations of energy is that it is the fastest, the most delicate, the most free from inertia and charge, of all these manifestations. If, therefore, we now extend the meaning of the word "matter" to all forms of energy, we will truly be able to say, as has been previously stated, that light is the most refined form of matter.

Studying in succession the different properties of light, we have seen why it holds a particularly exalted place in the totality of the phenomena which physics studies. Proceeding continuously from matter or being absorbed in it, it acts as a connecting link between all the material particles on the microscopic scale. It is light also which, rushing with a terrific speed, traverses the sidereal spaces and acts as a messenger between the most distant stars. It is through it that we have become aware of the immensity of the universe; it is light which reveals to us the existence of nebulae situated at such enormous distances that, in spite of its speed, it takes hundreds of millions of years to traverse them.

Carrying with it neither appreciable mass nor electric charge, light ploughs its way incessantly through space without requiring any support, and physicists with their minds' eyes see in it a conveyance of the electromagnetic field in the purest form. For us, as mysterious as it is familiar, it manifests itself under two aspects which at first seem to us to be contradictory. To interpret its nature, our mind, which is never able to ignore entirely the images suggested by our senses, evokes in turn the corpuscle which describes its trajectory and the wave which spreads out in vibrating; but it has recognized the insufficiency of these two representations considered separately and the necessity of merging them in a superior synthesis which considers them as complementary. This immense effort of abstraction has led us to entirely new conceptions of which the scope in the philosophic as well as in the scientific domain appears considerable. Taught by light, we have penetrated into the unknown spheres of thought.

Finally, light has just revealed itself to us as capable of condensing into matter, whilst matter is capable of dissipating into light.

Giving free scope to our imagination, we could suppose that at the beginning of time, on the morrow of some divine "Fiat Lux", light, at first alone in the universe, has little by little produced by progressive condensation the material universe such as, thanks to light itself, we can contemplate it today. And perhaps one day, when time will have ended, the universe, recovering its original purity, will again dissolve into light.

[1] The most recent determination of the velocity of light is $299,789 \pm 0.4$ km./sec. and it has been suggested that $299,790$ km./sec. should be adopted. This is equivalent to $186,281$ miles/sec., approximately.

CHAPTER IV

WAVE MECHANICS AND THE STUDY OF SURFACE STATES*

THE Doges of Venice were never allowed to leave the town that they ruled. Circumstances having led one of them to Versailles to the Court of Louis XIV, when asked by Louis what he admired most in this town then at the zenith of its splendour, he replied: "It is to see myself here!"

In assuming today the presidency of your closing conference, I would be tempted to say, like the Doge: "What astonishes me most is to see myself here." And for this reason: When in 1919, at the end of the First World War, I began researches in theoretical physics on the theory of quanta, which were to lead me to submit four or five years later in my thesis for a doctorate the first principles of wave mechanics, all thought of applying it technically was very far from my mind. Having much more the state of mind of a pure theoretician than that of an experimenter or engineer, loving especially the general and philosophical view, I was drawn towards the problems of atomic physics where the quanta rule, in the following way:

It was the conceptual difficulties which these problems raised; it was the mystery which surrounded that famous Planck's constant, h, which measures the quantum of action; it was the disturbing and badly defined character of the dualism of waves and corpuscles, which appeared to assert itself more and more in the realms of physics (especially in the realm of the X-rays which I was then studying with my brother).

It is to these stimulating and difficult problems that I sought to find some solution by making an appeal to the whole storehouse of old and modern theories of mathematical physics, from geometrical optics and analytical mechanics to the theory

*An address delivered at the closing meeting of the 'Journées des états de surface', held in Paris in October 1945.

of relativity and the quantal theories of Planck, Bohr and Sommerfeld. If anyone had then told me that studies so completely and, of choice, abstract could have given me twenty-five years later some title to preside over an important conference in a congress devoted to the very concrete study of the surface state of bodies, he would have astonished me.

Nevertheless the phenomenon of the diffraction of electrons and, to a great extent also, the present methods of electronic optics, are closely attached to the concepts which were then germinating in my mind and which with youthful audacity I was soon to set forth in my thesis. Now the diffraction of electrons and the electronic microscope constitute today two of the most powerful means at our disposal for the deeper study of surface states. And this is why, whilst remaining surprised to see how, by the unexpected scientific developments, certain techniques today can in a sense be considered as proceeding from my formerly purely speculative researches, I do not feel myself entirely unworthy of the honour of presiding at the present reunion.

And if we desire to draw the moral from this affiliation of discoveries, we should have to insist on the fact that the progress of pure science, the efforts accomplished in high spheres of scientific thought, have almost always had repercussions in the realm of applications and of techniques.

A long time ago Emile Picard wrote in his book, *La Science Moderne*: "The scientific dreamers who seem lost in their speculations are, in their own way, practical men; the application sometimes follows quite unexpectedly." And, as food for thought, he added this useful warning. "The source of this progress would soon dry up if an exclusively utilitarian mind should come to dominate our society, too much preoccupied with immediate enjoyment."

The example of the present practical applications of wave mechanics, that science which appeared so abstract at its origin, is undoubtedly one of the finest illustrations of the thought processes of that great mathematician.

I shall now leave these general considerations, and by way of prologue to the interesting communications which you are going to hear this morning, I should like to examine rapidly for what profound reason the new ideas of wave mechanics, when they were shown to conform to facts, should necessarily lead to new and powerful means of studying very small structures of matter, such as those which are the subject of your researches.

You are acquainted with the origins of wave mechanics. Towards 1920 physics was in a kind of blind alley. On the one hand the works of Fresnel, more than a century old, had accustomed us to regard light as formed by homogeneous waves transmitted through space and these views had been confirmed during the whole of the nineteenth century by experiments of an altogether remarkable extent and precision. The discovery of the photoelectric effect, however, had just proved to us that luminous energy possesses a granular structure entirely unrecognized by Fresnel's undulatory conception, and each day furnished new proofs of this discontinuous structure of light. Now, no means could be seen of reconciling this granular structure of light with the undulatory conception of Fresnel, a conception which itself was based on solid experimental proofs also.

On the other hand, the progress of the physics of matter had proved, with a wealth of incessantly increasing precision, that matter possesses a corpuscular structure, and had shown the role which "electrons" or grains of negative electricity played in this structure. But we had the surprise of establishing the fact that corpuscles of matter and electrons in particular, in certain cases and especially in the interior of atomic structures, showed paradoxical properties expressed by the theory of quanta, and of which the classical picture of the corpuscle could give no explanations.

In 1923, after deep reflection, I put forward an idea well known to all, in an attempt to probe more deeply into these obscure problems. This idea today forms the basis of the vast and complex edifice of wave mechanics. I announced that, in the case of light as of matter, it is always necessary to consider waves and corpuscles simultaneously in order to obtain a unique synthetic doctrine, capable of interpreting at the same time the corpuscular and undulatory aspects which the properties of light and of matter present. In the case of light this worked pretty well. We very quickly obtained a synthesis of the undulatory theory of Fresnel and Maxwell and of the new corpuscular theory of radiation, which Einstein had developed in 1905, known as "the theory of photons". Although the precise definition of this synthesis was subsequently long and difficult, for reasons which I am unable to enlarge upon, it was felt from then onward that one was on the right road. In the case of matter it was very different; my views appeared more daring and hypothetical for, up till then experiment had only made it possible to establish the corpuscular aspect of the elements of matter such as the electrons. The undulatory nature of the electrons remained unknown and if I had succeeded in interpreting the quantization of electronic movements in the atoms as an aspect of this undulatory nature, it was still a very indirect proof and one which was not yet very sound.

It was the discovery in 1927 in the United States by Davisson and Germer of the diffraction of electrons by crystals, soon confirmed by numerous investigations carried out in different countries, which gave a striking and complete confirmation of the conception which served as the basis of wave mechanics. It led especially to the verification that the wave-length of the wave associated with an electron of momentum p is given by the formula

$$\lambda = \frac{h}{p}$$

previously demonstrated by wave mechanics.

I shall also recall that subsequent experiments have shown that the other material particles, protons, atomic nuclei, etc., are also associated with waves, conform to the general schema of wave mechanics, and can give rise to phenomena of diffraction. The formula $\lambda = h/p$ applies, therefore, to corpuscles other than the electrons, as well.

And now why were these fresh discoveries capable of supplying us with new means of studying very fine material structures? It is because they showed us the existence of new phenomena of an undulatory nature corresponding to types of waves unknown up till then, the electron waves, for example. Now it is always with the assistance of undulatory phenomena that we have been able to analyse the very fine material structures and, as I shall recall, certain limitations of the processes of analysis, up till then employed, were related to the nature of the waves utilized and might be cancelled by the use of waves associated with the electrons (or with particles of matter).

The oldest method for the study of very fine material structures consisted in the use of apparatus giving an enlarged luminous image of the object to be examined—a magnifying glass or better, microscopes. But there exists a limit, imposed by the nature of things, to these magnifications. The length of a wave of luminous vibrations is of the order of half one-thousandth of a millimetre ($0 \cdot 5\mu$) for the middle of the visible spectrum, and it is shown in the classical theory of separation power that we can never distinguish from each other two points of an object when their distance is appreciably smaller than the wave-length. We can gain a little by using immersion objectives, but the advantage is relatively small. This limits the magnification of microscopes to two to three thousand at the most. The ultramicroscope enables one to go further, but with this arrangement we suspect the details of the objects rather than see them.

Indeed to go further we must use waves of much shorter wave-length. The discovery of X-rays which have wave-lengths shorter than those of light might appear at first to provide us with the means of studying very small structures in greater detail. Here wave-lengths range from 10^{-7} to 10^{-9} cm., and are a thousand times smaller than those of light. But a great difficulty presents itself; we cannot construct optical instruments for X-rays because all the media have an index of refraction practically equal to 1 for X-rays, whilst the construction of an optical instrument always implies the juxtaposition of media with appreciably different indices of refraction. Hence it is impossible to make an X-ray microscope. (It should, however, be noted that Mlle Cauchois succeeded quite recently, by means of ingenious apparatus, in obtaining images with X-rays.)

Fortunately there is the phenomenon of the diffraction of X-rays by crystallized media. In bodies partly or entirely crystallized, the distribution of material centres in the crystal presents a great regularity and the distances between these centres are of the order of 10^{-8} cm., that is, of the order of the wave-lengths of X-rays. Hence crystallized bodies play the role of a three-dimensional screen for X-rays and a beam of X-rays striking a crystal experiences a phenomenon of diffraction analogous to that which is experienced by light falling on an ordinary optical screen, but more complicated because here the screen is three dimensional.

The diffraction patterns obtained with X-rays allow us to deduce the structure of the medium which promoted the diffraction. This method has made possible not only the study of crystalline structures properly so named, but also that of superficial structures and of thin layers, for example, of oily substances.

Numerous results, often valuable for technical application (the lubricating properties of oily substances) have been obtained in this way. We know especially the excellent work in France on this subject carried out by J. J. Trillat and his school.

Nevertheless, the method of the study of fine material structures by the diffraction of X-rays presents some disadvantages. X-rays being very penetrating, they are specially well adapted for the study of the deep layers of the structures of matter. The superficial states, properly speaking, often escape them. Furthermore, the diffraction of X-rays does not allow one to see the structures but merely to deduce them with the assistance of theoretical considerations, starting with the observed appearances of the diffraction; and this deduction—somewhat indirect—is sometimes difficult or uncertain and leads to results which are not uniform.

The discovery of other methods better adapted to the study of surface states, enabling us to see the structures directly, remained, therefore, eminently desirable. The utilization of the wave properties of electrons would supply these new methods.

In the first place, the diffraction of the electrons by crystals is a phenomenon completely analogous to the diffraction of X-rays by crystals. In fact, in the usual conditions of obtaining them, the beams of electrons procured by accelerating the electrons by a difference of potential, correspond to associated wave-lengths, also of the order of 10^{-7} to 10^{-9} cm., that is, of the same order of size as the wave-lengths of the X-rays. Now it is the ratio of the wave-length to the distances between the centres of the crystal which controls the diffraction in the crystal, consequently the phenomena observable with electrons will present a marked analogy with the phenomena observable with X-rays. Evidently the wave of X-rays is an electromagnetic wave united to photons, whereas the associated wave of the electrons has not the same character (here is a difficult question which we begin today to understand much more clearly than we did some years ago); but this difference of constitution does not prevent the complete analogy of the phenomena of diffraction.

There is, nevertheless, a difference, which particularly interests us here, between the two kinds of phenomena. Electrons penetrate much less easily into matter than X-rays, and consequently their diffraction by crystallized matter very often takes place principally in the superficial layers, or even through the centres situated on the surface itself. This is why at the commencement of the studies on the diffraction of electrons, we had observed with a certain surprise phenomena of diffraction corresponding to a two-dimensional lattice—a purely superficial lattice. One readily understands that this circumstance is particularly favourable to the study of surface states and it explains why the diffraction of electrons has become quite an important method of investigation. But the diffraction of electrons, no more than that of X-rays, does not allow the superficial states to be seen and here again the deduction of the structures is indirect.

It is not the same in the case of the electronic microscope, for, contrary to what occurs in the case of X-rays, we are able to construct optical instruments for the waves associated with electrons. In fact in a region of space where electric or magnetic fields prevail, the trajectory of an electron is curved exactly as is a ray of light, that is to say, the trajectory of a photon in a non-homogeneous refracting medium. Wave mechanics shows that the region of space where the fields prevail plays for the wave associated with an electron the same role as a refracting medium with variable index does for a luminous wave. An appropriate combination of electric and magnetic fields is therefore capable of making the electrons emitted by a point source converge more or less exactly to a point. We can, therefore, obtain with electrons a more or less perfect image of an object which emits or diffuses electrons.

To be sure the electronic image obtained is not directly visible to our eye but it can induce fluorescence on a screen or make an impression on a photographic plate, so that with the aid of these simple contrivances we can finally see it. The electronic microscope, by providing the enlarged images, allows us, therefore, to see very small structures directly.

The great interest of the electronic microscope is that it provides very much greater magnifications than the optical microscope. The wave-length of electrons in the usual conditions of their use, is in fact of the order of the wave-lengths of X-rays, that is, 1,000 times smaller than the wave-length of light, and the theory of the separation power, always applicable as in optics, shows us, therefore, that the separation power of the electron microscope is much greater than that of the ordinary microscope; from which arises the possibility of very much greater magnifications. In place of magnifications of two to three thousand times at the most, we attain an enlargement of fifteen thousand to twenty thousand, even fifty thousand times, and we shall perhaps attain a magnification of one hundred thousand. And this is not all; it is possible that we might go further for by utilizing particles heavier than electrons (protons, for example) we shall obtain for a given energy still shorter wave-lengths (as the formula $\lambda = h/p = h/mv$ shows) and in consequence greater magnifications, going perhaps to five hundred thousand.

Professor Dupouy has shown you the magnificent results that he has obtained with his electronic microscope with magnetic field. Other lines of research of the same kind are being studied in France. Abroad electronic optics has already developed much further in certain countries but we hope to retrieve lost time. It has already brought us real revelations concerning surface states and micro-organisms. It is a wonderful instrument and it in impossible at present to imagine all that it will teach us. For the investigations of surface states, it seems certain that it will be a very valuable tool.

CHAPTER V

SOME CONSIDERATIONS ON THE CONCEPT OF QUANTITY IN PHYSICS

PHYSICS, like all other sciences, seeks to establish, to classify and to interpret a certain category of observable phenomena. It rests, therefore, essentially on observation, with the assistance of the senses provided for us by nature, of certain facts of the material world which are ascertainable. But this science only succeeded in emerging from a qualitative state to attain that of exact quantitative science by constantly resting on measurement; that is, in always seeking to characterize the aspects of truth by the aid of numbers, of which she asserts the value at certain epochs, and concerning which she seeks to follow a progressive variation in the course of time. Not being able at each instant to represent in its entirety the infinitely complex state of the real world of which, moreover, each observer at every instant perceives but a minute part, physics has sought to discover in the uninterrupted flux of phenomena certain elements capable, at the time, of being detached from the totality by theoretical abstraction and of being characterized by precise numerical values. These elements are the "observable physical quantities" and the aim of physical science is to establish the relations which exist between the values of these quantities and their variations, then to interpret these relations, to show their scope, by co-ordinating them in those vast constructions of the mind, which are called theories.

One should not believe that the different quantities considered by the physicist appear quite naturally to him and as imposed on his attention by the observation of reality only. It is but by the measures of length, of surface and volume, and perhaps for certain quantities introducing the idea of substance supposed indestructible, that it can be so. Already the precise definition of the quantity "interval of time" raises grave difficulties and can only be given with the aid of conventions where the constructive activity of our mind materially intervenes. Even more so is it the same in the cases where the physical quantities only present themselves to us in a veiled form, where it is necessary to accomplish an effort of abstraction or to depend upon the ideas previously acquired, to extricate the exact definition. The history of science shows, for example, how long a time and how many discussions, often acrimonious, it took to succeed in clearly discerning the momentum of energy, the inert mass of weight, the quantity of heat of temperature. . . .

The usual language still bears the mark of confusions which for a long time existed on this subject, and we readily say that one body is hotter than another when we should say that its temperature is higher.

Some philosophical scientists, such, for example, as Pierre Duhem and Edouard Le Roy, have long insisted on the fact that all the definitions of physics and that of quantities in particular, are based on conventions or hypotheses, and imply an adherence, often implicit, to generally admitted theories. The measure of every quantity is effected through the intermediary of a measure of length or of a measure of angle, and it is only indirectly, with the aid of theoretical conceptions, that we build up geometrical assertions about the quantity itself. Although it would be unnecessary to press the critical spirit to a paradox, it is certain that nature does not generally offer us of her own accord the quantities the study and the measure of which must serve as bases to the speculations of physics. It is necessary for us to extract these quantities from reality by an effort of abstraction which requires the whole of our theoretical knowledge and of our habits of thought. The description of the physical world effected by a being whose intellectual structure or sensory organs differed profoundly from ours, would undoubtedly be vastly different from ours. It has been said of art that it was "Man added to Nature". The same definition also applies to science.

The quantities which physicists use in their reasoning are not all observable and measurable. Certain of these serve only as intermediaries; they come into the calculations but are eliminated when comparison is made with experiment. We have attempted, by taking a purely phenomenological point of view, to eject all the non-measurable quantities from physical theories. The doctrine of energy and, more recently, the doctrine of quantal mechanics by Heisenberg are remarkable examples of this kind of effort. But these attempts have never completely succeeded; there always exist in the theories quantities which are non-measurable, and for example, in wave mechanics the well-known wave function Ψ belongs to this category. Nevertheless the measurable quantities retain a basic importance for it is through them that the indispensable experimental control of the consequences of the theory is carried out.

Here arises the question of knowing if it is possible, in the case of observable quantities, to distinguish those which can be fairly measured from those which can only be assessed. Many authors indeed make this distinction. The quantities which are fairly measurable would be those for which we could say that of two quantities of this nature the one is greater than the other and for which we could speak of the sum of two quantities of the same nature; the quantities which can only be assessed would be those for which these assertions would have no meaning. The first correspond to factors of capacity; they could be represented either by the addition of independent elements (lengths, surfaces, volumes), or by the variation of the quantity of an indestructible substance (mass, amount of electricity, etc.). The second, on the contrary, would correspond to factors of intensity and could in no wise be representable by a juxtaposition of elements or by the variation of a quantity of substance; electric potential and temperature would be typical examples of these.

At first sight this distinction of measurable quantities and of merely assessable quantities seems justified. To say that a metre is greater than a centimetre, that a weight of a kilo is greater than a weight of a gramme, are affirmations of which the sense is obvious. In the same way, we immediately understand the addition of lengths, some to others, in a work of land surveying; and the addition of some weights to others in the scale of a balance. To say, however, that one temperature is greater than another, that it is double or triple of it, does not seem to have a very precise meaning, and it is certain that we do not add temperatures as we place graduated rulers end to end. Nevertheless, looking at it closely, the distinction of the two kinds of quantities appears as more artificial than might have been thought at first sight. In fact, to say of a quantity that it is measurable is to affirm that we can fix its value by making it correspond to a well-determined number. Thenceforth, we can always say that, of two measurable quantities A and B, the one A is greater than the other B if the number which measures A is greater than that which measures B, and similarly if A, B, C are three measurable quantities, we can say that C is the sum of A and B if the number which measures C is the sum of those which measure A and B.

It is true that one can reply to that, with an appearance of reason, that for the quantities which are only assessable, we can choose an arbitrary scale to express their value whilst for the fairly measurable quantities there exist the natural scales such that in the first case the statement that C is the sum of A and B is disputable because it will be true only if certain scales are used, whilst in the second case the statement will have a precise meaning, thanks to the use of the natural scale. Two metres, it will be said, will always be twice one metre whilst a temperature will or will not be double of another according to the process used to assess them.

But in the definition of "natural" scales is there not something a little arbitrary, such as an unconscious appeal to custom or to more or less justified intuitions? We could very well measure lengths with rulers graduated logarithmically like slide rules and then a length of two metres would no longer be double the measure of the length of one metre. We admit as evident that in adding on the scale of a balance a weight of one kilo to another weight of a kilo, we make the scale support a weight of two kilos. But let us imagine—and it is not inconceivable—that the fact of placing side by side two weights of a kilo promotes the emission of a light radiation, then in accordance with the conceptions of relativity theory (the principle of inertia of energy) the two copper masses of a kilo each placed side by side would not have a total weight equal to the sum of the weights which they had when they were separated. It would be easy to multiply examples and thus to show to what point our conception of natural scales relative to quantities supposed to be rightly

measurable, and our assertions on the equality or on the ratio
of two such quantities of the same nature, depend on somewhat
arbitrary intuitions or on preconceived theoretical ideas.

Conversely, the quantities usually considered as simply
assessable can appear under another guise following the
theoretical conceptions which we introduce for the purpose.
Let us, for example, consider temperature. For all energetists
—for Pierre Duhem in particular—it was the type of a quantity
of intensity merely assessable. But already in the classical
framework of abstract thermodynamics, the introduction,
thanks to Carnot's principle, of the idea of absolute temperature as the inverse of the integral factor of the quantity of heat,
makes possible the definition of a natural and privileged scale
of temperatures. Further, the molecular and statistical theories
of matter, by defining the temperature of a body as proportional to the mean thermal energy of its molecules, reconciles
the idea of temperature to that of energy and in consequence
attaches it to an entity which is conserved: a perfect gas
comprising N molecules has a temperature double that of
another perfect gas also formed of N molecules if the internal
energy of thermal agitation of the first gas is double that of the
second.

And, moreover, for the electric potential can we not say
that in counting two piles in series, we add the differences of
potential existing at their extreme terminals?

In brief, it seems to us that we must not exaggerate the
scope of the distinction between measurable quantities and
quantities simply assessable. This distinction can be of practical
use in certain cases, but it depends in great measure on the
usual conditions of our experiments, of our habits of thought
and of the theoretical interpretation that we attribute to
the various quantities.

The measurable quantities can be divided into different
categories. Some are defined independently of any three
dimensional framework of reference in space and are characterized by a unique number. In classical physics such are,
for example, temperature, mass and electric charge. They are
called scalar quantities because they suggest the picture of a
scale of values independent of all idea of orientation. To

express the value of a scalar quantity we must choose the unit which will serve to measure it and the origin from which we start to measure. In this case the choice of a system of reference, reduces, therefore, to the choice of the origin. This choice is sometimes imposed by physical considerations as in the case of a quantity of substance or of that of absolute temperatures; in other cases, as that of measure of length or of time, it remains arbitrary. Regarding the choice of unit, it is always arbitrary. The number which measures a quantity always varies in inverse ratio with the unit chosen. A simultaneous change of origin and unit imposes on the number which measures the scalar quantity a linear transformation.

Besides scalar quantities there also exist quantities which are bound to one another and presenting amongst themselves a kind of solidarity—quantities the values of which depend on the three-dimensional frame of reference used to assess points in space. Such quantities define a unique mathematical "being" having an "intrinsic" significance, that is, independent of the system of reference employed; but in each system of reference the being in question resolves itself into "components" which themselves depend upon the system employed. The simplest example of this kind of mathematical entities is the vector of three-dimensional space which, in every system of reference formed by rectilinear axes, has three components. The vector is known in magnitude and direction if its three components are known. If the system of reference is changed, the components experience linear transformations depending on the displacement of the origin and on the change of orientation of the axes when passing from the first to the second system. Here the choice of reference involves, in addition to the choice of the origin, that of the orientation of the axes. Of course it will be necessary to choose a unit of length which will generally be the same for all three axes. If at the same time we change the unit of length, the origin and the orientation of the axes, the vector components will undergo a general linear transformation which will take account altogether of the three modifications that have been effected.

We can, moreover, in three-dimensional space, consider mathematical beings having an intrinsic character more complicated than vectors. Such are the tensors of different orders. The distinct components of a tensor of order k are in general 3^k in number. When there is a change of the system of reference, these components also undergo a linear transformation depending on the change of origin and on that of the orientation of the axes.

If we consider abstract space of more than three dimensions, we can also define vectors and tensors, generalizing those of the usual physical space. In a space of n dimensions a vector will have n components and a tensor of order k will have n^k of them. These components are linearly transformed when we displace the origin of co-ordinates and change the orientation of the axes.

These abstract definitions have assumed an important physical significance since the development of the theory of relativity; this latter has, in fact, introduced the conception that the totality of physical phenomena must be represented within the framework of a four-dimensional continuum uniting the space and time co-ordinates of different observers. The vectors and tensors of this "space-time" have an intrinsic significance, independent of the observers and of the systems of reference, but their components, which are the quantities physically observable and measurable, differ according to the observers and the systems of reference that they use. In the relativity theory there is no universal time common to all the observers, as was recognized in the old physics; two observers in motion relative to one another use different times, and since, in addition, the axes of reference which they use to locate the phenomena in space are no longer the same, the passage of one to the other corresponds to a change of the axes of reference in space-time, a change accompanied in general by a variation of all the components of vector and tensor quantities which characterize in an intrinsic manner the phenomena of the physical universe.

In addition to the vectors and tensors it is expedient to say a word about the "invariants". The invariants or tensors of order 0 are the quantities characterized by a single numerical datum which is independent of the system of reference used. For example, in classical physics the time intervals, the energies, the mass and the electric charge of a particle as well as the entropy or the temperature of a body, are invariants; their value is in no wise affected by a change of the axes of reference in space. But it should be remarked that the character of invariance of a quantity depends essentially on the theories that we admit. If we pass from classical physics, in which we judge the localization of phenomena in three-dimensional space by accepting the existence of an invariable universal time, to relativity physics in which we localize phenomena in the four-dimensional space-time framework, some of the invariants of the old doctrine lose their character in the new whilst others preserve it. Thus time interval and energy cease to be invariants and become the fourth component (or components of time) of a space-time vector; their values are not modified by a simple change of axes of reference in space, but they vary if one passes from the first observer to a second who is moving with respect to the first, for then a change of the system of reference in space-time is effected. Electric charge and entropy, on the contrary, remain invariants which are in no wise influenced by a change of system of reference of space-time.

The question is a little more complex in the case of mass; there, where atomic physics saw nothing but a single invariant quantity—the mass of a body—relativity physics distinguishes two quantities; the mass of a body at rest, which is a relativity invariant, and the mass of the body in motion, which is a function of its speed, and which in consequence is not a relativity invariant. The principle of the inertia of energy allows us to consider the mass of a body in motion as proportional to its energy and in consequence to liken it to the component of time of the space-time vector.

Is it expedient to distinguish invariant from scalar quantities? The two ideas are certainly extremely close to each other; scalar like invariant quantities are characterized by the fact that they are determined by a unique number and that they are independent of the system of reference employed. Nevertheless we could attempt to separate them by allowing that for a scalar quantity the essential property is to be characterized by only one numerical datum, while for an invariant quantity the essential property is to be independent of the system of reference. We could then say that energy, for example, is in classical physics at the same time a scalar and an invariant quantity, while in relativity physics it is always scalar but is no longer invariant. Nevertheless, as we have seen, the energy in relativity physics is really the time component of a vector and has thus become conjointly responsible for the momentum whose components form the other components of the same vector, so that, from the relativity point of view, the scalar character of energy is debatable. Perhaps it would be fairer to take as an example temperature, a scalar quantity and an invariant in classical physics, which ceases in relativity physics to be invariant without becoming the time component of a vector and whilst retaining a scalar character. In every way the ideas of scalarity and of invariance are very much akin and their distinction very narrow.

Here, we might again speak of the question of physical dimensions and of the equations to the dimensions, but this is so well known that it seems to us useless to press it. Some of the questions that we have touched on in this exposition are rather abstruse and undoubtedly would deserve a more complete examination; what we have said about them, however, seems sufficient to orientate the thoughts of those who would wish to examine them more thoroughly.

CHAPTER VI

ON THE FORMATION OF IMAGES IN CORPUSCULAR OPTICS

THE considerations which I wish to put forward have been suggested to me by an examination of the existing relation between the separating power of an electronic microscope and Heisenberg's uncertainty principle. The interesting thing about these considerations appears to be the fact that they demonstrate especially in the realm of corpuscular optics, the uncertainty relations and the phenomena which are associated with them, a fact which can assume a great importance in the near future, both theoretically and practically—for these are the phenomena which will at first render it difficult, then undoubtedly impossible, to "see" with the corpuscular microscope the details of smaller and smaller structures. The improvement in corpuscular microscopy is such that already we foresee the time when we may meet the first difficulties.

I shall divide this outline into two parts; in the first I shall recapitulate certain well-known theoretical ideas relating to the formation of images in instruments of ordinary optics and in those of corpuscular optics; in the second I shall confine myself more especially to stating precisely the questions relative to the separating power, to the starting of the object in motion, and to the quantal uncertainties in corpuscular optics.

I

First of all, let us recall a few classical ideas of ordinary optics and let us consider a source of light. From the point of view of geometrical optics which we shall adopt at first, this source sends out in all directions around it rays of light which today we can consider as being trajectories of photons emitted by the source. We will assume at first that the source is a point so that all the rays diverge from the point of origin.

An optical instrument is an arrangement formed by the

juxtaposition of different refracting bodies, the object of which is to give a point image of a point source. In other words, we want the luminous rays received by the apparatus, after they have passed through it, to converge as exactly as possible to a point image. Optical instruments in general exhibit a cylindrical axis of symmetry, and we say that they are centred. They are generally constituted by the juxtaposition of optically homogeneous media, for example by lenses joined together or separated by spaces filled with air (or by oil in the immersion objective). The rays are, then, broken lines, the breaks being produced at the surface of separation of the homogeneous media. There is, however, nothing to prevent us from imagining that in optical instruments we make use of non-homogeneous media with a continuously variable index; the rays would then be curves with a continuous curvature, but we could always try to arrange matters so that they intersect to give a point image. If I mention this possibility, which seems a little odd in ordinary optics, it is because this is what takes place in the apparatus of corpuscular optics.

The laws of geometrical optics (laws of Descartes, Fermat's principle, etc.) theoretically permit us to follow the paths of the rays in the optical instrument and to see if they reintersect exactly in a point image. The result of this study is that unfortunately this exact reintersection does not generally take place. The rays near the axis of the apparatus and very slightly inclined to it, which we call the "central rays", intersect well, with the usual apparatus employed, in an exact image the position of which is given by the well-known formulae of Gauss's homographic optics. But the rays at a distance from the axis or appreciably inclined to it do not intersect at the same point. The deviations of their points of intersection from the Gaussian image constitute the "aberrations".

The calculation of the aberrations is very important in optics because it gives indications on the manner of diminishing or finally of annulling them. This calculation is effected either by simple, though disjointed methods, which separately supply the different kinds of aberrations, or by a powerful and synthetic method, namely the more complicated method of iconal functions.[1] In one way or another we thus come to calculate and classify the most important aberrations, those which appear at first approximation when we pass beyond the Gaussian dioptric being called aberrations of the third order.

We find five kinds of aberrations of the third order, some particularly appreciable when the aperture of the instrument is large, the others when the point source is far from the axis. These are: spherical aberration, coma, curvature of the field, astigmatism and distortion. I am not dwelling on their nature which is well known to all those who are interested in geometrical optics, and equally I pass by chromatic aberration which appears when the source is not monochromatic.

All the preceding considerations on the formation of the image in an ordinary optical instrument are based on the laws of geometrical optics, and in particular on the idea of the luminous ray.

But it is well known that geometrical optics can provide only an approximation; the transmission of light can be described exactly only by wave equations and it is only in cer- tain—although extensive—cases, that the transmission of luminous waves is explained by the existence of rays obeying the laws of geometrical optics. In other cases, notably when the luminous wave, in order that it may penetrate into a region of space, must pass through an aperture of limited dimensions so that only one portion of the wave is admitted into the posterior region, phenomena of diffraction are produced. We can foresee this only with the aid of rigorous solutions of the wave equations, and there where the phenomena of diffraction intervene, geometrical optics and the idea of a luminous ray lose all significance. There, are then, no longer trajectories of photons; I need not recall here the difficulties to which this circumstance gives rise in the synthetic theory of waves and of the corpuscles for light.

Now, optical instruments have always a limited aperture, limited for instance by the mounting—by the circular edge of the objective. There is, then, diffraction of the wave admitted into the instrument through this limited circular opening. The theory of this diffraction, put forward a century ago by Airy, and requiring the use of Bessel functions, teaches us that, in consequence of this effect, the luminous intensity in the vicinity of a point object undergoes fluctuations; outside this point there are circular fringes alternatively bright and dark the intensity of which, moreover, rapidly decreases. Thus, even if geometrical aberrations are corrected or are negligible, the image of a luminous point is not a point but a circular spot where the intensity rapidly decreases over the whole towards the exterior, but presenting alternatively maxima and zero minima. Naturally, in the general case, the lack of definition of the image is due at the same time both to this diffraction effect and to the geometrical aberrations. Moreover, it is not sufficient simply to add the diffraction effect to the aberration effect to obtain a correct description of the lack of definition of the image; we must develop a rigorous undulatory theory containing at one and the same time the two effects, which can be done with the aid of a method previously developed by Debye.

So far we have assumed that the source of light is a point. As is understood, this is an abstraction. The objects which we examine with an optical instrument, whether they are self-luminous or whether they diffuse the light, are always extended. Each point of their surface can be regarded as a point source which would give in the optical instrument, if it were perfect, a point image; the juxtaposition of these point images in the image plane would give the perfect image of the surface of the object, and the correspondence between the points of the image and those of the object would be, as the mathematicians say, one-to-one. Unfortunately it is not so because the different images of the different points of the source are affected by the aberrations and the diffraction, and in consequence encroach on each other. There is no longer one-to-one correspondence between the points of the image and those of the object, and hence we are unable to see two very close points of the object as clearly separated from each other. Since we can almost wholly correct aberrations in ordinary optical instruments, it is especially diffraction which limits the "separation power" of these instruments. It is generally accepted that we can separate two points of the object if the distance between the centres of the diffraction spots which they form in the image plane is equal to the distance of the centre of one of these spots from the nearest dark circular fringe; this definition is somewhat arbitrary, but it is evident that such a definition is of necessity a little arbitrary because it depends especially on the very variable acuity of vision of the observer. If we adopt this definition it can be shown that, for a microscope, the smallest distance apart of two separable points is equal to:

$$d_{min} = \frac{0 \cdot 61 \; \lambda}{n \sin \epsilon} = \frac{\lambda}{2 \, n \sin \epsilon} \qquad (1)$$

$n \sin \epsilon$ being the numerical aperture of the microscope,[2] and λ the wave-length of the light employed. This formula shows that even in using the shortest wave-lengths and immersion objectives $(n > 1)$, we can hardly hope to exceed useful magnifications of the order of two to three thousand. Greater magnifications would only increase the distance of points of the image which might correspond to the same point of the object and in consequence would not in any way increase the separation of the points of the object.

We may consider that the different points of the object diffuse photons in succession. To secure a good image it is evident that the object must not have moved appreciably during the successive diffusion of these photons. But if a sufficiently heavy object is placed on the stage of a microscope, there is no reason why this object should move; in particular, the objects examined in an optical microscope are always much too heavy to be set in motion by the radiation pressure of the light which illuminates them. Here, therefore, there is no difficulty; we shall see that it is not the same for corpuscular optics.

Let us now consider corpuscular optical instruments. Here the source emits electrified corpuscles (electrons or eventually protons) and the optical instrument is an apparatus containing electric or magnetic fields arranged so that the corpuscles emitted or diffused by a point object converge as nearly as possible to a point image. Here again we shall consider centred optical instruments, that is, instruments presenting symmetry of revolution.

The region where the fields prevail is analogous to a region having an index of refraction—to an optical refracting medium; in the case of an electric field the so-called refracting medium is isotropic, and in the case of a magnetic field it is anisotropic;

in the one case as in the other the index varies in a continuous manner. From the point of view of wave-mechanics the trajectories of the corpuscles are the rays in the sense of geometrical optics corresponding to waves associated with the corpuscles. The geometrical optics of these rays is identical with the dynamics of the electrons, Fermat's principle, which determines the form of the rays, becoming identical with Maupertuis's principle which determines the form of the trajectories. In calculating the form of the trajectories we can see whether it is possible to make the electrons emitted by a point source converge to a point image. We ascertain that this is possible for the central rays (trajectories near the axis and not greatly inclined to it) and we recover the Gaussian approximate formulae. But here again there are "aberrations" in the case of trajectories which are far from the axis or which are appreciably inclined to it.

The calculations of third order aberrations which can be effected with the aid of corpuscular dynamics without explicitly introducing ideas of wave-mechanics, leads to the rediscovery of the five fundamental aberrations (see page 89). These are here also spherical aberration, coma, astigmatism, curvature of the field, and distortion, to which are added, if there are any magnetic fields, three supplementary aberrations characteristic of corpuscular optics: anisotropic coma, anisotropic astigmatism and anisotropic distortion.

To these geometrical aberrations are further added chromatic aberration when all the corpuscles emitted by an object have not the same speed—an aberration which in general causes little inconvenience—and an aberration of a special type—relativity aberration studied by Chanson, Ertaud and Magnan, which occurs in the case of very fast corpuscles when the tension is not exactly constant. Of all these aberrations that which is of much the greatest importance is spherical aberration; it is proved that this aberration can never be completely eliminated. To diminish it as much as possible we are led in electronic optics to use very small angles of aperture of the order $0^{0}\cdot01$ to $0^{0}\cdot0001$, greatly differing from ordinary optics in which much larger apertures are used.

All the preceding considerations are based on the study of corpuscular trajectories, a study which from the point of view of wave mechanics corresponds exactly to the geometrical optics of waves associated with corpuscles. But here as in ordinary optics one must needs take into account the diffraction of waves associated with corpuscles when they penetrate into the aperture—always very small—of the optical instrument. These phenomena of diffraction can only be predicted by the introduction of wave mechanics, that is, the theory of waves associated with corpuscules. In the region of diffraction geometrical optics is no longer valid, there are no longer any rays and trajectories can no longer be attributed to corpuscles. We therefore again reach the same general conclusion, of which the wide scope has already been indicated in the case of light and photons (see page 68).

The calculation of the phenomena of diffraction by the always circular aperture of the optical instrument is carried out as in ordinary optics, for it is based on undulatory considerations alone. As the result of diffraction the image of a point object is not a point but a circular spot the intensity of which decreases rapidly whilst oscillating as one moves away from the centre, so that there are clear and obscure rings around this centre. We are thus led, as in optics, to introduce the "separating power" of an instrument, and to define this idea exactly we adopt the same somewhat arbitrary convention—which has previously been fully explained (see page 91).

In the case of the microscope, the minimum distance apart of two separable points of the object is again given by formula (1), but here, owing to the smallness of the apertures, we can use ϵ for sin ϵ and, as the object is generally outside the fields, we can also make $n = 1$. We have then approximately

$$d_{min} = \frac{\lambda}{2\epsilon} \tag{2}$$

λ being the wave-length of the wave associated by wave mechanics with the incident corpuscles, given by the formula

$$\lambda = \frac{h}{p} \tag{3}$$

where p is the momentum of the incident corpuscles. When the corpuscles have not got speeds comparable with that of light, we can write

$$\lambda = \frac{h}{mV} = \frac{h}{\sqrt{2mE}} \qquad (4)$$

where E is the kinetic energy of the incident corpuscles.

Formula (2) shows immediately that with the corpuscular microscope we can obtain separating powers much greater than with the optical microscope. In fact, if $1/\sin \epsilon$ is here from 100 to 1,000 times greater than in ordinary optics, *per contra*, the wave-length of the electrons of a few dozens of kilovolts usually employed is of the order of 10^{-9} cm., or more than 10,000 times smaller than that of visible light. We can, therefore, hope to obtain separating powers from 10 to 100 times greater than those of the optical microscope, and allowing magnifications 10 to 100 times as great. In fact with the electron microscope magnifications from 10,000 to 50,000 are readily obtained and undoubtedly we can go further. I need not recall the sensational developments in the study of very small structures which have been already obtained by the use of these enormous magnifications.

To increase the separating power and the magnifications that can be used, still further, it is natural to consider employing, in the place of electrons, heavier particles, protons, for example. In fact formula (4) at once shows that with equal energy the wave-lengths are in inverse ratio to the square root of the masses; the proton therefore has, with the same energy, a wave-length more than 40 times as small as that of the electron, the ratio of the masses being about 1,840. It follows from this that d_{min} is diminished in the same proportion, which theoretically permits the use of magnifications 40 times greater. We could gain still more with particles heavier than the protons. We can, therefore, without exaggeration, envisage the possibility of magnifications of the order of 500,000. Claude Magnan has undertaken the construction of a proton microscope in France; many difficulties remain to be overcome to bring such apparatus to perfection, but it seems probable that excellent results are to be expected in this direction.

II

The theory of separating power, as we know, is closely connected with that of the quantal uncertainties brought to light in 1927 by Heisenberg. This is particularly well seen when we resume the famous argument developed by Heisenberg to which the name of "Heisenberg's microscope" is given. We shall resume this argument whilst insisting on certain points, but instead of considering an electron examined with the optical microscope by means of a luminous pencil, as is customary, we shall consider a *point* object of proper mass M examined under the electron microscope by means of a beam of monokinetic corpuscles.

The point object is placed on the stage of the microscope and bombarded with corpuscles arriving normally at the stage from underneath; it is supposed to be at rest in the initial state. λ will denote the wave-length $=h/p$ of the "illuminating" corpuscles. We shall consider all geometrical aberrations to be negligible, thus placing ourselves in a more favourable position than is actually the case. (See diagram on page 96.)

In accordance with this last hypothesis the position of the object can be known with as much precision as the effects of diffraction allow. By formula (1) the abscissa of the object can only be deduced from the scattering of an incident corpuscle by this object with an uncertainty equal to

$$\delta x = \frac{\lambda}{2 \sin \epsilon} \qquad (5)$$

In fact, if diffraction effects did not exist, since we imagine all geometrical aberrations negligible, the image of the point effect in the image plane π would be a point P and every corpuscle scattered by the object and penetrating into the aperture of the microscope would pass through P. The arrival of a single corpuscle at the point P, an observable phenomenon which can be registered on a photographic plate, for example, would therefore suffice to localize exactly the object to the point M of the stage. But the existence of diffraction has as a consequence that the arrival of a corpuscle at P may be due to the scattering of this corpuscle in a point of the stage situated at a distance from M which can be as much as $\lambda/2 \sin \epsilon$. We easily see, therefore, the origin of the uncertainty

as to the localization of the point object on the stage and we
see at the same time that the existence of this uncertainty is
not connected with the use of an intense incident beam, that is,

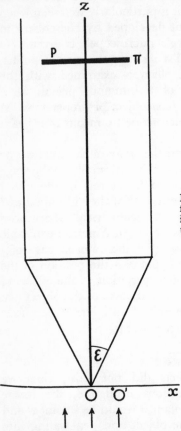

Diagram illustrating the effects of diffraction on the image of a point object
in an electron microscope. For explanation see page 95.

containing a large number of corpuscles, since we see it appearing in the case of a single diffused corpuscle.

The scattering of a corpuscle by the point object is due to a
brief interaction—a collision—which occurs between them.
In this collision the corpuscle yields some energy and some
momentum to the object supposed initially at rest, this cession
being in accordance with the conservation principles.

It is essential to remark that, in order that the microscope
should function in the way which has always been presumed

in what precedes, the point object must not borrow from the incident corpuscle more than a minute portion of energy and of momentum. If it were not so, the wave associated with the incident corpuscle would have its frequency and its wavelength profoundly modified by the process of the collision, and the functioning of the microscope would be completely disturbed thereby. Moreover, the resultant phenomenon could only be described by studying the propagation of the wave associated with the "object-incident corpuscle" system within the configuration space of that system.

This remark being well understood, let us denote by $\vec{p}'$ the momentum of the corpuscle after the collision, its initial momentum being by hypothesis equal to p—h/λ and vertical. Let us suppose that, which in consequence of the symmetry of revolution of the microscope does not vitiate the generality of the case, the trajectory of the incident corpuscle after the collision remains confined in the plane of the figure. Let us call a the angle made by $\vec{p}'$ with the axis of the microscope. Finally, let P_x be the momentum along ox, of the diffusing object after the collision.

The conservation of the momentum along ox gives us

$$P_x = p' \sin a \qquad (6)$$

and as we know that the collision must modify the momentum of the incident corpuscle only very little, we have $p' \simeq p$ and

$$P_x \simeq p \sin a = \frac{h \sin a.}{\lambda} \qquad (7)$$

Now the diffused corpuscle must enter into the microscope to be able to arrive in the image plane and this requires that $a \leqslant \epsilon$, whence

$$|P_x| \leqslant \frac{h \sin \epsilon.}{\lambda} \qquad (8)$$

After the collision P_x can have any value in the interval $-\frac{h}{\lambda} \sin \epsilon \rightarrow \frac{h}{\lambda} \sin \epsilon$ of magnitude $2\,h\sin\epsilon/\lambda$, and the observation of the arrival of the corpuscle in the image plane does not allow us to say what is the value of P_x in that interval. Therefore, after the observation of the arrival of the corpuscle in the image plane, we shall know the position of the point object on the stage with an uncertainty given by formula (5) and the component of the momentum with the minimum uncertainty

$$\delta P_x = \frac{2h \sin \epsilon.}{\lambda} \qquad (9)$$

Taking the product of δx with δP_x, we find

$$\delta x. \ \delta P_x \geqslant h. \qquad (10)$$

This is the Heisenberg uncertainty relation which thus appears as closely connected to the effects of diffraction and consequently to the undulatory nature of the corpuscles.

It will be remarked that, in the preceding we have argued about a *point* object and on the scattering by this object of a *single* incident corpuscle. The ascertained arrival of a single corpuscle scattered into the image plane provides us with information on the point object's position and momentum immediately after the collision, but this information is affected by Heisenberg's uncertainties.

However interesting from the theoretical point of view these considerations may be, they do not exactly correspond to the technical problem of the observation of images in the corpuscular microscope. In fact, the objects examined through the microscope are always extended and not points. As we have explained in the case of ordinary optics, the image of an extended object is obtained by successive scattering of numerous incident corpuscles by the different points of the object; if we ignore aberrations and diffraction, each scattered corpuscle gives in the object plane a point image of the point of the object which has scattered it, and the juxtaposition of all these point images provides the image of the extended object. But to obtain a good image, it will obviously be necessary for the object to remain sensibly immobile during the successive scattering of the different corpuscles which contribute to the formation of the image, without which we would obtain a "blurred" image, as photographers call it.

Now, in resuming the classical analysis of Heisenberg we have just seen that the scattering of each corpuscle by the object is accompanied by a movement of the object and it is necessary to seek under what conditions this movement will do no harm to the formation of the image. In theory the question already arises in optical microscopy, for the scattering of photons is accompanied by motion of the object (as Heisenberg's early argument on the electron illuminated by photons shows), but *in practice*, this circumstance is in no way important. In fact, the phenomena of diffraction do not allow the use of light to examine the structure of an object if this object has not at least dimensions of the order of μ; but an object of this dimension has always much too large a mass to be put in motion to any appreciable extent by the impact of a photon.

It is altogether different in corpuscular optics for here we can already study the structure of bodies having dimensions of the order of 100 $m\mu = 10^{-5}$ cm. (e.g. Herelle's bacterio-phages)[3] and there is hope of going further. Now a body with dimensions of the order $m\mu = 10^{-5}$ cm., and density close to 1, has a mass of the order of 10^{-21} gm., which is only about 1,000 times that of the proton and 10 times that of the atom of silver; the recoil effect in a microscope using heavier protons or atoms may, then, be important and will militate against the securing of good images. Even more so would this be the case if we wished to study the structure of molecules and atoms with the corpuscular microscope. The problem therefore deserves to be studied closely; it is no longer one of simple doubts of the theorist, but concerns obstacles which might arise in the future in the path of progress in microscopic technique.

Let us then consider an object of very small mass M on our scale. This object is placed at the centre of the stage of a corpuscular microscope of which the angle of semi-aperture is ϵ (see the preceding figure). We expressly suppose that *the object is free to move in the plane of the stage*, that is, it is not submitted to any restraint. It is "illuminated" by corpuscles of momentum $p = h/\lambda$ parallel to the axis of the microscope. For a collision contributing to the formation of the image (that is, accompanied by the scattering of a corpuscle in the aperture of the microscope), the component P_x of the momentum of the object after the collision will have the following maximum value

$$P_x^m = p' \sin \epsilon. \qquad (11)$$

p' being the impulse of the diffused corpuscle. Here again we have $p' \simeq p$ and the aperture ϵ in practice is always very small, so that we practically have

$$P_x^m = p' \epsilon \qquad (12)$$

On the other hand we can write

$$P_x = MV_x, \quad p = mv \qquad (13)$$

where V_x is the speed of the object in the object plane after the collision and v the initial speed of the incident corpuscles. In the formulae (13), M and m are the "masses in motion" in the relativity sense, that is, taking account of the increase of the mass with the speed. The speed of the object being always very small with reference to c, M can be regarded as the intrinsic mass of the object; on the other hand m can be sensibly greater than the intrinsic mass of the incident corpuscle, notably when the latter is an electron. For the maximum value of V_x we find

$$V_x^m = \frac{mv\epsilon}{M} = \frac{h\epsilon}{M\lambda} = \frac{h}{2\ Md_{min}} \qquad (14)$$

from (2) and (3). Here we come across the idea which is at the base of Heisenberg's argument; further, to increase the separating power, the more we decrease λ the more the maximum value of V_x increases.

To obtain a good image of the extended object, it is necessary for this object to scatter into the microscope a great many incident corpuscles. If $\bar{\tau}$ is the average interval of time separating the arrival of two consecutive corpuscles on the object, it is obvious that, in order to obtain a clearly defined image, it will be necessary that the product $V_x^m \bar{\tau}$ should be very small compared with the mean dimension l of the object, without which the latter would risk displacement in an appreciable manner in the object plane during the interval of time which separates two successive collisions and then the image could not be sharp. We must, therefore, have

$$V_x^m \bar{\tau} \ll l. \qquad (15)$$

Let us evaluate $\bar{\tau}$. Let i be the density of the current corresponding to the flow of illuminating corpuscles and e the charge of each of these. The surface of the object being of the order l^2, the number of corpuscles arriving per second on this object will be il^2/e approximately, and the mean interval of time between the arrival of two consecutive corpuscles will be

$$\bar{\tau} = \frac{e}{il^2} \qquad (16)$$

Substituting (14) and (16) in (15) we obtain

$$\frac{\epsilon he}{M\lambda il^2} \leqslant l \quad \text{or} \quad \frac{he}{2Mil^2 d_{min}} \leqslant l. \qquad (17)$$

Let us apply this result to the electronic microscope or to the protonic microscope for which $e = 1 \cdot 6 \times 10^{-19}$ coulomb. To be able to distinguish the details of the object, it is reasonable to assume that d_{min} must be at the most equal to $l/10$. Further, if the object has a density close to that of water, we can make $M \simeq l^3$ in c.g.s. units. As for i, it does not seem that it could exceed even in the most favourable case of electrons, the value $i = 10^{-1}$ amp. per c.c., corresponding to 1 milliamp per square millimetre. Finally the relation (17) gives us

$$l^7 \geqslant \frac{6 \cdot 5 \times 10^{-27} \times 1 \cdot 6 \times 10^{-19}}{2 \times 10^{-2}} \simeq 10^{-43} \qquad (18)$$

whence

$$l \geqslant 10^{-6} \text{ cm.} \qquad (19)$$

It seems, therefore, that starting a *free* object in motion will make it difficult to see with the corpuscular microscope the details of free objects having dimensions less than 10^{-6} cm. $= 10m\mu$. Nevertheless, it can be said that, the object receiving a whole series of impulses whose directions are distributed at random, there is a tendency to a certain statistical compensation of these impulses, so that the previous predictions are no doubt a little too pessimistic.

The starting effect which we have just analysed is different from the simple diffraction effect which leads to the definition of separating power. The diffraction due to the passage of the associated waves through the circular aperture of the microscope and the limitation of the separating power which results from it, already appear when we envisage the scattering by the object of each corpuscle separately; it is necessary to take it into account even for an object too heavy to be set in motion by the impact of the incident corpuscles; it would be necessary to take it into account even for a point object. On the contrary, the effect of starting intervenes only as a consequence of the following fact. To obtain an image of an extended object, it is necessary to collect in the microscope a great number of corpuscles scattered by the object. Heisenberg's argument shows well the connexion which exists between diffraction effect and starting effect, but these two effects intervene differently to diminish the sharpness of the image.

Furthermore, it is necessary here to notice that, for an object which is at rest, there is added another cause to the starting effect, which can prevent the procuring of a good image—thermic agitation. At the absolute temperature T, the small object of mass M will in practice have a thermal agitation such that V_x would be of the order of $\sqrt{kT/M}$, where k is Boltzmann's constant, equal to 1.37—10^{-16} c.g.s. To have a well-defined image it will therefore be necessary to have

$$\sqrt{\frac{kT}{M}} \frac{e}{il^2} \leqslant l \qquad (20)$$

from which we derive for the electronic and protonic microscopes with the hypotheses previously accepted,

$$T \leqslant 10^{52} l^9. \qquad (21)$$

We see that for $l \sim 10^{-6}$ cm., extraordinary low temperatures would be necessary to avoid this injurious effect to the sharpness of the images. Hence for a *free* object, the effect of thermic agitation, like the starting effect, must become very troublesome when the dimensions of the object are diminished to about 10 $m\mu$.

It is appropriate now to remark that we have discussed an object free to move on the stage; this would be the case of a particle in a vacuum or in a very rarefied gas. But in general the object has not got this freedom of motion; either it will adhere to the stage or it will be a part of the structure of a heavier object, like an atom in a solid body. This *solidarity* of the object with a heavier body will obviously greatly diminish the starting effect; it will also diminish the displacement by thermic agitation which will then be effected around a position of equilibrium.

To what extent will this solidarity of the object with its support or with its surroundings be maintained when this object is submitted to the bombardment of corpuscles of very great energy? This is a delicate question on which I can offer only somewhat incomplete views.

To sum up, let us consider an atom which is part of the structure of a solid or a liquid and let us ask ourselves if it will be possible to see the structure of this atom through the corpuscular microscope. We must remember that to liberate an atom which is part of a solid or a liquid body, it is necessary to supply it with an energy of the order of a fraction of an electron-volt, and to extract an intra-atomic electron from an atom, an energy of at most a hundred kilo-electron-volts is always sufficient, even for the most strongly bound electrons.

Let us now write down the equations of conservation of energy and of the impulse at the time of the collision of an incident corpuscle with the atom considered as the object. With the notation previously used, we have, neglecting the corrections for relativity (which are of little importance for this kind of calculation).

$$p = p' \cos a + P_z; \ p' \sin a = P_x \qquad (22)$$

$$\frac{p^2}{2m} = \frac{p'^2}{2m} + \frac{(P_x^2 + P_z^2)}{2 M} \text{ or } p^2 = p'^2 + \eta \ (P_x^2 + P_z^2)$$

making $\eta = \dfrac{m}{M}$. The rigorous solution of these equations gives

$$p' = p\left[\frac{\eta \cos a \pm (1 - \eta^2 \sin^2 a)^{\frac{1}{2}}}{(\eta + 1)}\right] \qquad (23)$$

$$P_x = p \sin a \ \left[\frac{\eta \cos a \pm (1 - \eta^2 \sin^2 a)^{\frac{1}{2}}}{(\eta + 1)}\right],$$

and

$$P_z = p \ \left[1 - \frac{(\eta \cos a \pm (1 - \eta^2 \sin^2 a)}{(\eta + 1)} \cos a\right]$$

$$W = \frac{(P_x^2 + P_z^2)}{2 M} = \left[1 - \left(\frac{\eta \cos a \ \pm (1 - \eta^2 \sin^2 a)^{\frac{1}{2}}}{\eta + 1}\right)^2\right]\frac{p^2}{2m} \quad (24)$$

W is the energy borrowed by the object from the incident corpuscle at the moment of the collision which deviates the latter through an angle a. The solution with the — sign corresponds to the rebound backwards of the corpuscle and does not interest us; we therefore, retain, only the + sign.

We shall call the "efficient collisions" those collisions which contribute to the formation of the image in the microscope, that is, those for which $a \leqslant \epsilon$. The aperture ϵ being very small we shall be able to use formulae (23) and (24) for the efficient collisions by retaining only the terms of the second degree at the most in a, which gives

$$p' = p \left(1 - \tfrac{1}{2}\eta a^2\right); \; P_x = pa; \; P_z = \tfrac{1}{2}pa^2 \left(\eta + 1\right) \qquad (23')$$

and

$$W = \frac{\tfrac{1}{2}\eta a^2 p^2}{m} = \frac{\tfrac{1}{2}h^2 a^2}{M\lambda^2} \qquad (23')$$

The maximum value of the energy borrowed by the object from the corpuscle in an efficient collision is, therefore, by (2)

$$W_m = \frac{\tfrac{1}{2}h^2 \epsilon^2}{M\lambda^2} = \frac{h^2}{8Md^2_{min}} \qquad (25)$$

The dimensions of atoms being at the most of the order of the Ångström unit, to be able to study the nature of our atom it is necessary that d_{min} should be equal to 10^{-9} cm. at *the most*. On the other hand, the mass M of the atom is, in order of magnitude, between 10^{-22} and 10^{-24} gm. Formula (25) thus shows that W_m is of the order of the electron-volt, that is, sufficient to set the atom free.

Instead of considering the collision of a corpuscle with the whole atom, let us consider the collision of a corpuscle with one of the outlying electrons of the atom. Formula (25) gives the maximum value of the energy borrowed by the electron in an efficient collision, but we must give to M the value of the mass of the electron, that is about 10^{-27} gm. We see then that, in all cases for $d_{min} \smallsmile 10^{-9}$ to 10^{-10} cm. the energy W_m can assume values of the order of 10,000 to 100,000 electron-volts. The efficient collision is, therefore, capable of tearing off the outlying electrons of the atom.

In short, from these approximate calculations we reach the following conclusion: "When the incident corpuscles will be sufficiently rapid (that is, will have a wave-length sufficiently short) for us to discern the details of the structure of the atom, they will be capable from the first efficient collisions of tearing the atom from the body of which it is a part and even of upsetting its internal structure by carrying off some of its electrons." In these conditions it scarcely seems to me permissible to hope that we could come, even in using protonic microscopes of very high tensions, to "see" with the corpuscular microscope the structure of atomic edifices. It is not, moreover, by chance that this is so, and this impossibility is closely linked with the very existence of the quantum of action.

Although the practical scope of the remarks on which we have enlarged in the second part of this exposition cannot be stated precisely in their entirety, it seems that they are of great interest in the period of the rapid development of the corpuscular microscope, which today appears to open up before us.

[1] Iconal functions. This is mathematical function whose analytical form characterises the image-forming properties of an optical system. [*Definition supplied by Dr. E. H. Linfoot.*]

[2] The numerical aperture of a microscope is not the aperture of the objective but is found as follows:—Let n be the refractive index of the medium (air, oil immersion, water immersion, etc.) and ϵ the semi-vertical angle of the cone of rays entering the objective, then the numerical aperature is $n \sin \epsilon$.

[3] Herelle's bacteriophages were first described in 1915 by F. W. Twort and afterwards—in 1918—by F. d'Herelle, whose experiments led to the view that they are ultramicroscopic living organisms which are parasitic and reproduce themselves in bacteria.

SECOND PART

SCIENTIFIC PHILOSOPHY

CHAPTER VII

THE REVELATIONS OF MICROPHYSICS

THE development of contemporary physics has brought about very important changes in the ideas which we entertained on scientific knowledge, on its nature and its limits. These theories can only really be well understood by following their details in the precise language of mathematical analysis; but, bordering on these theories and based on their results and their successes, new conceptions have been formulated, new suggestions have been put forward, of which the interest from the point of view of philosophical thought is beyond dispute, and which today must be known in their broad outlines by all cultured minds. Certainly not everything is clear or definitely established in this mass of new points of view which shock our most deeply rooted habits of thought and of which the strangeness is sometimes so great that our language does not always supply the words necessary to express them well. But how curious and worthy of reflexion are the conclusions to which we are led! This is what I wish, from the outset, to give a glimpse of in summing up the main points amongst them.

The scientist, in the presence of nature, is not like the art amateur before a picture, who has only to look at it attentively to perceive all the details. The scientist must observe and experiment to gain knowledge of the laws of phenomena; he can only really know what takes place around him if some effect, directly observable by his senses, produces a response in him. But the phenomena of physics, and those, above all, in the realm of microphysics newly presented to us by the skill of the experimenters, are very ingenious and very subtle, and any arrangement made with the object of causing them to produce observable effects risks disturbing them. The deeper study of microphysics revealed that this possible disturbance of the observed by the means by which the observation is made, is inevitable, for it is the necessary result of the existence of an element which physics had for a long time ignored.

This new and strange element which introduced itself as a spoil-sport into the speculation of physicists about fifty years ago is the so-called *quantum of action*. Without entering into too many technical details I shall attempt to give an idea of what the quantum of action is. For the moment I shall simply say that its existence—at least in microphysics—renders inevitable, and of great importance the disturbance which the experimenter necessarily exercises on what he wants to observe; the numerical value of the quantum of action fixes the lower limit of this disturbance, a limit which all the skill of experimental technique is, by the very nature of things, incapable of diminishing. The quantum of action being very small in comparison with our usual limits, these conditions are of little importance in physics of bodies on our scale, or on a superior scale, where everything sensibly occurs as if the quantum of action did not exist. This, on the contrary, is no longer the same in microphysics, on the scale of atoms, where the existence of the quantum of action and the disturbance that it entails, play an essential role.

The quantum of action expresses, as we shall see, a connexion of a new and, up to the present, little understood kind, between the geometrical and the dynamical aspect of things. This connexion makes it impossible to give in a general way to the analysis of natural phenomena, the form of a detailed description by figures and movements which would be in accordance with Descartes' ideal; such a description, just possible in Macrophysics, becomes quite impracticable in Microphysics. In classical physics we had postulated the possibility of describing natural phenomena by figures and by motion in the framework of space and time, and this hypothesis has met with an astonishing success; it had seemed capable of allowing, always and everywhere, the establishment of rigid and precise ties of inevitable succession amongst all natural phenomena, and had thus suggested the hypothesis of a universal determinism. The intervention of the quantum of action no longer allows us to obtain as clear and also as well determined a picture of the evolution of things; it involves a certain weakness which asserts itself in uncertainties of which the numerical value of the quantum of action determines the importance.

Other peculiar circumstances, all emanating more or less directly from the quantum of action, unite with the preceding in the description of the phenomena on very small scales. For example, the particles which form these systems seem to lose the individuality and the autonomy with which our very conception of the idea of particles seemed bound to endow them; these particles are in some way built into the systems which incorporate them and from diverse points of view the system appears to be more than the totality of the particles of which it is formed. Some novel consequences associated with the inaccurate localization of the elementary particles in the framework of space proceed from it, such as that mysterious principle of exclusion, the importance of which is fundamental, seeing that on it the whole stability of matter rests and concerning which the verifications are numerous and precise. Here are facts which are well established today, which we are able to express in a precise mathematical form, but which we hardly understand, for they are altogether opposed to our conceptions and intuitions.

All this train of surprising statements gives, when one reflects on it, the very clear impression that the framework of space and time, such as we conceive it, is not well adapted to the description of the phenomena of microphysics because it implies a severance between geometry and dynamics, which is contrary to the essence of the quantum of action. This check to our usual conceptions of space and time, when we seek to extrapolate them on the very small scale, is perhaps less surprising than one might at first think, seeing that our habitual framework of space and time is suggested just as well by the observations of phenomena, directly perceptible to our senses, such as they take place around us on our scale.

Now these phenomena are in reality statistical phenomena bringing into play an immense number of elementary processes, and the only thing that we could reasonably require from microphysics is that it should allow us, when considering very complex systems, to return to the conceptions of space and time. It is not, on the contrary, by any means necessary to require that the descriptions of the elementary processes themselves should be effected within our statistical framework of space and time. But we are human beings and all our perceptions seem to us as ordained in space and time; we can scarcely imagine a description of the evolution of things which did not make an appeal to these primordial conceptions. Also we are always led, willy-nilly, to make use of them in our description of microphysical phenomena, particularly since the phenomena observable by our senses, thanks to which we seek to deduce indirectly what takes place on the very small scales, appertain to the realm of sensations and are localized for us in our framework of space and time. But in thus seeking to arrange microphysical phenomena in a frame which does not appear, at least not in its usual form, even if we allow for the fact of the existence of the quantum of action, we encounter difficulties at which perhaps we must not be too much astonished.

In the course of the difficult investigations pursued by physical theory to arrive at an adequate representation of the phenomena which take place on very small scales, there has been introduced an entirely new concept of great scope—the concept of complementarity due to Niels Bohr. To obtain a complete description of the phenomena of microphysics our mind is obliged to call up in turn pictures which appear contradictory to it and which it is, nevertheless, very necessary for it to envisage successively if it wants to take account of the different aspects of reality. Such are, for example, the pictures of waves and of corpuscles which are both necessary to explain the known properties of light and of the material entities like the electrons. Wave mechanics have taught us to juxtapose these two images and to establish a certain correspondence between them which allows them to complete each other without ever entering directly into conflict.

Bohr saw there a new characteristic, of great scope, of contemporary physical theories, and noted that the pictures of the wave and of the corpuscle never enter into direct conflict because the more we want to specify the one, the more the other becomes obscured, and from this he has concluded that there can exist in nature "complementary aspects" of which the wave and the corpuscle offer us a relatively simple example. This new idea, both profound and flexible, appears, moreover, to adapt itself to many other cases and Bohr him-

self has attempted an interesting application of it to the phenomenon of life. To this attempt others have been added, notably
those of Jordan, which seem to hold out great interest in the
present state of biology.

From this brief résumé it is seen how original are the
reflexions which lead us to make somewhat surprising statements about microphysics. We shall endeavour to extend them
in resuming and completing the general indications which we
have just given.

Commencing with the seventeenth century, the science of
modern times has spread its wings, and its advances—more
and more rapid and surprising—have succeeded each other
with an accelerated rhythm. As soon as different categories
of phenomena, of established facts, were discovered, it was
necessary to relate them to each other in order to disentangle
the general laws, to bring out the more or less hidden connexions, and endeavour to extract from them a comprehensive
view of the physical universe. This work of synthesis was
necessary because it permitted, in place of a collection of a
greater and greater number of separate established facts, the
enunciation of the laws which summarize them all in a few
words of the precise language of mathematics, and effecting, to
use Mach's well-known expression, a vast "economy of
thought". Moreover, this work of synthesis was equally necessary because the general theortical conceptions allow us, commencing with the laws already known or from the hypotheses
which analogy or intuition leads us to envisage, to predict new
facts and to guide the experimenter in his task, which is to
interrogate nature.

It is unnecessary here to recall in detail the fine work of
classical physics, the great physical theories which arose from
the seventeenth century to the beginning of the twentieth
century; the theory of the phenomena of equilibrium and of
the motion of bodies in mechanics, the theory of the motion of
the stars or celestial mechanics based on the law of gravitation,
the theory of the phenomena of light or optics definitely
constituted under the form of an undulatory theory following
upon Fresnel's admirable researches, the theory of electric
and magnetic phenomena finally combined with the whole of
the optical phenomena in the vast and magnificent synthesis of

Maxwell, known under the name of the electromagnetic
theory; the theory of the phenomena of heat or thermodynamics, based on the two great principles of the conservation
of energy and of the increase of entropy. What concerns us here
is not to explain or to discuss the different forms or the particular branches of these brilliant syntheses; it is to endeavour to
see what they have in common, to explain exactly the postulates
that they implicitly admit at their point of departure.

A first postulate of this kind seems to us to be the following:
it must be possible to arrive at a description of the material
world which does not in the least take into account either the
scientist who experiments and reasons, or the means of investigation which he uses to observe the phenomena. It seemed
quite natural to many scientists, not all of whom had a philosophical mind, to suppose that it was possible for the material
world to have become known quite independently of the rules
of the functioning of our mind, and especially of the processes
necessarily associated with our faculties of sensation and perception through which we gain our knowledge of it. That our
scientific theories should be connected with the rules of the
functioning of our mind, to the structure of our reason, to the
concepts of which we dispose, that is certainly a point concerning which no scientist endowed with a mind, let it be
ever so feebly critical, has naturally ever been able entirely
to rid himself; the science of man is human and can never
cease to be so; on this point there is no possible doubt.

Nevertheless, the question of knowing if our means of
observation and the fact that they necessarily utilize phenomena
capable of being directly perceived by our senses, allow us to
trace out a truly objective picture—precise and unequivocal—of
what takes place in the material world, is another question less
easy to solve. The whole of the conceptions that we use in our
theories, and of the arguments that we develop in them, has
an essentially human form, but the scientist, who always
admits more or less implicitly the reality of the external world,
might very well think that there can exist a precise one-to-one
correspondence between the external world and the picture that
we can succeed in forming of it, even if he has a sufficiently
philosophical mind to remember that, after all, science is
only man-made.

He will then admit that observations or experiments carried out with sufficient skill and precision will always succeed in bringing to our knowledge with exactitude the quantities which are necessary for a complete description, if not of the material world in its entirety, at least of certain of the phenomena which occur in it. No doubt we cannot forget that in observation and experiment there always exist causes of error which it is impossible to eliminate completely and of which every conscientious physicist must always appreciate the importance. But, if such errors are inevitable, a skilful experimenter will know how to diminish them by means which are capable of ever greater efficiency. He will also know how to evaluate the errors which remain possible, and to assign narrow limits to them. We can thus hope, at least in principle, to see a tendency towards zero of the uncertainties, by which our knowledge of the parameters which must finally serve us in a description of the state of the material world, is affected. We can, therefore, hope (and this was one of the postulates of classical science) to succeed in expressing, obviously only in human language, but nevertheless in a perfectly precise manner, the evolution in the course of time of everything which happens in the space around us.

The mention in our last phrase of the two words "time" and "space" now leads us to give an account of another postulate common to all the theories of classical physics— the possibility of localizing in a precise and unequivocal manner in space and time all the transformations which operate in the physical world.

All our perceptions, all our activity, all our relations with the external world are, as it were, confined within the framework of space and time. Are these conceptions of space and time innate ideas, *a priori* forms of our sense perception? or have they, on the other hand, been slowly acquired in the course of the evolution of the human race or spontaneously extracted by our mind from the data of perception? These latter are questions the discussion of which we shall leave to the philosophers. What is certain is that the framework of space and time is imposed on us each time that we want to arrange our sensations and to follow the evolution of phenomena of which they show us the existence. Scientists have given a precise de-

finition to the conception of space and time by fixing
positions in space with the aid of co-ordinates related to geometrical solids serving as systems of reference and the positions
in time with the aid of a variable t, the time of classical mathematical physics, defined in relation to the movement of the
stars by the cycles of periodic systems called clocks.

In thus transforming into an abstract and schematic
framework these empirical realities—time and space—have
scientists not falsified the true meaning? Have they not substituted for a moving and qualitative continuity, namely the
duration perceived by consciousness, a "spatialized" representation which would deprive true duration of its profound
significance, of its evolutionary character, to replace it by a
static concept, incapable of making it possible to understand
its real nature? Even in the case of space, have they not mis-
understood its essence, which should be a continuous and
indivisible extension, to substitute for it an amorphous and
indefinitely divisible picture, thus bringing into being, if we
may say so, an excessive spatialization of space? These, then,
are the questions which the adepts of Bergsonism propound;
but again this is the business of the philosophers and meta-
physicians. Whatever may be the opinion one may have on
these problems, what must be admitted is that with these
co-ordinates of space and time, classical mathematical physics
was in a condition to represent in a precise way the succession
of phenomena which our senses allow us to verify around us.

From that moment a way opened quite naturally before
theoretical physics and it boldly entered upon it. It was thought
that all evolution of the physical world must be represented by
quantities localized in space and varying in the course of time.
These quantities must render it possible to describe completely
the state of the physical world at every instant, and the description of the whole of nature could thus be given by figures and
by motions in accordance with Descartes's programme. This
description would be entirely carried out with the aid of
differential equations or of partial derivatives enabling us to
follow the localization and the evolution in the course of time
of all the quantities defining the state of the physical world.
A magnificent conception for its simplicity and confirmed by
the successes which it has achieved for a long time! It

sustained and orientated all the efforts of the great schools of mathematical physics of the nineteenth century.

Assuredly not all scientists agreed to this description of the world by figures and movements exactly in the same way. Some with lively and concrete imagination sought to picture the elements of the material world so as to make the phenomena observed by our senses flow from the existence and movements of atoms or of corpuscles too small to be directly observed; they wanted to dismantle the machine to see all the wheels functioning. Others, more cautious and above all endowed with a more abstract mind, wanted to content themselves by uniquely representing phenomena by means of directly measurable quantities, and mistrusted the hypotheses—in their eyes too speculative and useless—of the atomists. And whereas the atomists were thus boldly advancing, opening new ways and allowing science to make astonishing progress, the energetists, impeded by their more formal and timid methods, retained a certain advantage from the conceptional point of view when they denounced what was simple and a little naïve in the pictures invoked by their bold rivals. But, without being aware of it, both admitted a great number of common postulates of which the future was to prove the frailty.

They were, in fact, agreed in admitting the validity of the abstract framework of space and time, the possibility of following the evolution of the physical world with the aid of quantities well located in space and varying continuously in the course of time, and the legitimacy of describing all phenomena by groups of differential equations. If the energetists, like Pierre Duhem, refused to allow the intervention everywhere of the "local movement" which could be represented by a displacement of parts, they fully admitted the consideration of "general movements" defined more abstractly by the variations of quantities in the course of time. In spite of their differences of view on the manner of carrying out this programme, all theorists were then in agreement in representing the physical universe by well-defined quantities in the framework of space and time and subject to differential equations.

The differential equations (or the partial derivatives) of classical mathematical physics have the common character of allowing us to follow rigorously the whole evolution of the phenomena which they describe, if we suppose that there are certain known data relative to an initial state corresponding to a particular value of time. From this there was deduced the possibility of establishing a kind of inevitable interconnexion of all the phenomena, and thus was reached the conception of a universal determinism of physical phenomena. It is not my purpose to examine from the philosophical point of view the idea of universal determinism, and I have not to ask myself, for example, if the mind, which, after all is said and done, is the creator of mathematical physics, could recover its place in a nature conceived of in such a rigid manner. What is certain is that physical phenomena, in so far as they were exactly represented by the differential equations of classical physics, were submitted to a very precisely defined determinism.

Classical physics thus represented the whole physical universe as projected with absolute precision into the framework of space and time, evolving from it according to the laws of an inexorable necessity. It completely set aside the means used to arrive at a knowledge of the different parts of this vast mechanism for, if it recognized the existence of experimental errors, it only saw in them a result of the lack of precision of our senses and of the imperfection of our techniques, and accepted the possibility of reducing them indefinitely, at least in principle, by an adequate improvement in our methods. All these representations rested essentially on the classical ideas of space and time; for a long time they appeared sufficient for a description of the evolution of the material world. Can we say as much today? That has become very doubtful since the astonishing discoveries of microphysics: I shall try to demonstrate this.

A first and somewhat grave attack on our classical conceptions of space and time has been brought about by the development of relativist ideas. The general public is greatly interested in the theory of relativity, and as a consequence of this particularly, many inaccuracies and even nonsense have been spoken on the subject. Relativity theory is actually a difficult theory which can only be well understood if one follows the mathematical development in detail. From the point of view which interests us here, its essential role has been to show that, between the space and time of physicists, there exist certain relations up till then unsuspected and utterly contrary to our habits of thought. The variables of space and time defined by the measures and clocks which are used by two observers in motion relative to each other are not related to one another in the way that was previously accepted without discussion; they depend on each other in a way which does not at all conform with our usual intuitions. In particular, we cannot define a "universal time" which would be the same for all observers. What is curious in this matter is that the new conceptions relative to the interconnexion between space and time have been imposed on physicists by the necessity of explaining experimental facts; left to themselves physicists would not have willingly wanted to adopt ideas so surprising and contrary to their usual intuitions, but the study of actual phenomena has led them to it.

The consequences which ensue from the new relations accepted between the co-ordinates of space and time of different observers are rather disconcerting at first sight; thus a body in motion seems shorter in the direction of its motion for one who sees it pass before him than for one who accompanies it in its displacement; a clock seems to go slower for one who sees it in motion than for one who is motionless beside it. Certainly these effects are generally very small—unobservable in most cases of ordinary experience; they only become notable if the relative speeds become very great—of the order of that of light *in vacuo*. Nevertheless, these effects of relativity, as they are called, are not always negligible; their existence necessarily entails certain modifications of the laws of mechanics and the deviations which follow from them with reference to the laws of classical mechanics become very important for bodies endowed with speeds close to the speed of light *in vacuo*. The particles of atomic physics, such as the electrons, often attain high speeds of this order, which has provided an opportunity of verifying by experiment the real existence of these effects of relativity. The speed of light *in vacuo* plays, moreover, a role of primary importance in all this theory; it appears there as the upper limit of the speeds which a material body can attain.

However important and radically new may have been the

ideas introduced into physics by the theory of relativity, never-theless they have not overthrown the spatio-temporal frame-work accepted by classical physics. Undoubtedly in relativity physics one must no longer consider space and time separately, or give a universal character to time; in a manner it is necessary to merge space and time in a four-dimensional continuum, the space-time of Einstein or the universe of Minkowski, where each observer carves out in his own way his space and time. But in this continuum one will always locate exactly all the "events" of which the whole constitutes the story of the physical world. All the past, the present and the future will be written, therefore, in the framework of this space-time and each observer will see them succeed one another each in his own present time, in accordance with the rigorous laws interpreted by differential equations. The picture of space and time henceforth as one, space and time having become conjointly responsible, continues to rule as master and physical determinism remains as rigorous as in the past. Far from overthrowing classical physics, the theory of relativity would rather appear to be its crowning work.

Much more profoundly revolutionary has been the theory of quanta. By introducing into physics the quantum of action measured by the constant h of very small but precise value $(6.62 \times 10^{-27}$ erg. sec.), Max Planck, about 1900, launched physics into ways which, in truth, were quite new. We cannot here take up the story of that memorable discovery, nor that of the extraordinary developments which Planck's ideas have undergone in a few years, leading finally to that new and specifically quantal form of mechanics which to-day is known as wave mechanics. What is now specially important for us to understand is the profound meaning of this rather mysterious idea of the quantum of action. Up till now the space and time of classical physics, or its successor—the space-time of the relativity physics—had appeared to us as a framework given *a priori* and quite independent of what one could put into it, quite independent particularly of the move-ments and evolution of the bodies which were localized in it. Indeed, the generalized theory of relativity had accepted the existence of an influence by the bodies situated in space-time on the curvature of this space-time, but this influence of the contained on the containing has nothing to do with the quantum of action.

To localize an object in space, there was no necessity to define exactly its motion and its speed; it could be affirmed that it had passed into such a position at the instant t in a well-defined system of reference without concerning oneself with its energy. To use the Cartesian expressions, form and motion appeared to be quite independent matters, data which no condition connected together *a priori*.

Now it is precisely this very natural supposition which the existence of the quantum of action compels us today to abandon. What we really call action in mechanics is a somewhat hybrid quantity which can be expressed as the product of energy by time or again as the product of momentum by length. But since the success of the astonishing hypothesis introduced by Max Planck in the theory of black body radiation we know that this action behaves as if it were formed of indivisible parts, of real atoms, of which the magnitude—always the same—is expressed by Planck's constant h. As the action cannot in any way be likened to a substance the total quantity of which would be conserved (there is conservation of energy in isolated systems, but not conservation of the action) this atomism of the action has nothing to do with material atomism. What, then, does it express? It is this which has emerged, little by little, from the advances made in the theory of quanta and the truth which we have thus succeeded in glimpsing is somewhat disturbing to our judgement.

The real significance of the quantum of action has been disclosed to us notably by the discovery of Heisenberg's uncertainties to which I shall presently return. It seems certain today that the existence of the quantum of action expresses a formerly totally unsuspected union between the framework of space and time and the dynamical phenomena which take place in it. The picture of space and time is essentially static; a body, a physical entity, which has an exact location in space and in time is, by this very fact, deprived of all evolutionary property; on the contrary, a body which is developing, which is endowed with dynamic properties, cannot really be attached to any point of space and time. These are philosophical remarks which go back to Zeno and Elea and his disciples. Heisenberg's uncertainty relations appear akin to these remarks; they teach us, in effect, that it is impossible to attribute simultaneously to a body a well-defined motion and a well-determined place in space and time. The more an experiment or an observation allows us to state precisely the spatio-temporal localization of a system, the more it leaves us in doubt as to its exact state of motion and vice versa. In the exact expression of Heisenberg's uncertainties Planck's constant h naturally comes in in an essential way. For example if p_x is one of the components of the momentum of a mobile point and x the corresponding co-ordinate, the uncertainties Δp_x and Δx, which, after every observation, depend on the exact values of the quantities, will be, according to Heisenberg, always connected by the inequality

$$\Delta p_x \cdot \Delta x \geqslant h$$

An analogous relation, but with a slightly different interpretation, $\Delta E \cdot \Delta t \geqslant h$ exists between the uncertainty in the energy and the uncertainty in the localization in time. The quantum of action then appears to us as marking the limits between which are compatible the conceptions of localization in space and time and the evolutive motion, between which Zeno of Elea, more than 2,000 years ago, had already discerned a certain antagonism. Therein, without any doubt, lies the most profound sense of the mysterious concept of the quantum of action.

Before proceeding further and studying the aspects and consequences of the idea of the quantum of action, let us insist on its smallness with reference to the quantities which are directly accessible to our senses. We usually employ in our measurements the c.g.s. system of units, which takes the centimetre as the unit of length, the gramme as the unit of mass, and the second as the unit of time. These three units have the advantage of being relatively small for us, whilst being directly perceptible, the first two to our senses, the third to our consciousness of duration. They are, therefore, appropriate to our scale. But in this system of units Planck's constant has the inconceivably small value $6\cdot55 \times 10^{-27}$, that is, it is equal to $6\cdot55$ divided by a number which is expressed by 1 followed by 27 zeros. This is to say that for our human scale, the quantum of action appears as completely negligible; in macroscopic physics its effect will be practically nil, everything will take place as if the mechanical action were continuous and not divided into atoms. A powder formed from grains sufficiently fine appears to us as a continuous medium; the grains exist, but they are so small, they are so numerous in any perceptible mass of the powder that we are no longer able to see them.

In macroscopic phenomena it is the same as regards action; the quanta of action still exist, but they are so small, they occur in such great numbers in all observable macroscopic phenomena that we can no longer discern them. These remarks are essential because they explain to us why macroscopic physics has been able to develop with so great a success by ignoring the existence of the quantum of action and by considering the framework of space and time as being able to provide for an absolutely precise description of dynamical phenomena. It is only when contemporary microphysics entered upon the study of phenomena on a very small scale, such as those which occur in the interior of atoms at distances less than 10^{-8} cm. and with periods of movement less than 10^{-14} sec., that the necessity for taking account of the quantum of action was clearly established.

On the large scale, the separation of the framework of space and time and of the phenomena which we localize there seems natural to us and corresponds to our intuition. We can always imagine a solid body serving us as a reference body to define the positions of points in space . . . such a body, for example, would be a collection of three rulers at right angles to each other and conveniently graduated, which would constitute a system of rectangular Cartesian co-ordinates in the sense of analytical geometry. Similarly, the time would be measured by the isochronous oscillations of the pendulum or a clock, regulated according to the movement of the fixed stars of the celestial vault. With these rulers and these clocks, we can assign exact co-ordinates to every material point or exactly fix the position or the orientation of a solid body in space at each instant recorded by the clocks; more generally, we can represent all the phenomena by well-localized quantities in space and time.

We shall thus recover the usual representations of phenomena in classical physics; we shall come to regard space and time as a kind of unchangeable framework in which all the successive aspects of the physical world are exactly located and inexorably unfolded. The theory of relativity will, indeed, show us afterwards that the information furnished by the rulers and clocks of different observers in relative motion is not connected in such a simple way as had been at first thought, that there is no universal space and time, that each observer defines his own individual space and time, and that the individual spaces and times of different observers are as though cut out of a four-dimensional continuum, space-time, which would be the true universal spatio-temporal framework. But it is nonetheless true that each observer can describe the evolution of the physical world, so far as it is accessible to him, by locating it exactly in the framework of *his own* space and of *his own* time; each event of the physical world will be represented by a point of the space-time which will not have the same co-ordinates for all observers, but which, nevertheless, will have very exact co-ordinates for each observer. Further, we can continue to suppose that the evolution of the physical world takes place in accordance with rigorous laws of a strict determinism. There is, therefore, no essential opposition between the conceptions of relativity physics and those of classical physics.

It is quite different if, examining the phenomena of the atomic scale, we introduce the idea of the quantum of action. In the atomic realm we no longer have solid or liquid bodies, and we cannot imagine a ruler or a clock; we only find corpuscles of an extraordinary lightness (the mass of the electron is about 10^{-27} gm.!) and no longer have we at our disposal any frame of reference for locating the positions, or any observable periodic movement to measure durations of time. Still further, the inequalities of Heisenberg's uncertainty show that we cannot imagine any system of spatial reference actually realizable, any clock capable of measuring time exactly, which has not a mass very much greater than that of the constituents of the atomic systems.

It is, therefore, by indirect means alone that we shall be able to seek to relate the phenomena which unfold on the very small scale to our usual framework of space and time constructed with the aid of macroscopic rulers and clocks. But then, in this somewhat spurious attempt to compel the elementary phenomena to conform to a framework which is merely statistical, there will appear Heisenberg's uncertainties demonstrating the impossibility of representing in this framework the dynamic evolution of the elementary entities in precise fashion. The possibility of separating the geometric and dynamical aspects, which was very approximately realized on the large scale by reason of the minute size of the quantum of action, ceases entirely on the very small scale and, as all our habits of thought have been formed according to the indications which our senses bring us on the phenomena on our scale, we remain very disconcerted in face of an acute reality to which our most inveterate intuitive conceptions no longer apply.

The double corpuscular and undulatory aspect of elementary physical entities is closely associated with the discovery of the quantum of action. We shall not here resume the history of the discovery of this double aspect, first for light, then for material particles. Let us merely say that, to give an account of the phenomena of the action of light or of the elementary entities of matter, it is sometimes necessary to use the picture of corpuscles localized in a point of space and sometimes that of periodic waves occupying the whole of an extended region of space and propagating themselves in a certain direction. Further, if we wish to establish a correspondence between these two pictures—for example— connect the energy and the momentum of a particle with the frequency and the wave-length which we associate with it, we are led to formulae in which Planck's constant h figures in an essential way; this shows that the duality of waves and corpuscles, the necessity of employing two pictures—apparently contradictory—to describe the same phenomena, is closely associated with the existence of the quantum of action. It is easy enough to understand, in a qualitative way, why it is so.

The corpuscle is a sort of ideal concept created by our mind to represent the localization of something at a point of space at a given instant; in classical mechanics we gave it the name of "material point", which, in that respect, is characteristic. The corpuscle therefore symbolizes the exact localization in the framework of space and time. It is more perplexing to define the sense of the wave; for that we must examine a little more closely the manner in which theory, guided by experimental results, has established a parallelism between waves and corpuscles, that is to say, wave mechanics envisages the wave associated with a corpuscle.

This wave envisaged in its simplest definition, in all its purity, one might say, is a plane monochromatic wave in the usual sense of mathematical physics; it is homogeneous throughout space and throughout the course of time and in consequence does not attribute any privileged role to any particular point of space, or to any particular instant of the duration of time; further, it is propagated in bulk in a certain direction. We can therefore say that, setting aside all spatio-temporal localization, it symbolizes a movement, it represents, in the pure state, a dynamic condition. Corpuscle and wave are, therefore, "idealizations" of which one is the symbol of the strict localization in space and time, while the other is the symbol of directed motion conceived in all its purity without any prejudice as regards localization. "That which is in a point cannot be in motion or evolve; what moves and evolves cannot be in any point." Undoubtedly such is the profound sense which Zeno of Elea would have attributed to the opposition of the wave and the corpuscle had he lived in the century of wave mechanics.

Now the quantum of action, as we have seen, expresses the existence of a profound and for a long time unsuspected relation between the geometrical and the dynamical aspect of things. It is, therefore, natural to see it occurring in the equations connecting the quantities which define the corpuscle and those which define the associated wave. The presence of the constant h in the formulae of wave mechanics is simply the sign of the necessary intervention of the quantum of action in the connexion which these mechanics attempts to establish between the geometrical and the dynamical aspect of the elementary physical entities.

But if the localization in space and time symbolized by the ideal concept of corpuscle on the one hand, and the dynamical evolution symbolized by the ideal concept of a plane monochromatic wave on the other hand, are really contradictory things, the correspondence established by wave mechanics between the two images must necessarily be incomplete and limited. The more the corpuscular aspect is in evidence the more the wave must efface itself, and *vice versa*, because, if one of these aspects is fully defined, the other must completely vanish. It is the great merit of Bohr and Heisenberg to have been able to extricate from the equations of wave mechanics the existence of a reciprocal limitation of the corpuscular and undulatory pictures.

What is it necessary to do to define exactly the corpuscular picture? It must be possible to measure exactly the co-ordinates of the corpuscle at a given instant. What must we know to define exactly the wave picture which, we have seen, represents the dynamical tendency of the entity that is studied? It is necessary to know the quantities which define the dynamical state, the energy and the momentum or, if we consider the associated wave, it is necessary to know its frequency and its wave-length connected with the energy, and the momentum, by the classical formulae of wave mechanics. Now Bohr and Heisenberg have shown us that no process of measurement can give us the exact position of a corpuscle in space and its momentum, or the energy of a corpuscle at a well-defined moment of the interval. Interpreting these conclusions in a quantitative form, Heisenberg has expressed them by inequalities connecting uncertainties which exist after an operation of measuring the values of the co-ordinates and the components of the momentum, of the energy, and of the instant when it is measured. The constant h appears in the right-hand term of these inequalities and its presence serves to remind us that it is the existence of the quantum of action which renders the strict localization in space and time incompatible with the rigorous determination of the dynamical states.

As Planck's constant is very small in comparison with man's units, the strict localization in space and time and the rigorous determination of dynamical states will appear very sensibly compatible in the realm of macroscopic physics; it is on the scale of microphysics that their fundamental incompatibility will stand out without dispute. In the macroscopic, Zeno of Elea appears wrong, pressing too far the claims of a too keen criticism, but in the microscopic, on the scale of the atoms, his perspicacity triumphs and the arrow, if it is actuated by a well-defined motion, is no longer able to be in any point of its trajectory. Now it is the microscopic which is the profound reality, for it underlies the macroscopic; it is in it that it is necessary to seek the ultimate mysteries of reality which, in the macroscopic, conceal themselves under the lack of precision of the sensory data and in the confused mass of statistical averages.

It is, perhaps, in the light of the results of microscopic physics that it will be necessary, one day, to resume the study of certain great problems of philosophy. To express this idea is, moreover, to underline the difficulty of these problems for us, poor humans; to resolve them, it would, perhaps, be necessary to see things through the eyes of microscopic being on the atomic scale, and where the quantum of action is affirmed. But, without organism of terrifying complexity, with our relatively coarse senses, we live on a scale of averages and of statistical effects and it is only through the mind's eyes that we have recently succeeded in obtaining a glimpse of the world of elementary phenomena and of the quantal processes; it is, nevertheless, this world which underlies all physical reality and without doubt it is in it that is found the solution of many of the great enigmas of the universe.

But let us return to the physics of the quanta and let us specify some essential consequences of the Heisenberg uncertainties.

First of all, why is it that experiments suitably arranged and carried out in the smallest details could never let us measure the geometrical and dynamical quantities simultaneously with more precision than the Heisenberg uncertainties permitted? Bohr and Heisenberg have given the explanation of this by analysing the processes of measurement which we could effectively seek to use to avoid the quantal uncertainties; they have shown that no process of measurement effectively attainable can make them disappear and that they will never fall below the limits which are assigned to them by the Heisenberg inequalities. And that always holds for the quantum of action; as a consequence every attempt to modify a process of measurement in order to allow it to give,

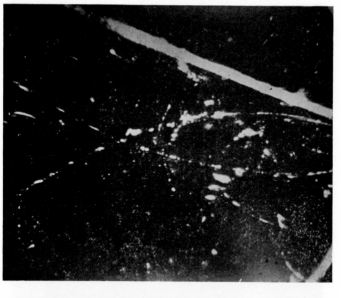

Positive electron and negative electron ejected from a sheet of lead irradiated by photons emanating from the action of beryllium submitted to the action of alpha-ray sand polonium.

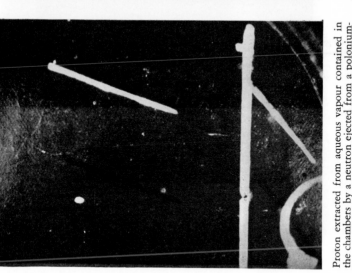

Proton extracted from aqueous vapour contained in the chambers by a neutron ejected from a polonium-beryllium source situated underneath (*Joliot-Curie*).

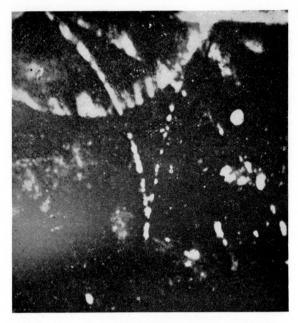

A pair of positive and negative electrons created in gas by a photon from thorium-C".

Trajectories of electrons in a magnetic field

A sheaf of beta-rays from radium-E deflected in a
magnetic field

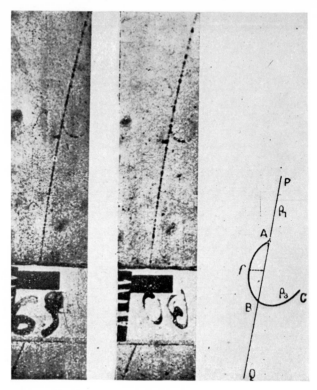

Stereoscopic view permitting the measurement of the mass
of the mesoton = 240 times that of the electron

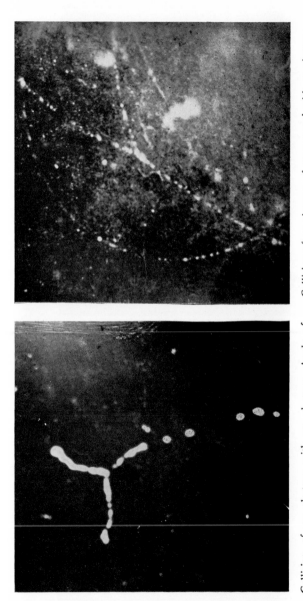

Collision of an electron with an electron. Angle of bifurcation = 90°

Collision of an electron of great speed with an electron. Angle of bifurcation = 60°

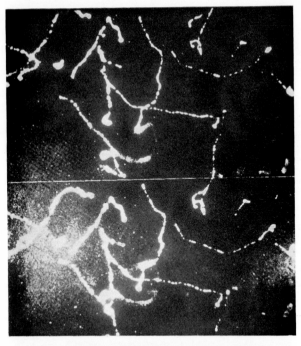

Trajectories of electrons in a Wilson Cloud Chamber

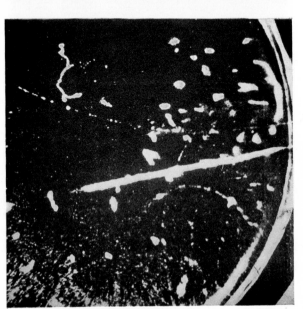

Trajectories of electrons and protons

Transmutation of a nucleus of nitrogen with the capture of an alpha-particle and emission of a proton

Alpha-rays from plutonium

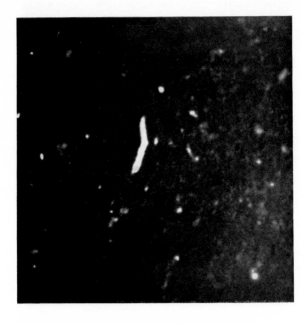

Ray of nitrogen projected by a neutron. Elastic collision.
(Joliot-Curie)

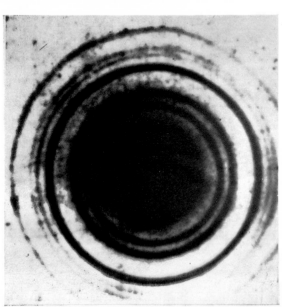

Diffraction of electrons by a thin gold leaf

for example, a more exact value of a geometrical co-ordinate, makes it give proportionally a less exact value of the corresponding dynamical quantity; what is gained on the one hand is lost on the other, so that Heisenberg's inequalities are always satisfied.

We shall not here give examples of the arguments which Bohr and Heisenberg have set forth, because, to understand them properly, a fairly deep knowledge of the results and the methods of atomic physics and wave mechanics is necessary. We shall only say that after discussions which have been of interest in that they clarified several points, the ideas of Bohr and Heisenberg appear today fairly universally adopted by physicists. What interests us here is to deduce the philosophical conclusions which develop from them.

Why does a well-made experiment of measuring never come to assign both perfectly accurate geometrical and dynamical aspects to the physical reality studied, whilst classical physics assumed without discussion that this must be possible? It is because an experiment in measurement always involves from the point of view of quantal physics, a partly uncontrollable perturbation of what one wishes to measure. This perturbation is bound up with the existence of the quantum of action which fixes its minimum limit and this limit, negligible in the macroscopic measurements, becomes important on the microscopic scale. This presents us with a totally new conception of the relation which exists between the scientist trying to know with precision the external reality and that reality itself.

In classical physics the universe was conceived of as formed from objective realities developing with a perfect precision in the immovable frame of space and time (or the Einstenian space-time); the scientist was, on the contrary, regarded as altogether external to this physical universe, the object of his studies, and as capable of measuring exactly all the parameters necessary to describe the successive states of the Universe, without thereby disturbing these states in the least. Also, in this classical physics, there was admitted the possibility of knowing exactly the dynamical states in the perfectly accurate framework of space and time. Altogether different is the position of the scientist in the physics of the quanta; he finds himself in the presence of physical realities which he cannot study without disturbing them. By appropriate measurements he can extract from this reality certain geometrical aspects capable of taking place in the framework of space and time which the conditions of his macroscopic perceptions impose on him; he can also extract from them some dynamical aspects corresponding to his conception of pure motion.

In certain cases, by pushing the spatio-temporal localization of the elementary physical entities far enough, he will come to represent them as corpuscles; in other cases if he presses the precision in the determination of the dynamical characteristics far enough, he will have to abandon the corpuscular picture and fall back on a purely wave picture. In most cases he will take up a position between these two extremes, he will know with a certain lack of precision only the geometrical and dynamical quantities and will then have to combine the wave and corpuscular pictures. But at all events Heisenberg's uncertainty relations will be satisfied. The essential point in all this is that the results of the measures constituting the scientists's knowledge will not describe the physical universe such as it is, but such as it is known to the scientist, following on experiments admitting of unknown and uncontrollable disturbances. Physics will, therefore, no longer have as its object to trace the general laws of the universe independently of those who study it; it must content itself with the much more modest role of representing the knowledge which each physicist has been able to acquire and to say what predictions this knowledge allows him to make in the matter of phenomena to come. A particularly important example will enable us to understand better the difference which divides the old from the new point of view.

In wave mechanics a certain quantity which is called the wave function and which is represented by the Greek letter Ψ is constantly interposed. This quantity is a function of the co-ordinates of space x, y, z, and of time, that is, it is defined in each point of space at each instant. If this quantity was a quantity of the classical type, it would have to represent a local and instantaneous state of the physical universe and in consequence have the same value for all observers. In carrying out precise measurements, they all would have to give it the same value. Now it is not so for the Ψ function of wave mechanics; its value varies for the different observers *according to the measures which each one of them has carried out*. The Ψ function, in fact, does not represent something which would have its place in a point of space at a given instant; it represents, taken in its entirety, the state of knowledge of an observer, at the instant considered, of the physical reality that he studies; there is nothing surprising, therefore, in the fact that the function varies from one observer to another since they do not, in general, possess the same information on the world which surrounds them, not having carried out the same observations nor the same measurements. One observation, one new measurement, can completely change the form of the function Ψ, which would be inconceivable if this function described an external reality, independent of the observer.

Quantal physics, therefore, no longer leads to an objective description of the external world, conformable—in a way instinctive—to the ideal of classical physics; it no longer furnishes anything but a relation between the state of the external world and the knowledge of each observer, a relation which no longer depends solely on the external world itself, but also on the observations and the measurements made by the observer. Science thus loses a part of its objective character; no more is it the passive contemplation of a fixed universe; it becomes a hand-to-hand struggle where the scientist succeeds in snatching from the physical world, which he would like to understand, certain information, always partial, which would allow him to make predictions that are incomplete, and in general, only *probable*. And this last word now leads us to explain how the intervention of the quantum of action, after having rendered human science less objective, has also rendered it less deterministic.

The determinism of classical physics postulated the inexorable unfolding of the evolution of the physical universe in the space-time framework. Improving on this conception, relativity physics registered all the events of the physical universe in its space-time where all the past, the present and the future were thus contained. Quantal physics has not been able to maintain these—undoubtedly too daring—assertions. How, in fact, could we assign a perfectly determined course in space and time to dynamical developments if the knowledge of the spatio-temporal localizations and that of dynamical developments are never rigorously compatible? How could a physics, which no longer knows a purely objective reality and no longer knows how to give anything but relations between the observer and the observed, arrive at a picture of the universe so totally objective as is implied by an entirely deterministic description of the phenomena? In classical mechanics, to be able to predict the motion of a material point it is necessary to know exactly its position and its speed at the same initial instant; it is necessary, therefore, to state exactly at that initial instant its spatial localization and its dynamical course. With classical ideas nothing prevents these initial data from being known, and in consequence nothing prevents a rigorous prediction of the subsequent motion in conformity with the determinist ideal.

It is no longer the same in quantal physics; the initial data which would be necessary for the calculation of the subsequent motion will never be known with exactitude by the physicist; the Heisenberg inequalities are opposed to it, and the uncertainties, with which the initial data are thus affected, no longer allow anything but predictions which in their turn are uncertain. There, where the classical physicist believed himself able to say: "Such and such event will necessarily occur at such and such an instant", the quantal physicist must be more unassuming and announce only that various more or less probable eventualities are possible. Probability will be installed as mistress in the enunciations of theoretical physics and it is only in a few very exceptional cases that indubitable predictions will be possible.

In short, quantal physics in its appropriate realm of very small scale phenomena is incapable of maintaining determinism, that is to say, the perfect prediction of observable phenomena.

But, the partisans of determinism will say, that does not prove that there is not a complete determinism of natural phenomena—it only proves that we do not know all the elements on which the unfolding of natural phenomena depends, and that certain of these elements escape us, the knowledge of which should provide evidence for determinism. If new advances come from experimental physics revealing these ignored elements, then it will be possible to restore determinism. And some will readily speak of "hidden variables". What, then, are these "hidden variables"? In classical physics, especially in thermodynamics, we had also met with phenomena of which the description appeared incomplete, and had recourse to the existence of "hidden variables" which escaped our experimental investigations, variables the knowledge of which would have been necessary to arrive at a complete description of the system. It is thus that in the thermodynamic theory of gases we could consider the positions and the individual speeds of the molecules of the gas as "hidden variables". Can we not, then, suppose that the present quantal theories, themselves also, disregard the existence of certain "hidden variables" which, if they were accessible to us, would permit the completion of the description of microphysical phenomena and subject them to determinism?

In reality it does not appear to be so; indeed the very form of the laws of probability, as it has been possible to show, which appear in quantal physics, is not that which corresponds to the existence of "hidden variables". One of the ways by which we could hope to restore physics to determinism is thus closed. Can we find another? That hardly seems probable if we reflect on the way in which the intervention of the quantum of action, by introducing a new relation between the geometrical and the dynamical aspects of the universe, prohibiting as it does an exact knowledge of the two aspects, has thus brought about the impossibility of establishing laws of rigorous succession between observable phenomena.

But, you will say to me, there is, all the same, determinism in the physical world. If I press the switch which puts on the current supplying this electric lamp, I see it light up . . . on condition, however, that the supply is not cut off, the lamp filament not burnt out, nor the fuses blown, but these are all circumstances easily controlled. Yes, in the macroscopic realm, which is that of classical physics, determinism exists practically, whilst it is no longer apparent to us in the microscopic realm. How is that possible? Quite simply because in quantal physics if there are no longer rigorous laws, there are yet laws of probability. It does not seem possible to be able to foresee in advance the individual phenomenon, but taking a very great number of elementary phenomena it can be said that such a proportion will be produced in such a way and such another proportion will be produced in such another way.

We can compare this situation to that which exists for the statistics of actions depending on the human will. Each week in Paris there are a certain number of people who commit suicide; this number is very nearly constant but it is conceivable that it varies slightly as a function of the circumstances. Thus it would increase a little in periods of crisis and privation and diminish in the quiet and prosperous periods (unless, perhaps, it may be the contrary, I do not know). Nevertheless this constancy of the statistical laws does not at all prevent us from believing that men are free to commit suicide or not to commit suicide. If I take a name from the Telephone Directory by chance, I am completely ignorant whether the person who has this name will commit suicide or not in the coming week, but I know that the number of people who are going to end their lives in this next week will be about the mean normal value. The indeterminism of elementary phenomena is, then, perfectly compatible with the determinism of the macroscopic phenomena and that because there still exist, even in microscopic physics, laws of probability.

We must now say a few words about the new conceptions of microphysics in what concerns the whole collections of corpuscles and the possibility of stamping with an individual character the corpuscles belonging to such collections. These are questions so important and so difficult that here we can do no more than merely touch on them.

The representation of the evolution of an aggregate of corpuscles assumes in wave mechanics an abstract form which gives but little information. The Ψ wave which represents the observer's knowledge of this system and enables one to follow its evolution, is not in fact representable in our ordinary space of three dimensions; it must be represented in a fictitious space, the space of the configuration of the system, possessing as many dimensions as the co-ordinates necessary to define the position of all the constituents of the system. If the corpuscles of the system did not interact amongst themselves we could consider them separately and associate with them a wave in ordinary space. But if there exist interactions between the corpuscles, it is necessary to regard them as forming a system with which we must associate a *unique* wave evolving in the space of the configuration. It is, therefore, to the existence of interactions, explained analytically by the intervention of terms of potential energy, that the system owes the possession of a complete individuality in which those of the constituent corpuscles come to be more or less blended. The system thus appears as a sort of unit of higher order in the heart of which the constituents are so much the more difficult to isolate in that they are more strongly united between themselves by the interactions.

In particular, every attempt to localize one of the constituent corpuscles exactly requires that we tear it from the system of which it forms a part, hence that we mutilate this system. It thus seems that the concept of an elementary constituent and that of a system furnish us with pictures which are never rigorously valid simultaneously; every observation which shows the existence of the system is inconsistent with an isolation of the constituents and every effort to isolate the constituents destroys the system by this very action. Just as with the images of the wave and of the corpuscle, the pictures of constituents and of system can never be simultaneously defined with precision in physical reality such as we observe it. We shall return to this point in speaking about complementarity.

In the study of the systems of corpuscles by quantal physics, other new and very surprising ideas are introduced when we consider systems containing corpuscles of the same physical nature, such, for example, as an atom containing several electrons. In classical physics we always suppose that in an assembly of corpuscles we can distinguish each corpuscle, for example, by attributing a fixed number to it, and in consequence follow its evolution in the course of time by continuously distinguishing it from its companions. This hypothesis is perfectly logical in classical physics where we assume that the corpuscles are exactly localized in space at each instant; it is then possible to distinguish the different corpuscles from their position in space at that instant, then to continue to distinguish them by constantly following the series of positions that they occupy, starting from the initial instant. Otherwise expressed, although the corpuscles of the same physical nature may be absolutely identical amongst themselves, the possibility of continuously localizing them offers to classical physics a means of distinguishing them. It is no longer the same in quantal physics, at least in a general way; here, as we have seen, the corpuscles are generally, for each observer, badly localized because their co-ordinates are usually affected by some of Heisenberg's uncertainties. More often it happens, therefore, that the zones of possible localization of the corpuscles encroach on one another. This is what will always happen, particularly in the case of the constituents of the same system when they are strongly bound together. It is evident then that we will no longer be able to follow the individuality of the corpuscles, since, because of their resemblance to one another, the only way of distinguishing them was to localize them differently in space and this possibility has disappeared.

In quantal physics, when we have to deal with aggregates of corpuscles of the same physical nature, we can then no longer particularize them, mark them with a number. We must, for example, be content to say, in this collection of corpuscles there are so many of them in such a state, so many of others which are in such another state, etc. We shall never be able to say, this corpuscle is in this state, that other corpuscle in another state, etc. To be able to distinguish a corpuscle it would be necessary to tear it from the system to be able to consider it apart; to restore its individuality it would be necessary to isolate it.

It is not possible here for me to explain how this disappearance of the individuality for corpuscles of the same nature is interpreted in the formalism of the wave mechanics of systems. I shall merely say that the somewhat abstract formulae to which we are thus led are amongst those which, in wave mechanics, have received the most direct confirmation arising from experiment. It is notably on these that the theory of the spectrum of helium and that of the formation of the molecule of hydrogen are based, the confirmation of which by experiment is particularly brilliant.

One of the strangest conclusions to which the development of wave mechanics of corpuscles of the same physical nature has led is the principle of exclusion announced by Pauli. For certain categories of particles, and notably for the electrons, which are one of the most important constituents of matter, the states which the groups of such particles can assume are submitted to a very curious restriction; "two of these particles can never be in the same individual state." This we call the exclusion principle, for we can also say: the presence of one of these particles in a certain individual state excludes the presence of every other particle of the same nature in the same state. The accuracy of Pauli's principle is today beyond doubt; its confirmations are innumerable, and, in particular, the theory of the spectrum of helium, of which I have just spoken, adduces the most beautiful illustration which one could wish. Besides, the importance of the exclusion principle in atomic physics is supreme; it is to it that we owe the explanation of the stability and diversity of the various forms of atoms which correspond to the ninety-two simple elements of chemistry; it is to it that we owe the explanation why these simple elements have different physical and chemical properties exhibiting a well-known periodicity in accordance with their atomic weights. Without the exclusion principle the physical world would be entirely different from what it really is.

It is even more curious to observe how much this principle is contrary to our intuitive ideas. Let us consider, for example, an enclosure containing a gas formed of molecules of the same nature obeying the exclusion principle. Let us fix our attention on two molecules situated at two opposite extremities of the enclosure; the exclusion principle tells us that they cannot have the same state of motion. How is that possible since our enclosure can be infinitely great and in consequence our two molecules infinitely separated one from the other? The answer to this objection is very ingenious and brings out well the insufficiency of our habitual intuition of space. Here it is.

Since we imagine the two molecules endowed with exactly the same motion, we imagine their states of motion to be perfectly known, but then, according to Heisenberg's uncertainty relations, their positions are completely unknown to us, they can be anywhere in the interior of the enclosure, and we have no right to suppose that they are very far from one another. Otherwise expressed, two particles having exactly the same motion would be found in a manner at the potential state in the whole of the enclosure which contains them, and it is henceforth less astonishing that each one of them could prohibit the other from having its own state of motion. We see how contrary to our intuition are the circumstances which we meet here. The principle of exclusion and also all the wave mechanics of the systems of corpuscles are things which our intuition does not assimilate and nevertheless their validity is absolutely imposed by experimental results. It is unnecessary to say that at the origin of all these difficulties we now, and always, find again the existence of the mysterious quantum of action.

We cannot lay stress on the difficult and very abstract wave mechanics of the systems of corpuscles and, to conclude, we shall touch on the question of the "complementarity" in Bohr's sense.

Niels Bohr, who was one of the chief founders of the modern theory of atoms, has also greatly contributed to the development of quantal physics in general. Having clearly seen the real sense of the duality of waves and of corpuscles, he thought that here was an example of a fact capable of being met with in other realms of science. To him the description of natural phenomena, such as are afforded us, especially by the existence of the quantum of action and the disturbance of the observed by means of the observation, has not necessarily the unequivocal and coherent character usually attributed to it in classical theories. To describe observable realities, it may be necessary to employ in turn, and even simultaneously, two or more apparently contradictory pictures.

All that can be insisted on in this multiform representation is that the different pictures never enter into sharp conflict and never lead us to contradictions. Now—and this is the great lesson which Bohr has drawn from Heisenberg's uncertainty relations—the duality of waves and corpuscles in wave mechanics shows that it can be perfectly so. In virtue of the uncertainty relations, the wave aspect asserts itself only when the corpuscular aspect vanishes and vice versa. For example, the examination of the phenomena of interference of light shows that, if we thoroughly examine the interference fringes, we are unable to say where are to be found the corpuscles of light—the photons—and if, conversely, we modify the arrangement in such a way as to be able to specify exactly the trajectory of a photon, it becomes impossible to observe the interferences exactly.

As though by a curious precaution of nature, the two aspects—the corpuscular and the wave—play a sort of hide-and-seek game, so that they never come to oppose one another. Bohr says, that here are "complementary aspects of reality", aspects which appear contradictory to us but which are, in reality, complementary, since it is necessary to consider them in turn to obtain a complete description of the observable facts. But there is nothing to prevent us from thinking that these circumstances can be found in other questions than those of waves and corpuscles. As we have said, the system and the elementary constituent appear also, in a certain sense, to make up complementary aspects of reality, aspects which are completed by opposing each other.

Bohr has made a very original attempt to apply the idea of complementariness to the phenomena of life. Life appears to us under opposing aspects; sometimes it seems to reduce itself to a collection of physico-chemical processes, sometimes it appears to assert itself as characterized by an evolutionary dynamism which transcends physico-chemistry. Bohr questions whether there might not here be two complementary aspects of reality somewhat analogous to the wave and corpuscular aspects of physical entities. And this is how he has attempted to develop this idea.

To succeed in reducing the functioning of a living being to physico-chemical processes, it would be necessary to submit all its tissues, all its cells, or fractions of cells, to a complete physico-chemical analysis including the isolation and the separate examination of all their parts; but it is quite obvious that such an analysis would have the effect, long before pressing it to its limits, of bringing about the death of the living being that is studied. At the moment when the physico-chemical analysis of the tissues would be complete, life, in so far as it is a dynamical organizer, would have disappeared. If, on the other hand, we wish to follow the functioning of the vital dynamism, it is very necessary to have regard for the soundness of the tissues and cells of the living being and then the physico-chemical analysis of the living matter will necessarily remain very incomplete. We see how interesting is Bohr's idea and how his conception of the complementary aspects of reality is capable, by its possible remarkable extensions, of interesting philosophers.

As I have had occasion to speak of the phenomena of life, I should like, in conclusion, to say a few words on the relations which, perhaps, will one day be confirmed between microphysics and biology. For this we shall follow the suggestions put forward by Pascual Jordan, an eminent quantal physicist, who for some years has been particularly interested in these questions.

At first sight it may seem extraordinary to believe that the new conceptions of microphysics should, perhaps, be able to assist us in understanding the mysteries of life. In fact, many living organisms, ourselves for example, belong to the scale which we have called macroscopic; they, in particular, are the seat of extremely complex phenomena where an immense number of elementary processes intervenes. Now we have seen that the macroscopic phenomena of this kind practically obey, by reason of their essentially statistical character, the laws of classical physics. But, says Jordan, the whole behaviour of living organisms appears ultimately to be ruled by some directive *centres*, the activity of which orientates all the vital dynamism. This is particularly well known to those who have studied, however little, embryology and have followed the astonishing progress of contemporary genetics. It is the nuclei of the sexual cells and even certain parts of these nuclei—the genes—which transmit from one generation to another all the hereditary characteristics with their immense complexity; it is a few "organizers" which direct all the work of the growth of the young living organisms in the path of development. We stand astonished before the smallness of these directive elements wherein lies the whole mystery of life. With great profoundity Bergson wrote in *Creative Evolution*: "The act of organization has something of the explosive; it requires the least possible room at the start, a minimum of matter, as if the organizing forces only entered into space with regret."

Even in adult organisms this directing role of microscopic elements continues; it is in a few cells of the grey matter of our brain that the mysterious powers which orientate all our activity, intellectual, sentimental and voluntary lie. When we have pondered deeply on this astonishing regulation of the vital dynamism by microscopic elements, we understand why Jordan was able to say that, in spite of appearances, a mammal, for example, belongs in a certain sense to the microscopic world. The directive elements of its vital dynamism are, in fact, of the order of magnitude of the atomic systems and it is, therefore, with the aid of the conceptions of microphysics that their functioning will undoubtedly have to be studied one day.

All this is still very conjectural; microphysics and biology will have, each in its own sphere, to make considerable progress before they can meet. If, in concluding, I have taken the risk of saying a few words to you on these hypothetical views of the future, it is to end my task of showing clearly all the philosophical implications of the young microphysics. It has shown us that space and time are purely statistical concepts; it has shaken determinism and cast strange doubts on the individuality of elementary particles; it has revealed to us the "complementary" aspects of reality; tomorrow perhaps it will help us to understand the mysteries of life.

CHAPTER VIII

PERSONAL MEMORIES ON THE BEGINNINGS OF WAVE MECHANICS

FEW chapters of general history are more difficult to write than those having to do with the history of scientific ideas. To study the history of a particular science, or even more modestly to relate with exactitude certain important episodes of its development, it is indeed necessary to know thoroughly the present state of this science and all the events which little by little have led to it being what it is today; this is an essential condition for the exact appreciation of the importance of each advance accomplished and the reasons for which these advances have operated in such and such a manner. But it is not sufficient for anyone who wishes to study the past of a science to have an extended and precise knowledge of its subject; it is also necessary to possess the essential qualities of the historian and the methods of historical criticism. As these different qualities are rarely united in the same individual, the history of the different branches of science can only be approached with advantage by a small number of specialists, and it does not seem up to the present to have developed as much as the great interest, which is attached to it, would justify.

If the study of the development of the sciences up to the contemporary period is already difficult, how much more so is it if we wish to include the most recent developments. The multiplication of publications in all countries and in all languages, the stupendous development of experimental discoveries, the enormous increase of theoretical ideas which in the epochs of rapid progress are often completely transformed from one year to the next, all this will offer to the sagacity of the future historians of science an almost inextricable skein of facts when tracing the exact course of the evolution of discoveries and doctrines and following the successive steps of the thought of innovators.

In order to facilitate, within the compass of what is possible, the work which historians of science will have to accomplish, it is no doubt of value that scientists who have participated in some of the great crises with which the advance of each science is sign-posted, should seek to summarize the successive states of mind through which they have passed and to give an account of the different circumstances which little by little have oriented their thought. One will then often perceive that the course of this thought must have described numerous meanderings before finally orienting itself in the path where it has been able to find its full fruition.

I have therefore thought that it might be of interest if I, too, looked back in retrospect on the subject of the origins of wave mechanics. Although it would assuredly be little laudable to speak too much about oneself, it seems to me that I may here be excused because, in tracing the course of my old ideas, I shall have as main object the provision of a document for those who would later wish to enter upon the history of the great crisis undergone by physics at the epoch when quanta made their disturbing appearance.

Moreover, I will not direct my principal attention in the present exposition to the germination in my mind of the original ideas which I had put forward in my first works, and which served as bases to later developments of wave mechanics. My intention is, on the contrary, to insist above all on the difficulties that I encountered and the hesitations which I experienced when I sought to interpret physically in a thorough manner the fundamental conceptions of wave mechanics and to understand the real import of the wave-corpuscular dualism implied in the very structure of the doctrine of which I had made myself the protagonist. I should also like to explain how, little by little, starting from the classical deterministic conception of physical phenomena which I adopted more from habit of mind than by philosophical conviction, I was led to range myself entirely on the side of the probability and indeterminist interpretation which Bohr and Heisenberg have given of the new mechanics and of which the famous "uncertainty relations" are the analytical translation.

Perhaps this "confession" will have the further advantage of preventing certain investigators one meets with pretty frequently in these days, forcing themselves to turn back to the past, to question again the new conceptions of the physics of uncertainties. All those, in fact, who attempt any effort of this kind, are led to take up again, in one form or another, the efforts which different investigators, of which I myself am one, had made twenty years ago, to try to save the exact pictures and the deterministic beliefs of classical physics. Such is, for example, the attempt, known as the hydrodynamic interpretation of Madelung, which I had summarized by calling it the pilot-wave theory and which I had afterwards to abandon.

One will thus see that it is not out of mere wantonness that I have given up the traditional positions of classical physics but rather was I compelled and constrained to do so; perhaps this statement itself will show the incredulous how much these traditional positions had become impossible to defend. The memory of unfruitful efforts, which are quickly forgotten precisely because they are unfruitful, is far from being useless for it saves many from starting a work destined to fail, and from entering blind alley ways where others before them momentarily went astray.

The evolution of my own conceptions in the critical period 1923-8 on the interpretation of wave mechanics, proves also at what point he who puts forward the fundamental ideas of a new doctrine often fails to realize at the outset all the consequences; guided by his personal intuitions, constrained by the internal force of mathematical analogies, he is carried away, almost in spite of himself, into a path of whose final destination he himself is ignorant. Having habits of mind formed in great part by the teaching he has received and by the ideas which prevail around him, he often hesitates to break with customs and seeks to reconcile with them those new ideas whose necessity he perceives. Nevertheless, little by little, he finds himself forced to arrive at interpretations which he had not in the least foreseen at the beginning, and often ends by being all the more convinced of them the longer he has tried in vain to avoid them. And therein lies the further interest which the following exposition offers to the psychological study of discoveries.

The Origins (1923-4)

In the course of the years 1922-3, there was clearly manifested to my mind the necessity of bringing together in one kind of synthesis the ideas of wave and corpuscle, employed for a long time by theoretical physics but in isolation from each other.

The idea of wave, at first associated with the intuitive picture of vibratory motion propagated in a material medium, had played an essential role in the development of the physics of solid bodies, liquids and gases; the theory of elasticity, hydrodynamics and acoustics had made great use and a deep study of this idea of wave. Then the waves had become, thanks to Augustin Fresnel who had revived Huygens's ideas, the key to the explanation of luminous phenomena and, in this realm of optics, they had appeared as representing the vibratory movements of a very fine medium penetrating all bodies—the luminous ether.

The properties of this ether appeared, moreover, as somewhat paradoxical since it had to be sufficiently attenuated not to exert any restraint on the bodies which move in it, and nevertheless infinitely rigid, for it could transmit only transversal waves, light never containing longitudinal waves of a detectable intensity (see Chapter VII). The electromagnetic theory of light had soon given to the luminous wave a more abstract character, for it had defined all radiations as constituted by electromagnetic fields propagated by waves in space, without being able to state clearly whether these fields really represented the vibration of a medium. The conception of an ether, as the support of electromagnetic fields, had encountered so many difficulties that it fell into a certain discredit; the development of the theory of relativity was to give it the death blow. But the hypothesis of waves representing vibratory fields propagated through space had remained the solid and indispensable basis of a complete explanation of the phenomena of physical optics, in particular of the phenomena of interference and diffraction the study of which admits so much precision.

On the other hand, the idea of the corpuscle, as old as scientific thought and already in honour amongst the philosophers of antiquity, had acquired an importance more and more marked in proportion to the development during the nineteenth century of the conceptions of atomic and molecular physics. The successive discovery of molecules, atoms, ions, electrons, supported by more and more numerous and irrefutable experimental proofs, had led to the conviction amongst all physicists that the explanation of natural phenomena must essentially call for the intervention of discontinuities of structure which schematize the idea of corpuscle. The corpuscle appeared to them as a physical entity, localizable in space at different instants, and even, as was admitted as evident at that epoch, theoretically susceptible of being localized in space at every instant. Physical quantities which characterized it, such as its mass and electric charge, were said to be attached to it in a permanent manner; it possessed at each instant an energy and a momentum, and these qualities were thought to vary only when it exchanged them with other physical entities in conformity with the great principles of conservation.

Such as they presented themselves to the minds of theorists, the pictures of waves and corpuscles were in striking contrast; whilst the fields of an undulatory character were by hypothesis distributed continuously and homogeneously in the extended regions of space, the corpuscles were essentially regarded as localized, endowed with individuality and constituting kinds of mobile singularities with permanent existence in space. Theoretically there was no logical objection to using one of these two pictures in certain branches of physics and the other in other branches, to introduce waves, for instance, in the explanation of electromagnetic and luminous phenomena, and to interpret from the existence of corpuscles and from their movements and interactions, the structure and properties of material bodies seen on a very small scale. But certain symptoms, the number and importance of which had been on the increase, appeared to me, about the year 1923, clearly to indicate that this dichotomy of the ideas of waves and of corpuscles in different regions of the physical world did not correspond to reality, and that it was necessary for the two rival images to be made to intervene everywhere simultaneously. In other expositions I have often explained what these symptoms were and here I shall only give a rapid résumé of them.

At the epoch to which I go back, the discovery and study

of the laws of the photoelectric effect, and of the more recent Compton effect and, one may say, the whole collection of the quantal phenomena of interactions between matter and radiation, irresistibility imposed the idea that it was necessary, according to the hypothesis suggested by Einstein, in 1905, to reintroduce into the theory of light the idea of corpuscles, by conceding that in every luminous monochromatic wave of frequency v the energy is concentrated in particles of value hv, where h is Planck's constant of quanta. These particles of light, these photons as we then began to call them, manifest themselves by local actions and we can attribute to them an energy and a momentum obeying the general laws of conservation. No doubt photons differed in more than one respect from the particles of light formerly envisaged by Newton and by the partisans of the theory of emission; their appearance in physics constituted no less a quite unexpected offensive return of corpuscular discontinuity in a domain where the continuity of waves appeared to have been absolutely imposed since the great work of Fresnel. Of course this great work was in no way disturbed so far as it concerned the explanation of the phenomena of physical optics, so that the conception of luminous waves remained just as necessary as before. It seemed, therefore, necessary to turn to a synthetic theory of light based on a wave-corpuscle dualism, the nature of which remained very mysterious.

If it was thus almost evident in 1923 to every physicist without bias that the corpuscles were invading *de novo*, a realm which was really believed to be definitely reserved for waves, without, moreover, succeeding in expelling these from that domain, a much greater boldness would have been necessary to suggest that the waves in their turn would invade the realm up till then reserved for corpuscles. Nevertheless this was the conviction which, little by little, was at that time, impressed on my mind. The analogy of Fermat's principle which holds sway in geometrical optics and of the principle of least action which regulates the motion of corpuscles, the very particular character of the quantized movements which, according to Bohr's views, the electrons possess in the interior of atomic systems and which are characterized by integers as interference phenomena in the theory of waves, and still other comparisons, appeared to me to indicate more and more clearly that the mechanics of corpuscles, at least on the atomic scale, must introduce undulatory pictures, wave-propagations which had not, up till then, been taken into account.

Further, the intervention of quanta and of Planck's constant h, as much in the theory of photons as in that of the quantization of the electronic movements, seemed to me to show clearly that the link between the two terms of the wave-corpuscle dualism took place through the intermediary of the quantum of action, and must in consequence be expressed mathematically for formulae in which the constant h would appear. This was already the case for the relations which, in the theory of the photon, expressed the energy and momentum of the corpuscle of light as a function of the frequency and of the wave-length of the luminous wave, and the form of these relations gave an indication of the interconnexion that had to be established in the general case of any corpuscle whatever, since the theory of the photons must evidently be included as a particular case in the general theory.

Still other considerations were able to serve me as a guide. Since the work of the geometer Hamilton, almost a century ago, we knew that if we consider a corpuscle of a given kind moving in a permanent field of force, the possible trajectories of this corpuscle are divided into classes, each class forming the collection of rays of a certain wave propagation of the type of geometrical optics. If, then, we imagine not a single corpuscle alone, but an infinity of identical corpuscles and without mutual interactions, they can simultaneously describe all the rays of a similar wave which would be propagated in the field of force, following well-defined laws in conformity with those of geometrical optics. But naturally, we are generally concerned with a single corpuscle which will describe one only of the rays of the wave. Nevertheless, if we imagine an infinity of identical corpuscles simultaneously describing all the rays of the same wave, we see that the propagation of each of these waves represents the total of the possible movements of the corpuscles which belong to the same class. Moreover, in geometrical optics each ray is uniquely determined by the physical conditions which confront it as it progresses, and it is possible in consequence to predict its form without having to concern oneself with those of the other rays of the same wave.

Now the form of each ray is wholly determined in geometrical optics by the classical Fermat's principle or by the minimum time; it is thus easy to foresee, since each ray is a possible trajectory of a corpuscle, that there must be a close link between this principle of Fermat which determines the possible forms of the rays, and Maupertuis's principle of least action which determines the possible forms of the trajectories. This analogy between classical dynamics of corpuscles and geometrical optics, so clearly put in evidence by the researches of Hamilton, and a little later by those of Jacobi, had appeared at this epoch only as a curious analytical equivalence permitting the development, in a very elegant and often very useful form, of the general theories of dynamics. Moreover, certain difficulties seemed opposed to any physical interpretation of this analytical equivalence and for nearly a century no effort was made in this direction. In the state of mind in which I found myself in 1923, I immediately succeeded in convincing myself that it would be necessary, on the contrary, to attempt the development of the parallelism between corpuscular dynamics and the propagation of waves by giving it a physical meaning and by introducing quanta into it.

I do not wish to recall here in detail how I succeeded in developing these new points of view, first in notes which appeared in *Comptes Rendus* of the Academy of Sciences at the end of 1923, then in a more complete exposition which constituted my thesis for a doctorate, submitted in 1924. I shall only remark that in these researches I succeeded in associating a propagation of waves to every movement of a corpuscle obeying the classical laws of dynamics, and in establishing the exact quantitative relations between the frequency and the wave-length of the wave on the one hand, and the state of motion of the corpuscle on the other, with the aid of formulae in which Planck's constant figured, and which made possible the indentification of the principle of Fermat with that of Maupertuis. I further showed how this quite general theory contained as a particular case the theory of photons, and how also, applied to interatomic electrons, it permitted the interpretation of the existence of stationary states for these electrons as being the effect of a sort of resonance of their associated waves.

Finally, knowing well that, from the general point of view of undulatory optics, geometrical optics appears only as an approximation valid under certain conditions, and avowing that the classical dynamics of corpuscles itself evinced the truth as intepreting the geometrical optics of the waves associated with the corpuscles, I put forward the view that it was necessary to make an effort to constitute a mechanics of corpuscles more general than classical mechanics and which would be, with regard to the latter, what undulatory optics is with regard to geometrical optics. Just as physical optics allows the prediction of phenomena such as interference and diffraction which completely escape the anticipations of geometrical optics, because they are beyond the limits to which this control can be applied, so also I foresaw, from that moment, that it must be possible to obtain with corpuscles, with electrons in particular, certain phenomena of interference or of diffraction altogether impossible to foresee with the aid of classical dynamics.

Obstacles and Progress (1925-6)

Thus I clearly saw in what direction it was necessary to move, and the subsequent development of wave mechanics has done nothing but confirm the correctness of the programme which I had then outlined. But at the same time that there clearly appeared to me the role which the new mechanics must play, I saw not less clearly what considerable difficulties one was going to encounter when one would wish to state precisely, in harmony with this new doctrine, the exact relationship of wave and corpuscle and to reconcile the two expressions of this dualism, without deviating too much from classical ideas admitting the possibility of representing all physical realities by pictures in the framework of space and time, and attributing a rigorous determinism to their evolution. It is, in fact, that all my previous scientific training and the principles which I had imbibed in the work of my precursors or from the teaching of my masters, led me to regard the totality of these ideas as forming—at least on purely scientific ground—the intangible basis of all future progress and the norm from which one could not depart without betraying the true method of positive science. But the more I sought to run into this pre-existing mould the new material furnished by my ideas on wave mechanics, the more obstacles I encountered and the constantly increasing consciousness of these difficulties contributed to prevent me during the whole of the year 1925 from rapidly developing the structure which I had undertaken. Let us then examine what were these obstacles and these difficulties.

In the theory of waves the magnitudes of fields which are propagated by undulations are distributed in space in a continuous manner; the different points of the wave do not differ essentially one from the other, which can be interpreted in the language of mathematics by saying that the waves of the usual undulatory theory do not present any "singular point". In the positively particular case, but so important in optics, of the plane monochromatic wave, all the points of the wave are even strictly equivalent; the wave is then completely homogeneous. To be sure, one can always very well trace the rays of the wave, when geometrical optics is valid, to describe its propagation, for these are by definition the orthogonal curves with surfaces of equal phase, and for plane monochromatic waves, the surfaces of equal phase then being parallel planes, they simply form a beam of parallel straight lines. But these rays all play exactly the same role and none of them is privileged.

In the Hamilton-Jacobi theory of which we have previously spoken, all the possible trajectories of a corpuscle, if they all belong to a same class, are assimilated in a field of given force, to the different rays of a wave, and this has regard for the equivalence of the rays since all *possible* trajectories are obviously equivalent. If we had to deal with an infinity of identical corpuscles describing all possible trajectories, the equivalence would be maintained in consequence of a statistical effect; but in practice we generally have to do with *one* corpuscle describing *one* of the possible trajectories. Then in the wave of the Hamilton-Jacobi theory there exists at every instant a point having a particular role, namely, the point occupied at that instant by the corpuscle, and the trajectory described by the corpuscle in the course of time is a ray having a *singular* character, since it is effectively described by the moving body, whereas the other rays are only possible trajectories, but not effectively described.

In the framework of the classical theory of Hamilton-Jacobi, these assertions do not imply any difficulty, since the wave and its rays there play only the role of a fictitious representation, permitting the grouping of the possible trajectories into different classes without having to consider in the least this wave as possessing a real physical existence. Quite different is the point of view of wave mechanics which, in a way, in associating the propagation of a wave with all corpuscular movement, places the two expressions of the wave and corpuscular dualism on to a footing of equality. In this case it then becomes very difficult to explain how the associated wave can have a character of continuity (and even of perfect homogeneity in the case of the plane wave) which the classical theory of waves postulates, whilst the presence of the corpuscle ought naturally to create at the centre of this wave a sort of singular point, the trajectory of this singular point defining in the course of time a privileged ray. And, nevertheless, it was absolutely certain that the wave associated with the corpuscle must have the continuous character of the waves of the classical undulatory theory; in the particular case of light, indeed, the explanation of the phenomena of interference and diffraction authoritatively demands the intervention of continuous waves employed in optics since Fresnel, and in consequence the waves associated with the photon must necessarily have this character. The development of wave mechanics, moreover, already proved, and would prove more and more, that the waves associated with every corpuscle must have the properties of continuity of classical waves.

A great difficulty was thus presented when the way in which the wave and the corpuscle must be thus associated was sought, and that even in the case where, geometrical optics being valid for the propagation of the wave, the movement of the corpuscle can be described by the equations of classical mechanics in the framework of the Hamilton-Jacobi theory. But even more formidable obstacles appeared to confront me when I sought to extrapolate my new conceptions beyond the domain of geometrical optics in attempting to construct wave mechanics in all its generality according to the programme which I had sketched for myself. Indeed we know that when the propagation of a wave can no longer be described by the processes of geometrical optics, as for example when interferences or diffraction intervene, the idea of ray entirely loses its meaning and physical optics must give up the defining of rays in the regions where, in consequence of interferences, a complicated redistribution of the vibratory luminous fields holds sway. Let us give an example of this which corresponds to the experiment described in all the classical treatises of optics under the name of Young's experiment with holes.

A plane screen is pierced with two circular holes of the same diameter. A beam of light is made to fall normally on the front face of the screen, forming a plane monochromatic wave. What happens on the other side of the screen? The answer is altogether different according as the diameter of the holes pierced in the screen is large with respect to the wavelength of the incident wave or, on the contrary, as it is of the same order. In the first case geometrical optics is applicable to the description of the phenomenon; from the posterior side of the screen two cylindrical and parallel pencils of light will emerge, each one of these being almost exactly defined laterally by the contour of one of Young's holes. In this case, if one wishes to follow mentally the movement of one of the photons which pass through the screen, one can imagine that it follows one of the rectilinear rays of the incident wave which passes through one of Young's holes and no difficulty will then be seen in affirming that such a photon must have passed through such a hole.

But let us consider the second case, that where the wavelength of the incident wave is of the same order as the diameter of Young's holes; there will then be diffraction at the passage of the light through each hole and on the posterior side of the screen each of them will play the part of a source of a small spherical wave. If the holes are not separated too much from each other, there will exist an extended region of space where the waves emanating from the two holes will fall on each other with a marked intensity and in this region will occur phenomena of interference; these are exactly the phenomena which Young had formerly observed, thus supplying a decisive argument in favour of the theory of waves, and which are carefully described and theoretically explained in all the treatises of physical optics.

In the region of interference where the distribution of vibratory magnitudes, when we analyse it in detail, appears somewhat complicated, there is no longer any means of defining the rays of light having a simple physical meaning, and in consequence we no longer know where are the trajectories of the photons; and nevertheless there is no doubt that localized photoelectric effects can occur in the bright fringes of this region so that the photons can there manifest their existence. Still more serious difficulties appeared on reflection. If we wish to preserve the classical description of phenomena with the aid of precise pictures in the framework of space and time, we must imagine that each photon of the incident wave penetrates into the posterior region of the screen by passing through one or other of Young's holes. But experiments of capital importance have shown that the phenomena of interference are obtained without any modification when the intensity of the incident light is very feeble—sufficiently feeble for the photons to arrive one by one at long intervals on the interference apparatus. It follows from this that the arrival on this apparatus of each photon considered in isolation must be associated with the arrival of a continuous wave which alone allows the exact prediction of the interferences that arise from the presence of the holes in the screen. But this continuous, homogeneous wave, must strike Young's two holes in the same way, for the classical theory of the phenomenon, which cannot be set aside, makes the two holes intervene in a completely symmetrical manner. How can we reconcile this symmetrical intervention of Young's two holes with the hypothesis that the photon necessarily passes through one or other of the two holes? Having closely analysed the problem, I found the obstacle insurmountable.

An examination of other phenomena, that for example of interference fringes which are produced in the vicinity of the surface of a mirror (Wiener's fringes), and again of the reflection and partial refraction which a luminous wave undergoes when it reaches the surface of separation of two unequally refracting media, raised problems which are analogous and as little soluble. I was wrong in wishing to solve these without thinking of doubting the too-well-established conceptions and the too-dogmatic affirmations of classical physics.

While I was struggling in the midst of these contradictions, the mathematical development of the new mechanics was making great advances. In 1925 Heisenberg, only twenty-five years old, by allowing himself to be guided by Bohr's correspondence principle and with the desire to adopt a strictly phenomenological point of view, was developing his quantal mechanics or the mechanics of matrices, the applications of which were immediately shown to be very fruitful. Then, at the beginning of 1926, in a series of basic memoirs, Schrödinger, expanding the ideas contained in my thesis, gave a complete analytical development of wave mechanics, applied it triumphantly to the rigorous determination of the quantized states to which the atomic systems are susceptible, and finally showed that Heisenberg's quantal mechanics was completely in accord with wave mechanics, of which it is basically only a transposition into a more abstract algebraic language. Soon afterwards a very young English scientist, P. A. M. Dirac, was to give all this new theortical construction a still more abstract form in his theory of q numbers.

The researches of Schrödinger had naturally aroused the keenest interest in the whole scientific world; numerous memoirs were then devoted to develop them and to apply their results. I need not say with what ardent interest I followed all this sudden efflorescence of new ideas, seeking to state precisely the bonds which united my primitive conceptions to the forms, sometimes rather different, which they assumed in the minds of other workers.

Nevertheless the true interpretation of the wave-corpuscle dualism seemed to me to remain obscure and did not cease to preoccupy me. In his brilliant researches Schrödinger had appeared to incline toward a solution of this problem which for a brief time appeared very attractive, but which in my view, had never really satisfied me. He proposed more or less explicitly to suppress one of the expressions of the dilemma by supposing that the corpuscles were only appearances due to the existence of small groups of waves. If, in fact, we consider a group of waves of small dimensions, it follows from the laws of geometrical optics, when they are valid, that this small group of waves must be displaced in space along one of the rays predicted by geometrical optics. If then this group of waves is sufficiently small so that on our scale we could liken it to an almost point object, it will constitute for us a sort of corpuscle describing in space one of the trajectories predicted as possible by classical mechanics. From that to the supposition that the corpuscles are in reality only small groups of waves, was but a step which Schrödinger appeared disposed to take. Unfortunately this attractive interpretation was unable for long to stand up to a critical examination. A small group of waves of this type must go on continually spreading out, hence the following inadmissible consequence.

At the end of a very short time that which at the inception would have constituted a corpuscle would have, so to speak, diffused itself into space and would have ceased to exist. Further, if in the case, where geometrical optics is valid, the conception of the corpuscle-group of waves could, setting aside the preceding difficulty, appear acceptable, it lost all clear meaning outside the realm of geometrical optics, for example, in the regions of interferences. Where can be found in the midst of Young's or Wiener's fringes small groups of waves in propagation capable of giving us a representation of the photon at the centre of these fringes? The attempt was hopeless; the interpretation proposed by Schrödinger had to be quickly abandoned.

In spite of the astonishing successes obtained by wave mechanics, the true interpretation of the wave-corpuscle dualism on which it was based thus still appeared as completely mysterious at the beginning of 1927, which was to be, in the evolution of this problem, a decisive year.

Last Attempts and Final Transformation (1927-8)

Let us first of all recall that the spring of 1927 was to give to wave mechanics the direct experimental proof which it still lacked. Davisson and Germer then announced that they had succeeded in obtaining diffraction phenomena by directing a beam of monokinetic electrons on to a nickel crystal, and this phenomenon, in every respect analogous to the diffraction of X-rays by crystals, was soon obtained again under varied conditions by G. P. Thomson, followed by many other physicists; it has made possible a more and more exact quantitative verification of the predictions of wave mechanics. It was a fine success for this theory!

Nevertheless this discovery, by bringing to light evidence for the electrons, of phenomena of the physical optical type, intensified the difficulties of interpretation which preoccupied me. How, indeed, could one imagine the motion of an electron when it underwent diffraction by a crystal? In the classical picture of the elastic impact of a corpuscle on a crystal, this rebounding should depend solely on the properties of the surface of the crystal at the point of impact only, and not at all on the whole structure of the crystallized body. Now the diffraction experiments showed, on the contrary, that the phenomenon was conditioned by the whole structure of the crystal. This was easily explained from the point of view of wave mechanics, since in Davisson's experiments the wave associated with the electron, just as the electromagnetic wave of X-rays in Laue's experiments, reaches an extended part of the crystal and experiences the reaction of the totality of the regularly distributed diffraction centres which are contained therein. But how are we to describe the trajectory of an individual electron in such a phenomenon? Such was always the stumbling block.

Beset by these difficulties, during the course of the year 1927 I made two successive and different attempts to break the circle of obstacles where the physical interpretation of wave mechanics appeared to me grievously circumscribed; these were the hypothesis of the double solution and the theory of the pilot-wave. These two attempts, which were both useless, had the advantage of making me see better the necessity for adopting entirely the new ideas which were developed during the course of the same year by Bohr and Heisenberg.

To make the nature of my efforts understandable, it is necessary that I recall one of the principles which had quite naturally arisen from the first developments of wave mechanics. In the undulatory theory of light, it is, we know, the square of the amplitude of the luminous wave, often called luminous intensity, which measures at each point of space the magnitude of the effects which light can produce there. This hypothesis is, in particular, absolutely necessary for the correct and exact.

prediction of the phenomena of interference and of diffraction. With only a little reflection we can see that in wave mechanics we will have to generalize this hypothesis under the form of the following principle, often called "the principle of localization" or "principle of interferences"—"The square of the amplitude of the wave associated with a corpuscle measures at each point and at every instant the probability with which the corpuscle manifests its presence at this point at that instant." This principle was at once one of the most obvious and the best established in the physical interpretation of wave mechanics.

Now, if we suppose that the form of the wave associated with a corpuscle is known, the intensity of this wave at each point and at each instant can be considered as defining the density of a fictitious fluid moving in space in the course of time, and then the quantity of this fluid contained in a small volume dv will give the probability that the corpuscle manifests its presence in the volume dv. If there is associated with the wave considered, not a single corpuscle but an infinite number —a swarm—of identical corpuscles, the fictitious fluid which we have just imagined would evidently represent the mean statistical distribution in space of the corpuscles of the swarm. A study of the equations of wave mechanics permits us, more-over, to define, reckoning from the appearance of the wave, the motion of all the parts of the fictitious fluid. It is then tempting to suppose that the movement of every corpuscle associated with the wave invariably coincides with the move-ment thus calculated for one of the elements of the fictitious fluid; the whole of the corpuscles of the same swarm would then be, in a way, the physical realization of the fictitious fluid, but even in the case of a single corpuscle the movement of this corpuscle would be completely determined by the knowledge of its associated wave and the principle of inter-ferences would be automatically satisfied. This physical inter-pretation of wave mechanics, which subsequently has had to be entirely abandoned, is often named "Madelung's hydro-dynamical interpretation" after the physicist who, independ-ently of me, had had the first idea of it. This hydrodynamical interpretation, which is in accord with the conceptions of classical physics, I tried to develop in two different ways in a more complete manner in 1927.

First of all—and this was the origin of my first attempt—it had appeared reasonable to me that, to remain really in agreement with classical ideas, it would be necessary to succeed in incorporating the corpuscle with the wave in order to obtain a clear and coherent picture of the wave-corpuscle dualism in the space-time framework. The only way in which this could be effected appeared to me to suppose that the corpuscles are in reality singularities of a permanent character central to an extended wave. The true wave associated with a corpuscle would then be a wave of singularity. But we have seen that wave mechanics, just as Fresnel's optics, had been led to consider continuous waves without singularities, of which the fundamental property was that their intensity would furnish at each point the probability of the presence of a corpuscle. How can we reconcile these two opposed conceptions of the wave associated with the corpuscle—conceptions which then seemed to me equally necessary?

To do this I attempted to develop the idea that the equations of wave mechanics would always admit of two linked solutions of which the one, having singularity, would really represent the structure of the wave-corpuscle dualism, while the other—continuous—would give only the statistical aspect of the displacement of a swarm of corpuscles. I thus hoped to obtain a theory representing the wave-corpuscle dualism, in conformity with the ideas of the older physics, whilst justifying the use of continuous waves and attributing to them the essential property expressed by the principle of interferences. We should thus recover Madelung's hydrodynamical interpretation, but duplicated, so to speak, by the structural picture of the waves with corpuscular singularities. This bold and ingenious attempt—too ingenious perhaps—was, I believe, the only one which was effectively tried to save classical ideas. I outlined it in an article in the *Journal de Physique* written at the beginning of 1927 and traces of it will also be found in the text of a section of the *Memorial des Sciences physiques* written about the same period.* I unfortunately discovered that the justification of my hypothesis, apart from altogether simple cases, such as that of uniform rectilinear

* *La Mécanique ondulatoire*, Paris, Gauthier-Villars, 1928.

motion, involved enormous mathematical difficulties and I did not delay in convincing myself that it was really impossible to advance in this direction. I then sought to establish myself more solidly on a sort of support position by adopting a point of view in principle less satisfying, but perhaps easier to defend. The opportunity for this was offered to me by the preparation of a report to the fifth Solvay Council of Physics which was to meet in Brussels in October 1927.

The immense interest which the development of the new mechanics had raised in scientific quarters in all countries had made the choice of the study of this doctrine under its different aspects the topic of the projected reunion. The famous H. A. Lorentz (who died at the beginning of the following year) entrusted with the organization and presidency of this Physical Council, wrote to me in June 1927, asking me to give him a report on wave mechanics and its interpretation, a report which would be distributed to the members of the Council before its assembly, and furnish one of the bases of the discussion. Convinced at that time that my hypothesis of the double solution was too difficult to be justified, I decided to adopt a more restrained point of view in my report.

I accepted on the one hand the existence of corpuscles imagined in the classical manner as small point objects, and on the other hand that of continuous associated waves, transposed from physical optics to wave mechanics. The corpuscle placed in the wave thus found itself coincident with a component part of the fictitious fluid of probability of which we have previously spoken; my hypothesis then was that the corpuscle at every instant followed the movement of the component part of the fictitious fluid with which it coincided and the principle of interferences immediately resulted from it. Thus I placed, in a way arbitrarily, the corpuscle central to the wave and I supposed that it was impelled in accordance with some well-defined law by the very propagation of the wave; so I recovered, stating it precisely, the hydrodynamic image of Madelung. In my hypothesis the wave in a way "piloted" the corpuscle, hence the name of "theory of the pilot-wave" which I gave to this conception. This theory was certainly much less complete than that which I had hoped to be able to build with the hypothesis of the double solution, since it no longer succeeded in *incorporating* the corpuscle in the wave, and established the wave-corpuscle dualism without attempting to penetrate more deeply into its nature; but in my opinion it had then the advantage of maintaining the traditional idea of a point corpuscle well localized in space, and of maintaining the rigorous determinism of its movements.

Such was the solution, an outline of which I gave in my report to the Solvay Congress. But here yet again difficulties appeared and above all—as always—when exceeding the limits of geometrical optics, one sought to imagine the motion of the corpuscles in the regions of interference. Certainly the formulae at which I arrived allowed me to describe this motion in a complete manner and in particular I studied the motion of the photon in the case of Wiener's fringes in the neighbourhood of a mirror. But the movements thus attributed to the corpuscles in the regions of interference had a somewhat artificial character, and the more I thoroughly developed this theory of the pilot-wave, the better I understood its weakness and difficulties.

The most serious of these difficulties were connected with the existence of a new principle which had been introduced into wave mechanics alongside that of interferences and which was beginning to play almost as important a role; I now speak of Born's principle of spectrum decomposition. This principle was itself also suggested by the wave theory of light.

Let us consider a beam of white light; we know that different arrangements, such as prisms or gratings, enable us to decompose this light into a spectrum, that is to say, to isolate the different monochromatic components which, by their "superposition" gave this white light. White light must then be represented by a wave function formed by the sum of plane monochromatic waves, and the arrangements in question have for effect the isolation of these different monochromatic components. Making use of mathematical language, we can say that the prism isolates the constituents of the Fourier series which represents analytically the incident white light. If we then introduce the idea of the photon we shall have to say that after its passage through the prism, an incident photon can reveal its presence in one or other of the coloured beams which emerge from it, and the wave theory then demands that the probability of the photon showing its presence in one of these coloured beams must be measured by the intensity of the corresponding Fourier constituent in the Fourier series which represents the incident wave. Born was the first to transpose these remarks from optics to wave mechanics and this transposition has led to the general principle of spectral decomposition, of which the following is the enunciation:

"In general, a corpuscle whose state is represented by a certain associated wave has not got a well-defined energy; its energy has only certain *possible* values. The probability that a measure of this energy should provide one of the possible values is given by the intensity of the corresponding monochromatic component in the Fourier series which represents the wave associated with the corpuscle in its initial state before the measurement."

This statement leads to the adoption of entirely new conceptions, completely foreign to classical physics, for it implies that in general a corpuscle has no well-defined state of movement, but that it is necessary to envisage the state of the corpuscle as a "superposition" of states of movement. This extension of the idea of superposition to the states of movement of a corpuscle, such as optics employs when it studies the luminous non-monochromatic waves, was in flagrant contradiction to the spatio-temporal system of pictures on which all the attempts at an explanation of phenomena in the older physics were based; it also led to the abandonment of the concrete character which up till then it had often been sought to attribute to the associated waves. It is for this profound reason that the theory of the pilot-wave and the whole of Madelung's hydrodynamic interpretation with the well-defined movements which they constantly attributed to the corpuscles, finally appeared irreconcilable with Born's principle.

If we thoroughly investigate this difficulty, we see that the theory of the pilot-wave being, if we wish to preserve the classical concepts, directly suggested by the principle of interferences, there exists in the framework of the classical concepts, a sort of contradiction between this principle and that of Born. As the development of wave mechanics has shown more and more clearly the necessity for admitting the simultaneous validity of these two principles, this development would then necessarily lead to the abandonment of the classical representation of phenomena with the aid of definite pictures in the framework of space and time and, in consequence, of the mechanical determinism which is connected with it.

These thoughts began to impress themselves on me when, on the eve of the opening of the Solvay Conference, I became acquainted with an account of the greatest importance published a little previously by Heisenberg, wherein, influenced by some suggestions of Bohr, the young German scientist formulated for the first time his famous uncertainty relations and developed all the new ideas with which they were connected, but I still hesitated to adopt a point of view which was so completely opposed to all my previously established custom. The discussions on this subject at the Solvay Conference were somewhat animated.* In a fine inaugural speech Lorentz had upheld and defined with great precision the point of view of classical physics. Born, Heisenberg and Bohr affirmed the necessity of the somewhat revolutionary conceptions which the uncertainty relations implied. Schrödinger preserved a classical bias still rather favourable to the picture of corpuscle-groups of waves. Einstein opposed the new ideas of Heisenberg with able objections which Bohr refuted by adroit arguments. Without allowing myself to be entirely convinced by the reasonings of Bohr and Heisenberg, I commenced to appreciate all their importance and profundity.

Having returned to Paris, I proceeded to reflect for a long time on Heisenberg's uncertainties. At that time I was giving a free course at the Sorbonne on wave mechanics; I still taught there the theory of the pilot-wave, but already I hardly believed in it any longer.

At the beginning of 1928 my decision was made; it was necessary in spite of the enormous effort of intellectual adjustment which they involved, to adopt the conceptions of Bohr and Heisenberg. Invited to deliver some lectures at the University of Hamburg in the spring of 1928, I there for the first time declared in public my formal adherence to the new ideas. In the

* See *Electrons and Protons, Rapports et discussions du Ve Conseil da Physique.* Solvay, Paris, Gauthier-Villars, 1928.

course of the following autumn, I was commissioned to hold an official course of instruction at the Faculty of Sciences, Paris; in the winter half of the scholastic year 1928-9 I gave a course where I developed the point of view of Bohr and Heisenberg and where I showed why the theory of the pilot-wave was inadequate.* Since that time (as my readers know) I have devoted considerable efforts to explain to physicists and philosophers the nature and the scope of the changes which the new orientation of theoretical physics in the microscopic domain implies for all our representation of natural phenomena.

Most physicists, with few but notable exceptions, belonging above all to the older generations, have progressively rallied to the probability interpretation of wave mechanics and to the uncertainties which are its consequence. A few attempts are still made from time to time to return to the past, for example, to take up again Madelung's hydro-dynamic interpretation. It does not seem that such attempts can have any serious chances of success today.

As can be seen from these personal recollections, the first period of the development of wave mechanics has been marked for me, after the initial discoveries, by several unfruitful attempts to interpret the principles of the new doctrine without overthrowing the bases—up till then always accepted—of our physical theories. These attempts have caused me a lot of worry and have made me lose much time. Never-theless, I do not regret them; they have had the advantage of making me see clearly the profound reasons for which the adoption of the concepts—at first sight so surprising—of Bohr and Heisenberg, had become a necessity imposed by the very existence of the experimental facts of which it is the duty of microscopic physics to give an account.

NOTE ADDED BY THE AUTHOR FOR THE ENGLISH EDITION

I have recently had information of a work by David Bohm (not yet published at the time of writing) which has brought my attention back to the theory of the pilot-wave. Bohm has, indeed, taken up again this theory exactly in the form which I had put forward at the Fifth Solvay Conference of Physics

*Introduction à l'étude de la Mécanique ondulatoire, Hermann, 1930.

in October 1927. Reflecting *de novo* on these problems, it always appears to me that this last form of my ideas of 1927 is impossible to accept; if we return to the objectivistic point of view of classical physics, we could not, in effect, admit that a corpuscle would be guided in its movement by a Ψ-wave of wave mechanics since this Ψ-wave is only a representation of probabilities. On the other hand, the initial form of my ideas of 1927, notably that which I had developed under the name of "theory of the double solution" in my article in *Journal de Physique de 1927*, seems to me more acceptable, because it admits the existence, behind the statistical Ψ-wave of wave mechanics, of a wave of singularity which would be the physical reality; the movement of the singularity would, then, quite naturally be conjointly responsible for the propagation of the wave of which it is part, and it would be only in appearance that the movement of the singularity would seem to be guided by the propagation of the statistical Ψ-wave; we would then recover all the formulae of the theory of the pilot-wave, but under a form which would no longer give rise to the same objections. I had only abandoned this theory of the double solution in 1927 because of the mathematical difficulties. There would, perhaps, be reason for examining them afresh.

For those whom the question would interest, I would point out that the theory of the double solution is set forth in the following article; *Journal de Physique*, Mai 1927, Serie VI, t. VIII, p. 225-41, and that this article has been reproduced in the English language in the following book: Louis de Broglie and Leon Brillouin—*Selected papers on Wave Mechanics*; Blackie and Son, London and Glasgow, 1928, pp. 113-38.

It is, moreover, probable that the theory of the double solution could only be developed in a satisfactory manner within the framework of a non-linear wave mechanics.

A Newcomer in Physics: the Nuclear Field

The idea of "field" is one of the most mysterious of physics. It has been progressively forced on the minds of scientists trying to explain the existence of interactions between different parts of matter. When mechanics was developed in the seventeenth and eighteenth centuries, it was assumed that it accounted for the facts, that there exist between small material particles (material points of rational mechanics), of which all bodies were supposed to be constituted, forces which would result either from the interaction of particles between themselves, or from the action of other bodies external to the system considered. Force was considered as an "action at a distance" and it is in this way that Newton conceived it when he introduced the idea of universal gravitation. But the conception of an "action at a distance" without any intervention of the medium—often empty—which separates the interacting bodies, did not fail to produce in the minds of physicists a certain uneasiness which Newton and his contemporaries already felt. Little by little physicists persuaded themselves that if a body placed in an empty region of space is submitted to a force, it is because that region of space is not really amorphous, that it contains a certain power of action. They understood that this region of space must be, in a certain manner, the means of interaction, and imagined a propagation of the actions in the medium from one place to the next.

These new conceptions were developed especially in the nineteenth century. Stated in perhaps too naïve a form by Faraday, they triumphed in the beautiful electromagnetic theory of Maxwell where the idea of the "field" appears clearly, that is, as a capacity for action defined at each point and at each instant by appropriate mathematical concepts. In Maxwell's theory, which is exclusively concerned with electric and magnetic phenomena, this field is the electromagnetic field; it is represented by the sum of two vectors—the electric field which acts on the charges at rest or in motion and the magnetic field which acts only on the currents, that is, on charges in motion. The propagation of the interactions through space with finite velocity has found in the framework of the electromagnetic theory precise expression in those formulae which give the "delayed potentials"; the state of an electromagnetic field at a point at a given instant depends, not on the position and actual movements of the electric charges, but on their position and their motion at an instant previous to the actual instant by the duration necessary for the propagation of the action from the charge to the point of space considered. Thus in the conceptions of Maxwell and his successors, the idea of field triumphed and the notions of force and of potential energy assumed a much more satisfactory form than in rational mechanics with action at a distance.

Let us add that in the electromagnetic theory, light and other radiations, which, with decreasing wave-lengths range from Hertzian to X-rays and γ-rays, appear as disturbances of the electromagnetic field which are freely propagated in space. Thus all the great collection of radiations enters into the general conception of the "field".

The conceptions of the electromagnetic theory relative to the fields are not immediately applicable to gravitation, and for a long time after Maxwell the forces of gravitation preserved the character of actions at a distance which they possessed since Newton. Einstein's generalized theory of relativity and the interpretation of gravitation which it proposed have been necessary for the reintroduction of gravitational attraction into the framework of the general conception of fields, and to allow us to consider it as propagating itself from one place to the next with a finite velocity.

The triumph of the new description of the field had thus led to a very marked opposition between matter formed ultimately of well-localized elementary particles, and the field spread out in a continuous manner in the empty spaces separating the elementary particles. Field and matter of corpuscular structure appear as symbolizing the inevitable antinomy of the continuous and the discontinuous, the material singularities being, moreover, the "sources" of the fields which they create around them. But this clear-cut distinction, which by its clarity could appear to be satisfying to the mind, has been demolished by the development of wave mechanics. The latter, based on numerous and substantial experimental proofs, teaches us that, in the case of the elements of matter as also in the case of fields, there is a need to introduce the dual picture of waves and of corpuscles, the relation between these two pictures causing the intervention of the quanta and being capable of correct expression only in terms of probability. Henceforth a new sort of extended and continuous field must be constantly associated with particles of matter, the Ψ-wave of wave mechanics, whereas with the fields of the classical theory of radiations it is now necessary to associate particles which, in the case of the electromagnetic field, bear the name of photons and which symbolize the discontinuity of the energy-exchanges between radiations and matter. From henceforth there is, therefore, a much greater symmetry between matter and radiation since both cause the intervention of waves and corpuscles, continuous and discontinuous.

How, then, can we today characterize the difference between the elementary corpuscles of matter and the field particles of the photon type? A first important difference is that the elementary material corpuscles cannot appear and disappear except in pairs, whilst field particles, such as the photons, can be emitted and absorbed singly. A second difference, of mathematical order, is that electromagnetic fields associated with photons are represented by vectorial quantities while the Ψ-wave of elementary corpuscles, of the electrons for example, cannot be represented by vectors, but by quantities of another nature called spinners. A third difference is explained by the fact that elementary corpuscles obey the statistics of Fermi-Dirac while the photons obey a different statistics—that of Bose-Einstein. All these contrasts can be connected with the following fundamental distinction.

The elementary corpuscles have a *spin* (internal rotation) which, expressed with the quantal unit $h/4\pi$, where h is Planck's constant, is equal to $\frac{1}{2}$, whereas the spin of the field particles expressed in the same unit always appears as an integer 1 for the photons associated with electromagnetic waves, and no doubt 2 for the "gravitons" which would be associated with the gravitational fields. On this basis we can today construct a theory of particles with a spin which permits the co-ordination of all the facts and gives a good account of the essential differences which exist between particles of matter and field particles in the old and restricted sense of the word.

Thus, in a more complex and profounder new sense, we can always oppose matter with these corpuscles and its Ψ-waves to the "field", the vehicle of interactions, with its particles capable of appearing and disappearing singly, and its waves of the vectorial type.

We now come to a fundamental question; how many fields of a different nature exist? Forty years ago the reply would very probably have been that there were two of these—the gravitational field and the electromagnetic field. It then seemed that with these two kinds of action we should be able to interpret all the observed phenomena.

The two kinds of fields appeared, moreover, of very different nature. The gravitational field, represented at each point by a single vector, was closely bound to the existence of the masses from which it seems to emanate and, in consequence of the strict proportionality which exists between inert mass and gravitational mass, the movements which result from it are independent of the nature of the bodies submitted to its action. The electromagnetic field, on the contrary, is represented at each point by two vectors, one of an electric nature, the other of a magnetic nature; it is bound to the existence of electric charges, and the electrified bodies which are submitted to it assume movements which vary according to their nature, more precisely according to the value of the relation e/m of their charge to their mass. Numerous attempts have been made to understand the nature of these two fields and to fuse them into the framework of a single theory.

Regarding the gravitational field, we know that Einstein's generalized theory of relativity has ended in giving it an interpretation which connects it with the space-time *curvature* induced by the very presence of material bodies, and in thus explaining in a truly remarkable manner the fact—up till then mysterious—that inert and weighty masses are proportional and that in consequence the trajectories of different bodies placed in the same gravitational field are the same notwithstanding the difference of their masses. As to the electromagnetic field which can very easily be made to enter into the framework of the restricted theory of relativity, he has not been able to find an analogous interpretation, and to attempt to construct "unitary" theories of gravitation and electromagnetism, it has been necessary to bring in new ideas such as those of the variation of standards of length when they describe closed circuits in space-time (Weyl), that of a fifth dimension which would be added to space-time (Kaluza), that of a torsion of space notably considered by Einstein in his recent researches, etc.

The multiplicity of these attempts shows that none of them

up till now has really given satisfaction. Besides, an acceptable theory of the electromagnetic field must today be "quantal" and take account of the existence of photons—particles of spin 1; in the same way the gravitational field is probably itself also quantized and must no doubt be associated with "gravitons" which probably have spin 2. Be it as it may, a genuine synthetic theory of the gravitational field and of the electromagnetic field remains a task for the future.

But the question of fields has been widened by the discovery of a new type of field—the nuclear field—the importance of which is certainly as great as that of the two others. This field of forces only acts at very short distances of the order 10^{-12} cm. at the most (order of magnitude of nuclear dimensions); it therefore intervenes in an essential manner in the internal cohesion of the nuclei of atoms, whilst it is without any influence as soon as the distance of the interacting particles attains the order of magnitude—nevertheless still very small—of atomic dimensions (10^{-8} to 10^{-9} cm.) and for this reason it is entitled to be called the "nuclear field".

The existence of the nuclear field was brought to light (without, moreover, its importance at this time having been fully taken into account) by Rutherford from 1910, when the great English physicist perceived that the deviations suffered by α-particles in passing close to atomic nuclei imply a law of interaction for very small distances departing from the Coulombian form. Nuclei and α-particles, being positively charged, exert an electrostatic repulsion on each other and we can calculate the deviations which must ensue therefrom when an α-particle passes near a nucleus; the outcome of the calculation is completely confirmed by experimental results when the impact is not too close, that is, when the particle does not pass into a vicinity too close to the nucleus; but if the impact is a close one, that is, if the particle approaches the nucleus at distances of the nuclear order, predictions from the calculation are at fault, which indicates the intervention of actions different from Coulombian actions.

A long time after Rutherford's experiments, after 1930, when it was understood that the nuclei are formed of protons and neutrons (that is, as we say at present, of "nucleons", some charged positively, the others neutral), it became evident that an attraction must exist between these constituents—even those not electrically charged; in other words, a proton and a neutron and even two neutrons must be mutually attracted although there are no electrical interactions between them, and in the same way between two protons there must exist, besides the Coulombian electrostatic repulsion due to their electric charges, an attraction of another nature, independent of the presence of the charge on the particles. We thus returned to the idea of the nuclear field and perceived all the importance of this field since it appeared to assure the stability of the nuclei of atoms. Further, various reasons which I am unable to give here, led once again to the belief that this field only acted at distances of the order of the nuclear dimensions.

But what is the nature of this new field? Must we suppose, as in the case of the electromagnetic field, that it is associated with particles, and what are these particles? We are indebted to Yukawa for having made important progress in the solution of the problem when, in 1935, he stated his reasons for assuming that the nuclear field is connected with the existence of particles of which the mass should be about 200 times greater than that of the electron. The general theory of the particles leads in effect to the view that the potential created by a corpuscle around itself must be of the form

$$V = \frac{\epsilon}{r} e^{-k_0 r}$$

where $k_0 = 2\pi\mu_0 c/h$, h being Planck's constant, c the speed of light *in vacuo*, and μ_0 being the appropriate mass of the particles connected with the field created by the corpuscle. In the case of an electromagnetic field created by an electrified corpuscle at rest, ϵ is the electric charge e of the corpuscle, μ_0 is the appropriate mass of the photon, which can be considered as zero, and the potential V is reduced to the electrostatic potential in e/r. If the corpuscle gives rise to a field of the nuclear type around itself, ϵ will be the charge relative to the nuclear field and k_0 must be sufficiently large for the exponential to approach zero at a distance of the order of 10^{-12} cm. from the corpuscle. It is easily deduced from this that the mass of the particles of the field must be at least 100 times that of the electron. Yukawa therefore boldly announced that there must exist particles of a mass intermediate between that of the electron and that of the proton for which the name "mesons" was soon used; he even adds a little later that these particles, being field particles, must probably have, like photons, a spin equal to 1. The discovery made a short time afterwards in cosmic radiation of unknown particles having a mass approximately equal to 200 times that of the electron brought an astonishing confirmation of the rather daring views of the Japanese physicist.

Following the path opened by Yukawa, physicists have constructed a whole theory of nuclear fields by considering these fields as "mesic fields". These theories are of great interest but it must be readily admitted that they still rest on somewhat frail bases. The complexity of the facts in the domain of nuclear physics and the insufficiency of our knowledge of the properties of mesons render precarious on many points the theoretical developments concerning the mesonic field and the calculation of the interactions which take place between the nucleons through its intermediary. The question has recently found itself still further complicated by the discovery of at least two kinds of mesons of different mass; μ-meson which was the first discovered in cosmic rays and of which the mass is about 200 times that of the electron, and π-meson more recently indentified and of which the mass appears in the neighbourhood of 275 times that of the electron. Moreover, we suspect the existence of yet other sorts of mesons[1] notably τ-meson the mass of which should be 800 to 1,000 times that of the electron.

There is some doubt as to the exact value of the spin of these particles, which only increases the weakness of our interpretations of the nuclear field. It seems that meson μ, the first brought to light, has a spin of $\frac{1}{2}$ and in consequence should be a "heavy electron" rather than a real meson; it could not then play the part of a field particle and it would be meson π which would possess a spin of 1 and would have to intervene in the theory of the nuclear field; but these interpretations are still very much subject to revision.

Be it as it may concerning these difficulties, the nuclear field certainly exists and there are strong theoretical reasons for thinking that it is associated with particles of the "meson" type. Perhaps there even exist several kinds of nuclear fields associated with mesons of different mass. Since charged nucleons (protons) give rise to a Coulombian field around themselves they possess at the same time an electromagnetic and a mesic field (or even perhaps several mesic fields). The question then arises of knowing if the electromagnetic field and the mesic fields must be considered as independent or, on the contrary, as very closely associated. Such a "unitary" theory of the electromagnetic field and the mesic fields (which must be carefully distinguished from the unitary theories of electromagnetism and gravitation, for here it is not a question of gravitation) has been considered by various physicists, notably, first of all, it would appear, by Stuekelberg.

Let us consider the case of a proton and let us suppose, to simplify matters, that there exists one kind only of mesic field with constant k_0. If the electromagnetic field and the mesic field are independent of one another, the electrostatic field of the proton will be derived from the Coulombian potential $V_1 = e/r$ and the mesic field from the potential $V_2 = \epsilon \, e \frac{\epsilon}{r} e^{-k_0 r}$, e and ϵ being respectively the electric charge and the mesic charge of the proton. The unitary theory to which we previously referred consists in blending together the two fields and in supposing that they are derived from the potential

$$V = V_1 + V_2 = \frac{e}{r} + \frac{\epsilon \, e^{-k_0 r}}{r} = e \frac{\left(1 - e^{-k_0 r}\right)}{r}$$

with the supplementary hypothesis $\epsilon = -e$.

This relation expresses that the fields are opposite, which allows us to give to this conception the name of the theory of "deductive field" because a mesic field comes to "deduct itself" from the Coulombian field. As soon as we are at a distance r from the proton greater than the nuclear dimensions, the exponential term $e^{-k_0 r}$ in V becomes negligible and V is reduced to the Coulombian potential, but at distances of the order of the nuclear dimensions, the mesic term makes itself felt and counterbalances the Coulombian field so that, for r approaching zero, V remains finite. The theory assumes more complex forms if we accept the existence of several kinds of "mesic fields", which, moreover, appears necessary to take account of the finite mass of the neutrons.

Personally I think that this fusion of the electromagnetic field and the mesic field corresponds to reality and that it must be examined thoroughly. Recently I tried to show that such a unitary conception of the two kinds of fields ought to lead to the removal of the well-known difficulties encountered by the quantal theory of fields, notably in what concerns the value of the intrinsic energy of the electrified particles. The solution of all these problems is certainly only at its commencement, but we already glimpse vast new possibilities of interpretation.

To end this rather brief statement on the nuclear field, we should like to insist on the danger which always threatens theorists and which is due to the temptation to consider the present state of our knowledge as definitive. Almost instinctively the human mind tends to construct syntheses which it imagines complete, on the basis of knowledge which is, and which no doubt will always remain, fragmentary. These provisional formulations often render great services in guiding scientific research, but it is always necessary to avoid considering them as definitive and of attributing to them a permanency which they have not got. Instances of this abound in the history of physical science and we shall cite a few examples.

The successes of rational mechanics in the explanation of the motion of the stars and of terrestrial bodies led physicists in the middle of the nineteenth century to think that a mechanical explanation of all physical phenomena was possible. After having rendered some service, this interpretation had to be abandoned because the discovery and the deep study of electromagnetic phenomena had shown that these are of capital importance in nature and that they cannot be explained on the basis of classical mechanics. Physicists then tried to reconcile the explanation of physical phenomena with the laws of electromagnetism, a reconcilation which was soon effected by the conceptions of the theory of relativity, and after a few notable successes, this synthesis crumbled in turn, following on the discovery of quanta, although nothing in the electromagnetic theory made it possible to foresee their existence. The discovery of a wave aspect of material particles (diffraction of electrons, etc.) came afterwards and obliged us to revise completely all our previous conceptions.

More recently still, at the beginning of the study of the structure of the nuclei, we recognized only protons and electrons as elementary particles, we attempted to describe this structure by conceding that nuclei are formed of protons and electrons. But the unexpected discovery of the neutron in 1931 led to a new change of conception: the nucleus would be formed of protons and neutrons (nucleons), the electrons emitted at the time of the transmutations being created when a nucleon passes from the neutral state to the positively charged state or inversely.

Finally, in a similar fashion, the appearance in physics of the nuclear field exhibits the variety of the attempts made to reconcile all fields with the electromagnetic type and the gravitational type, and the incomplete character of every unifying theory which only make these two kinds of fields intervene. The nuclear field certainly plays as important a role for the structure of matter as the electromagnetic and gravitational fields, and no doubt it is necessary and even urgent to attempt a unitary representation of the nuclear field and of the electromagnetic field, whilst waiting to add to it gravitation, the role of which appears less important on the nuclear scale.

Thus, at each stage of the progress of our knowledge in natural philosophy, new elements are introduced which often compel us to re-cast entirely the whole of our interpretation of physical facts. No doubt the theorists would prefer merely to perfect and amend the existing theories rather than to be obliged constantly to reconstruct them. But this obligation is the condition and the ransom of scientific progress.

On the Uncertainty Relation of the Second Quantization

The development of the new theories of physics has obliged physicists to adopt conceptions profoundly different from those of the older physics. The originality and the difficulty of these conceptions have as a consequence that neither philosophers nor physicists themselves have yet come to grasp the extent of their scope and their real significance. The necessity of making physical facts which are well established and appear contradictory enter into the framework of a single coherent theory, imposes today an obligation on the human mind of making one of the most laborious efforts which it has had to accomplish since it has sought to understand the laws of natural phenomena, and to conjecture beneath the complexity of appearances the profound correlations which unite them. Thus it is not useless in the presence of such difficult problems to consider them always under new aspects, by varying the points of view and the perspectives.

That is what we should like to do in this article whilst insisting principally on an uncertainty relation of which much less has been said than of those of Heisenberg, perhaps because it is still much more difficult to understand, but of which the physical importance and the conceptual scope is certainly considerable. I am alluding to the uncertainty relation which connects the "number" of particles of the Bose-Einstein type attached to a particular wave, to the "phase" of that wave.

In undertaking this exposition I must first recall that particles of the atomic scale are divided into two categories. In one they obey Pauli's exclusion principle and, when in a numerous collection, they are governed by the Fermi-Dirac statistics; in the other they do not obey the exclusion principle and when they are in a numerous collection they are governed by the Bose-Einstein statistics. The electrons, the protons, the neutrons, certain nuclei of atoms, belong to the first type; Dirac has proposed to name them "fermions". The α-particles, photons, certain nuclei of atoms, belong to the second category; Dirac reserves the name of "bosons" for them. There are reasons for thinking that elementary indecomposable corpuscles (as no doubt are the electrons) as well as all complex particles formed by an odd number of elementary constituents, are of the fermions type, whilst particles formed from an even number of elementary constituents are bosons. We shall not here insist on this point although it probably has great importance.

We shall first consider the fermions, the most familiar example of which, for physicists, is the electron. Fermions obey Pauli's exclusion principle, which implies that in the wave-corpuscle association for the fermions there is never more than one corpuscle per wave, each wave being defined by its frequency, its direction of propagation and the properties of spin which are associated with it. The fermion is a savage; it remains isolated on its wave and declines all collective work. Thence results that in a numerous collection, the fermions, because they remain isolated, observe the Fermi-Dirac statistics which, applied to electrons, permits us especially today to explain correctly the properties of the electric conductivity of metals. Thence results also, what is still more important, that each outlying electron plays a particular role; from which ensues, when we pass from one element to the following element in Mendéléef's classification, a variation in the chemical, spectroscopic and sometimes magnetic properties, due to the individual role played by the new electron which is added to the outlying structure of the atom.

Here now is an essential point. The waves associated with the different fermions are completely independent since each fermion forms a separate set: we are, therefore, unable to compare them between themselves, which implies that their relative phases are completely indeterminate. Let me make myself clear. The different parts of the wave of an individual fermion have perfectly defined differences of phase; it is this which allows the wave of an electron, for example, when occurrences taking place in the course of the path oblige it to superpose itself upon itself, to give rise to diffraction phenomena such as those observed when electrons are diffracted by crystals (phenomenon of Davisson and Germer) or by the edge of a screen (Borsch's phenomenon). But we are unable, by reason of the isolation of fermions, to say exactly what is the difference of phase between the wave of one fermion and that of another fermion. In mathematical terms, this is expressed in wave mechanics of the electron by saying that the phase of the Ψ function always contains an independent additive constant.

From this it especially follows that the wave of the fermions has not at all the character of waves of classical physics. No doubt the square of the modulus of its amplitude—its intensity—gives at each point the probability with which the associated fermion will reveal its presence at that point, which corresponds to an energy distribution conceived by classical wave theory; no doubt the spectral decomposition of the Ψ-wave associated with the fermion corresponds to the respective probabilities of the different possible values of the energy and of the momentum associated with the fermion, corresponding to the decompositions envisaged in the classical theory of light. But these correspondences between the properties of the Ψ-wave of the fermions and those of the waves of classical physics operate by introducing, with regard to the position and movement of the fermions, aleatory conceptions altogether foreign to the classical conceptions. Further, these analogies, which are far from being equivalences, stop there. It is impossible to assimilate the Ψ-waves of the fermions to genuine "vibrations" propagating themselves in space in the course of time, as are the elastic and electromagnetic waves of macroscopic physics, vibrations which would be capable of causing vibratory movement in receptor bodies sensitive to them. It is equally impossible to add the amplitudes of two fermionic waves, as in classical physics we can add together (vectorially) the amplitudes of macroscopic elastic or electromagnetic waves. That is impossible because each fermion and its wave are essentially isolated; the Ψ-wave is, therefore, nothing but an element of prediction, that is, the mathematical representation of the probability of observable events and of the results of measurement, its amplitude, determined by normalization with the aid of the principle of compound probabilities not having any direct mechanical or physical significance.

Thus the fermion Ψ-wave appears to us as a fictitious wave of a symbolic and mathematical character permitting only the prediction of the possible results of the discontinuous succession resulting from measurements made on the associated corpuscle. And nevertheless there exist waves, for example electromagnetic, which have the character of genuine vibrations for which we can add the amplitudes, and which are capable of communicating a mechanical vibration to a receptor body. If we consider, as appears natural, the electromagnetic wave as being the Ψ-wave of the photons, there is therefore a notable difference between the Ψ-wave of photons and those of electrons. To understand this difference we must start from the fact that photons are bosons and not fermions. We must therefore, now study the case of bosons.

Contrary to fermions, bosons are not subjected to Pauli's

exclusion principle; they can, therefore, group themselve in more or less large numbers on the same wave. This faculty of grouping is explained by the fact that, when bosons are in a numerous collection, they obey a statistics distinct from that of Fermi-Dirac—the statistics of Bose-Einstein—which expresses the possible existence of clusters of particles associated with the same wave. The validity of the Bose-Einstein statistics for photons, which are particles of the bosons type, involves the well-known form of Planck's law of spectral distribution for black body radiation, because this radiation can be likened to a "gas of photons".

The study of the grouping of bosons on a single wave has led to the development of the theory of the second quantization of which Dirac clearly developed the principles twenty years ago. Applied to the particularly important case of photons, the second quantization leads to the "quantal theory of electromagnetic fields" due to Jordan, Heisenberg and Pauli; this is what we see particularly well when we give to this last theory the form developed by the author of this present article under the title[2] of "Wave Mechanics of the Photon". The examination of these problems of grouping leads to new ideas of great interest and we meet again, but under a very different form, the concepts of uncertainty and of complementarity which are classical, since the researches of Bohr and Heisenberg, in the case of a single corpuscle and of its associated wave.

For greater clarity we are going to discuss the photons of light, although our arguments are in theory applicable to other kinds of bosons. We can consider the case of a single photon and of its associated wave; this is the case which is naturally presented when we consider the emission of a photon by an atom in a Bohr's quantal transition. Then, as in the case of the fermion, the associated wave has only the mathematical sense of a means of prediction, defining by its local intensity the probability of the possible localizations of the photon and by its spectral composition the probability of its states of possible movement. The wave attached to a single photon has never the character of a true observable vibratory phenomenon. But it is certain that it is no longer the same if we consider the emission of a Hertzian wave by the antenna of a wireless transmitter.

In such a wave there are, without any doubt, vibrating electric and magnetic fields of perfectly defined phase, able to communicate a synchronous vibratory state to an appropriate receiver. We can even state this assertion precisely by considering an arrangement for Hertzian emission, somewhat out of use today, but which has been used—the emission by high frequency alternator; with this arrangement we directly produce in an alternator a "sinsusoidal" current of high frequency and, by sending this current into an antenna, there is produced the emission of a Hertzian wave of the same frequency, the phase of which is directly connected with the movement of the alternator and the arrangement of its circuits. Here there is no way out; it is clearly seen that the electromagnetic field is a real vibration produced with relations of phase determined by the mechanical rotation of the alternator. But, as we know, since Maxwell, that an electromagnetic wave does not differ at all in nature from a luminous wave, we must suppose that it transports photons and we are led to ask ourselves why this case differs from that of the emission of an isolated photon.

In the case which we have just considered a Hertzian wave must be regarded as the Ψ-wave of the photons which are associated with it and yet it has here the physical characteristics of a vibration in the classical sense, that is, that it possesses a well-defined phase; that the amplitudes of two Hertzian waves which are superposed can be added (vectorially); that this vibration can be communicated to an appropriate receiver, etc. Why has this wave thus a character altogether different from that of the fermions or of the isolated photons? The reply to this question is as follows:

Photons, being bosons, can be grouped on a single wave and the usual Hertzian wave is precisely a wave to which are associated a very large number of photons. It is easy to ascertain that, because of the smallness of the quantum $h\nu$ each group of Hertzian waves transports a very large number of photons and this grouping of photons on a single wave gives it a character altogether different from that of a Ψ-wave associated with an isolated corpuscle. The emission of a Hertzian wave is due to the combined movement of the electricity in the emitting antenna (and eventually in the high-frequency alternator): regarded from the quantal point of view this movement in unison amounts to an infinity of small co-ordinated and *coherent* quantal transitions. This process is, therefore, altogether different from the process of emission of an isolated photon in an individual quantal transition; it is only rendered possible because photons, being bosons, can group themselves in large numbers on a single wave and such a process could not exist for the emission of fermions.

An electromagnetic wave detectable macroscopically, as is a Hertzian wave, is, therefore, characterized by two factors; the number—always large—of photons which it carries, and the phase—always well-defined—of the vibration which it represents. Now—and here is the essential point—between these two quantities, "number of photons" and "phase of the wave", the theory of the second quantization, and the quantal theory of fields, which is derived from it, have established the existence of a relationship of complementarity involving uncertainties altogether analogous to those well known today which exist between the position of any corpuscle whatever and its state of motion.

First let us recall of what consist Heisenberg's uncertainty relations and the complementarity which they express. We can measure by an experiment made at a given instant the position of the corpuscle at that instant; we can also measure its energy and its momentum by other kinds of experiments. But we cannot simultaneously measure a co-ordinate q_i of a corpuscle and the corresponding component p_i of its momentum. Every measure leading to a simultaneous evaluation of both these "conjugate" quantities allows the uncertainties δq_i and δp_i to be incorporated in their exact value such that the inequality

$$\delta q_i \cdot \delta p_i \geqslant h \ (i = 1, 2, 3)$$

(where h is Planck's constant) may be satisfied[2]. These are Heisenberg's uncertainty inequalities to which it is necessary to add the fourth inequality

$$\delta E \cdot \delta t \geqslant h \quad (E \text{ energy})$$

of which the significance is, however, a little different. The value of the co-ordinates and of the time t defines exactly the "spatio-temporal localization" of the corpuscle corresponding to its granular aspect; the value of the p_i and of E defines the "dynamic state" of the corpuscle corresponding, in accordance with the principles of wave mechanics, to its wave aspect. Heisenberg's uncertainty relations express therefore, as Bohr has strongly emphasized, the "complementary" character of the granular aspect and of the wave aspect of the elementary physical entities which we call corpuscles. The more we come to define exactly one of these aspects, the more the other becomes uncertain. Thus the existence of these two aspects which seem to us irreconcilable, nevertheless never entails a contradiction. This conception of complementarity is assuredly one of the most original and most profound which contemporary physics has introduced.

Let us now return to electromagnetic waves, carriers of numerous photons. The theory of the second quantization has shown us that there exists between the number of photons and the value of the phase of the wave a relation of complementarity. We could, for example, by estimating the photoelectric effects produced by the incident photons, determine the number of photons carried by an electromagnetic wave, but such a determination would not give any information as to the value of the phase of the wave. We can also, by observing the electrical or mechanical vibrations produced on a receiver by the action of the electromagnetic wave, determine exactly its phase, but such a determination would teach us nothing about the number of photons associated with the wave. More generally, every observation permitting a simultaneous evaluation of the number of photons and of the phase of the associated wave leaves incorporated in these quantities uncertainties δN and $\delta \Phi$, such that the uncertainty relation

$$\delta N \cdot \delta \Phi \geqslant l$$

may be verified. The "number of photons" and "the value of the phase" appear to us therefore, as observable, but in Bohr's sense complementary, aspects of a macroscopic electromagnetic wave. The more we define one of these aspects exactly, the more the other becomes uncertain.

We can say that here again there is a relationship of complementarity between the granular and the undulatory aspect of photons. Indeed, the possibility of "numbering" the photons is essentially related to their granular character of discontinuous units, whilst the existence of a well-defined phase would not be conceived without the possibility of associating a wave with the displacement of photons. Nevertheless the grain-wave complementarity here appears in an altogether different aspect. In Heisenberg's relations, the grain aspect is defined by the localization of the corpuscle and it could not be done by numbering the corpuscles since we are considering a single corpuscle; as to the wave aspect, it is defined by the momentum and the energy, that is, by the wave-length and the frequency, but in no way by the absolute value of the phase since this, as we have seen in the case of individual Ψ-waves, always admits of an arbitrary additive constant.*

The co-operation of a large number of photons (or more generally of bosons) in the same wave results in giving to this wave the character of a wave of the classical type, a real physical vibration in propagation with a well-defined phase, additive amplitude and the possibility of transmitting electrical or mechanical movements in phase to appropriate receivers. But to render evident the "classical" properties of the wave is only possible if we give up decomposing it into corpuscles and numbering these. Every enumeration of this kind, as an inevitable consequence, makes the classical properties of the wave disappear.

Thus the macroscopic electromagnetic wave appears to us as the result of the co-operation of a very great and undetermined number of photons. More generally, the macroscopic wave fields of well-determined phase appear to us as associated with particles of the bosons type which alone, by their ability of congregating on a single wave, render possible the appearance of these macroscopic wave fields.

Thanks to the theory of the second quantization applied to the quantal representation of electromagnetic fields, we have thus succeeded in accounting at one and the same time for two physically certain and, at the first appearance, contradictory facts: the emission of radiation by photons at the time of

* Moreover this follows from the fact that for $N = 1$ and $\delta N = 0$, the relationship $\delta N . \delta \Phi \geqslant 1$ gives $\delta \Phi = \infty$.

Bohr's quantal transitions and the macroscopic existence of electromagnetic waves with well-defined phases and with classical properties of the Maxwell type. But, just as it has not been possible to account for the double granular and wave aspect of particles on the atomic scale, except by introducing the Heisenberg uncertainties and the complementarity of which they are the expression, in the same way we have not been able to reconcile the quantal and classical undulatory aspects of electromagnetic radiation except by introducing the uncertainty relation $\delta N \cdot \delta \Phi \geqslant l$, that is, a new kind of complementarity between the number of photons associated with a wave and the phase of that wave.

In the expositions of philosophical character of the new physics, we have, in general, insisted less on this kind of uncertainty and of complementarity than on those relative to the wave-corpuscle duality to which are attached the names of Heisenberg and Bohr. Nevertheless, they have a very great importance, for without them it is impossible to understand how the passage of the quantal processes on the microscopic scale to certain essential phenomena on the macroscopic scale operates. They also show the importance of the distinction between fermions, always isolated and associated with individual waves without physical character, and bosons, capable of grouping themselves on a single wave which then assumes the properties of classical waves.

The importance of the quantal theory of the electromagnetic fields in the present development of theoretical physics could not be exaggerated. It is today the basis of all the arguments thanks to which physicists seek, with varying success, to explain the utmost details of atomic or nuclear phenomena (such, for example, as the Lamb-Rutherford spectral displacement which is making much ink flow at the present time). But absorbed in the carrying out of their calculations, theorists often seem little inclined to meditate on the bases themselves of the theory— bases which have, nevertheless, an essential importance, and which are not beyond raising some difficulties here and there. When, after the passage of time, we shall be better able to pass judgement on the whole of the new conceptions introduced by contemporary physics we shall without any doubt discover that the complementarity between the number of bosons associated with a single wave and the phase of that wave has an altogether fundamental import and significance.

---

[1]Brown and others at Bristol found that the mass of the τ-meson is about 969 times that of the electron. Cockcroft, 1954, quotes 966.

[2] See the author's book on this subject: *Mécanique ondulatoire du photon et théorie quantique des champs électromagnétiques*, Gauthier-Villars, Paris, 1949.

CHAPTER IX

CONCEPTIONS OF CONTEMPORARY PHYSICS AND THE IDEAS OF BERGSON ON TIME AND ON MOTION

[With the approval of the author this chapter has been merely summarized because it was felt that this would meet the needs of readers better than a full translation. The translator has given a very brief outline of Bergson's philosophy—sufficient it is hoped, to enable readers to follow the arguments put forward by the author. Those who wish to make a study of Bergson's philosophy are referred to the bibliography of his works which appears at the end of this chapter (page 194), but this is not necessary if they are content with the present outline which has been compiled only for the purpose of making clear certain analogies between his philosophy and contemporary physics.]

HENRI LOUIS BERGSON (1859-1941) reacted against the views which denied the reality of time and held that a considerable amount of confusion arose from the attempts to state reality in terms of space and to eliminate time. He believed that the principle of Duration is all-embracing and thus capable of generating and also of explaining reality; the attempted elimination of time was, he believed, characteristic only of knowledge which was dominated by conceptions of utility. He showed the fallacy in the method of intellectual analysis and the inadequacy of the rational and mechanical interpretation of the world to which such an analysis leads. On the other hand he regarded intuition as the method which can reveal the immediately given data that make up our concrete experience. Thus he informs us that

". . . intelligence and instinct are turned in opposite directions, the former towards inert matter, the latter towards life. Intelligence, by means of science, which is its work, will deliver up to us more and more completely the secret of physical operations; of life it brings us, and moreover only claims to bring us, a translation in terms of inertia. It goes all round life, taking from outside the greatest possible number of views, drawing it into itself instead of entering into it. But it is to the very inwardness of life that *intuition* leads us—by intuition I mean instinct that has become disinterested, self-conscious, capable of reflecting upon its object and of enlarging it indefinitely". See Bibliography (at end of this chapter) No. 4, page 186.

It must not be concluded that Bergson's philosophy has escaped severe criticism or that de Broglie accepts it *in toto*; indeed he thinks that many of the criticisms are quite justified but, on the other hand, he feels that justice should be done to a philosopher of Bergson's standing and hence refers to a number of analogies—some of which, he admits are not very good, whilst others display the brilliant mind of the French philosopher. Amongst the many criticisms put forward—too numerous to refer to in this summary—the translator would like to give a quotation from a work which attracted considerable attention nearly thirty years ago in the philosophical and scientific worlds.

"The theory of Evolution has made the aspect of time in the universe more important than ever before, and Bergson has rescued the concept of time from the confusion in which it had become entangled, not only in our empirical experience, but even in our scientific and philosophic ideas. But while freely conceding this great merit to Bergson I must confess that I fail to see how from pure Duration he has produced concrete reality. It simply cannot be done. From bare, undifferentiated, homogeneous unity you cannot reach out to multiplicity. You may call pure Duration creative, but it will create nothing until it is mixed with something very different from itself. And indeed Bergson has had to summon to his rescue another principle, which he has invested with all the characters of which he had so carefully deprived Duration. This is the intellect. The intellect is practical, analytical, selective, purposive; it is at once the

principle and the instrument of action; it can analyse the
material before it and choose what is useful for its purpose."
—J. C. Smuts, *Holism and Evolution*, pages 93-4.

Later on Smuts points out that Bergson went wrong in
impoverishing the creative principle by reducing it to the bare
empty form of Duration. He adds:

"In order, after that false step, to set his Creation going, it
was inevitable that another mistake should be made, and
that a relatively subordinate factor, like the Intellect, should
be overloaded with importance. Thus the intellect, which is
a sort of Machiavelli or Mephistopheles in the Bergsonian
system, has a role assigned to it which is accentuated both
unduly and in a one-sided manner. In order to understand
nature we have to proceed more modestly and in closer
touch with our ordinary observation of her ways." *Id.*,
page 35.

We shall now consider some of the analogies which de
Broglie discovers between a number of Bergson's views and
the quantal theory, and first of all Bergson's criticism of the
common idea of motion will be dealt with, summarizing de
Broglie's description on page 198 of *Physique et Microphysique*.

In describing the movement of a point as a continuous
sequence of positions successively attained in the course of
time, science falls into a profound error because it thus ignores
the essential of motion—mobility, dynamism. The variable *t*
of the classical mechanics, serving to mark the instants of the
passage of a moving body to the different points of its trajectory,
can be conceived as taking place with infinite speed without
altering in any way the coincidences foreseen. The whole
trajectory is then spatialized, and the strict relativists thus
imagine it in their space-time when they evoke the "world-
line" of the universe of a moving body. But Bergson has never
admitted this point of view which, according to him, deprives
duration of its concrete, and in some manner creative, character.
More than once in his criticism of the classical image of motion,
he has called to his aid the arguments of Zeno of Elea. The
most striking of these arguments is, in de Broglie's view, that of

the arrow which, according to Zeno, cannot at any instant of its flight occupy an exactly determined position, because, if it occupied such a position, *it would be at rest.* Bergson's comments on this are as follows:

"The passage is a movement and its arrest an immobility. When I see the moving object pass a point, I understand without doubt that it *could* stop at that point and, even when it does not stop, I am disposed to consider its passage as an infinitely short rest. Every point of space being necessarily fixed, I have great difficulty in not attributing to the moving object itself the immobility of the point with which it coincides. How would a *progress* coincide with a *thing,* a movement with an immobility?"

De Broglie then adds:

"So the philosopher of Duration maintains an invincible mistrust with regard to the representation of movement by the displacement of a point on a trajectory. He sees there an illusory description. 'At its basis,' says he, 'the illusion comes from the fact that the movement, *once effected,* has deposited along its path a motionless trajectory on which we can reckon as many immobilities as we wish. From this it was concluded that the movement, being carried out, deposes at each instant, underneath itself, a position with which it coincided' " (Bibliography 2, page 207).

De Broglie asks the question whether there is some analogy between Bergson's criticism of the idea of motion and the conceptions of contemporary quantal theories, and concludes that the answer must be in the affirmative. It has been pointed out (page 98) that one of the important results of the development of the new wave and quantal mechanics has been to show the impossibility of attributing simultaneously to an elementary corpuscle a well-defined state of motion and an accurately determined position. He concludes that the analogy appears real, and moreover, if Bergson's criticism of motion has erred anywhere, it would be more by excess of caution. To show the analogy more clearly we shall quote again from Bergson: "In space there is nothing but parts of space and in whatever point one considers the moving body, *one will obtain only a position*" (Bibliography 1, page 84). Borrowing the language of the quantal theories he would have been able to say, according to de Broglie: "If one seeks to localize the moving object, by a measure or by an observation in a point of space, one will obtain nothing but a position, and the state of motion will completely escape." But he wrote the lines quoted above in 1889, forty years before the appearance of Heisenberg's uncertainties.

Nevertheless there are serious discrepancies in the so-called analogies, of which the following is given as an example. Quoting from the same book, we read as follows:

> "Now, in the analysis of variable, as in that of uniform motion, there is only the question of spaces traversed once and of simultaneous positions once attained. We were then obliged to say that, if mechanics retains no time except simultaneity, it retains no motion itself except immobility" (Bibliography 1, page 90).

De Broglie points out that, while this statement may be true of classical mechanics, it seems much less exact in the case of wave mechanics in which precise localization and pure mobility can be encountered in turn, being, according to Bohr, complementary aspects of reality.

This and other examples show that certain phrases of Bergson should be greatly modified if one wished to state more exactly the analogies between his philosophical conceptions and the new theories of physicists. Nevertheless, at times the analogies appear quite clearly in the text of his books, as the following example from *Physique et Microphysique*, page 203, will show.

If today a professor of wave mechanics wants to explain to his students how the plane monochromatic wave represents the rectilinear and uniform motion of a corpuscle, he must commence his exposition by saying:

> "Let us consider a corpuscle endowed with a perfectly well-defined state of motion, that is, corresponding to an

energy and to a momentum exactly known, and let us completely disregard the position of the corpuscle in space; this state of motion without localization is described in wave mechanics by the propagation of a plane monochromatic wave. . . ."

And now let us hear Bergson: "Attach yourselves to the movement whilst disengaging yourselves from the divisible space which subtends it so that only the mobility is considered!" (Bibliography 2, page 232). Is there not here an undeniable analogy between the teaching of the scientist and the dictum of the philosopher?

Another example is given of the difficulty of avoiding consideration of the corpuscle of wave mechanics, which is represented by a wave extended over a whole region of space and which, not localized, can manifest its presence in every point of this region: "As the shrapnel, bursting before it falls to the ground, covers the explosive zone with an indivisible danger, so the arrow which goes from A to B displays with a single stroke its indivisible mobility" (Bibliography 4, page 334).

Another example from quantal physics is even more striking. From all that the reader has learned in the preceding chapters, and more especially on pages 122 *et seq.*, he is aware that in the quantal theories, much more so than in the classical theories, time as it flows on seems to bring forward new and unpredictable elements. Here are Bergson's words written nearly fifty years ago:

"The more I consider this point, the more it seems to me that, if the future is bound to *follow on* the present instead of being given alongside of it, it is because it is not completely determined at the present moment, and if the time taken up by this succession is something other than a number, it is because it ceaselessly creates itself from what is unforeseeable and new" (Bibliography 4, page 367).

On this de Broglie remarks that if Bergson had been able to study the quantal theories in detail, he would undoubtedly have joyfully stated that in the picture which they offer us of the evolution of the physical world, they show at each instant nature hesitating between several possibilities, and without doubt he would have repeated, as in his last work, that "time is this hesitation itself or it is nothing" (Bibliography 8, page 101).

In wave mechanics the possibility of two particles finding themselves at the same point of space leads to a weakening of the old idea of the impenetrability of matter. This idea thus becomes obscured while at the same time the permanent numeration of particles becomes impossible, and this fact can be compared with a profound idea of Bergson. "To admit the impenetrability of matter is, therefore, simply to recognize the solidarity of the ideas of number and space; it is to enunciate a property of number rather than of matter" (Bibliography 1, page 67).

The idea of *stationary states* was early introduced into the quantal theories. According to Bohr, structures on the atomic scale are capable of stationary or quantized states which do not allow of any evolution in time and are as though placed outside duration. But these quantized systems are also capable of passing by a sudden *transition* from one stationary state to another and it is by the succession of these sudden transitions, of which quantal physics today is able to calculate the probabilities, that the evolution of the material world, envisaged on the microscopic scale, is effected. The following words of Bergson seem relevant in this connexion: "Let us merely say that intelligence represents the becoming as a series of *states* of which each one is homogeneous with itself and does not appear to change" (Bibliography 4, page 177).

De Broglie speculates on what Bergson's reaction would have been to the philosophical aspects of the contemporary theories of physics, but unfortunately when the quantal theories had commenced to take their present form he was old and in poor health. Nevertheless in his last work he has referred to these theories in a note of which the following is the text:

"We therefore, can, and even we must, still speak of physical determinism even when we postulate in accord with the most recent physics the indeterminism of the elementary phenomena of which the physical fact is composed.

For this physical* fact is seen by us as subjected to an inflexible determinism and is radically distinguished thereby from the acts which we accomplish when we imagine ourselves free. Thus, as we suggest above, we can ask if it is not precisely to mould matter in this determinism, in order to obtain in the phenomena which interest us a regularity of succession allowing us to act on them, that our perception stops at a certain particular stage of condensation of elementary phenomena. . . ." (Bibliography 8, page 61.)

On this de Broglie comments as follows:

"A curious suggestion according to which living beings would necessarily have a 'macroscopic' perception, for in the macroscopic only there prevails the apparent determinism which renders possible their action on things. In reading this isolated text, how much one regrets that the great philosopher was unable to survey with his piercing glance the unforeseen horizons of the new Physics!"

In a footnote at the end of Chapter IX de Broglie has drawn attention to some other resemblances between the ideas of Bergson and those of modern physics; some of these were pointed out to de Broglie by M. André George and relate to Bergson's conceptions on causality and on the distinction between strong causality and weak causality which de Broglie himself had introduced some years ago especially in *Continu et Discontinu*, page 64. Speaking of weak causality Bergson writes as follows:

"If, therefore, we decide to conceive the causal relation in this second form, we can affirm *a priori* that a relation of determinism between cause and effect will no longer be necessary, for the effect will no longer be given in the cause. It will reside there only in a state of possibility and as a confused representation which will not, perhaps, be followed by the corresponding action" (see page 294 *et seq.* of the same work for further remarks).

---

* And (we should add) macroscopic.

The following are Bergson's chief works—for the guidance of any who may wish to study his philosophy:

1. *Essai sur les données immédiates de la conscience*, 1889. English translation, *Time and Free Will*, 1910.
2. *Matière et mémoire*, 1896. English translation, 1911.
3. *Le Rire*, 1900. English translation, 1911.
4. *L'Évolution créatrice*, 1907. English translation, 1911.
5. *L'Énergie spirituelle*, 1919.
6. *Durée et simultanéité*, 1923.
7. *Less Deux Sources de la Morale et de la religion*, 1932. English translation, 1935.
8. *La pensée et le mouvant*.

Amongst the books in English the following may be mentioned:

W. James, *A Pluralistic Universe*, 1909.
A. D. Lindsay, *The Philosophy of Bergson*, 1911.
H. Wildon Carr, *Henri Bergson: the Philosophy of Change*, 1912.
Hugh S. Elliott, *Modern Science and the Illusions of Professor Bergson*, 1912.

CHAPTER X

CHANCE AND CONTINGENCY IN QUANTAL PHYSICS

DETERMINISM reigned supreme in the theories of classical physics. It was supposed that all phenomena, from the smallest to the greatest, were governed by rigorous laws so that the state of the world at the instant t must be completely determined by its state at the initial instant t_0. In support of this conception which Laplace had summed up in a phrase that has become celebrated, we could invoke certain general philosophic reasons such as the principle of sufficient reason, but above all we could count on the continued confirmation which the development of science seemed to bring to it. The possibility of expressing the laws of astronomy, of mechanics and physics, by rigorous mathematical relations, and that of representing the evolution of phenomena by the aid of differential equations, the solutions of which are completely determined when certain initial data are known, explain in precise form the success of the hypothesis of universal determinism. It had so successfully become one of the best assured principles of scientific thought that Henri Poincaré, in spite of the boldness of his critical mind and the independence of his judgements, gave the impression of going astray when, by chance, he came to make allusion to the possible limits of physical determinism.

And, nevertheless, in the course of the last century and particularly in its second half, theoretical physics has played a larger and larger part in its speculations on the notion of chance, in the calculus of probabilities and in statistical laws. How was this science, which then accepted with complete confidence the conception of universal determinism, able without contradiction to introduce chance into its arguments? This depended on the conception that was entertained of chance, a conception which has often been fully defined by the scientists of that epoch and which had nothing to do with the pure contingency of philosophers. We shall first state precisely the point of view that they adopted.

To do this, let us admit in all its rigidity the validity of universal determinism. We must then reject the intervention of all contingency, of all real chance in the development of natural phenomena. If our judgements and our methods of observation were sufficiently refined to permit us to follow in detail all phenomena, in even the most fine-spun, if our minds were sufficiently powerful to analyse them all, we would always succeed in re-establishing the inexorable chain of determinism which binds them to each other. But one must confess that the human condition does not always allow us to attain this ideal goal. The skein of causes is sometimes so tangled that we do not succeed in unravelling it; very often our coarse senses and our imperfect experimental methods only allow us to establish general phenomena through the co-operation of an immense number of elementary phenomena, the inextricable complexity of which we are incapable of following. Then we say that chance intervenes, or again that the appearances established by our senses have a statistical character. But if we are determinists of the strict school, we shall not doubt but that it is only an appearance resulting from the imperfection of our means of knowing. Let us take a familiar example from a type often quoted.

While walking on a frosty day on a sloping pavement, we fall and break a leg; that is an unlucky affair which has serious consequences for us and, as we do not clearly see all the causes of it, we say that it is due to a lamentable chance. But, will say the determinist, this is nothing but an appearance due to the complexity of the causes which, having led us on to a sloping pavement just at the moment when very complex meteorological conditions brought about the appearance of a layer of ice, made us slip where others would undoubtedly have preserved their equilibrium.

Let us proceed to an example of another order; a physicist asserts that the pressure exerted by a gas on a wall of the receptacle which contains it is constant; yet the kinetic theory of gases interpreting the hypothesis—well established today—of an atomic structure of matter, informs him that this pressure is due to the encounters with the wall of the innumerable molecules of gas and that it is only the statistical result of these encounters. Our physicist, if he is a determinist, will admit that the movements of all the molecules of the gas are governed by rigorous laws and that, if he were able to follow them in detail, he could predict when and in what conditions each molecule would strike the wall, and from that deduce the instantaneous impulses, constantly varying, which this wall will experience in the course of time. But the coarseness of our senses does not permit us to see the molecules and to follow their movements, and, even if that were possible, the frailty of our mind would not allow us effectively to foresee by calculation the displacement of myriads of molecules. We must, therefore, be content to admit that everything takes place as if the molecules moved about at random and that the uniform pressure, stated to exist on the wall, resulted statistically from the average recoil of innumerable molecules with non-ordinated movements. In short, we shall introduce the idea of chance and laws of the statistical type not as interpreting an irreducible aleatory[1] character, a real contingency, of phenomena, but rather as a simple result of our inability to follow in its infinite complexity the violent agitation of elementary phenomena.

Perhaps we have not sufficiently insisted on the boldness of the act of faith which permitted the physicists of the nineteenth century, creators of the statistical theories of physics, to assume the determinism of the elementary phenomenon the evolution of which we are not able effectively to follow. Since the seventeenth century, the admirable precision of the predictions of mathematical astronomy, the rigour of the laws discovered by mechanics and physics had shown that on the celestial and human scale everything takes place as if the hypothesis of universal determinism were exact. Led to believe that on an infinitely smaller scale, which completely escapes our senses, matter and electricity have an atomic structure, physicists of the last century promptly admitted, without doubting that they were thus performing a very bold extrapolation, that the elementary particles of matter and of electricity, themselves also obeyed inflexible laws. Going much further, they even postulated that the mechanical and electromagnetic laws of the atomic world were identical with those which we establish for macroscopic bodies. Such daring suppo-

sitions could only be justified by the accuracy of their consequences, since we are unable to verify them by following the
detail of the elementary processes. It is, therefore, logical to
affirm that with regard to elementary processes, the onus of
proof devolves on those who want to transpose into this very
subtle realm the conceptions suggested by the evidence of
phenomena in a totally different scale. This is a point of view
which, we shall see, has been forcibly put forward by von
Neumann.

But, it must be admitted, the adventuresome attempt of
the creators of the statistical theories of matter and of electricity
appeared at first crowned with complete success. The kinetic
theory of gases and its generalization—statistical mechanics—
have succeeded in giving an account of a large number of
observable properties of matter under its gaseous form or
under the solid and liquid forms. They have reached an
admirable and valuable interpretation of that thermodynamic
quantity entropy, up till then so mysterious.

On the other hand, the theory of electrons, due to H. A.
Lorentz, started from the idea of transposing to the scale of
the electrons the macroscopic laws of electricity and of magnetism such as had been expressed by Maxwell's classical equations
and, doing so, it had obtained at the outset some striking
successes such as the prediction of the Zeeman effect, the interpretation of electro-optical and magneto-optical phenomena,
the demonstration of formulae representing very exactly the
diffusion and dispersion of light, etc. . . . . Further, the study of
the motion of electrons in electromagnetic fields, especially
due to Paul Villard and Jean Perrin, and the recording of their
trajectories by means of the Wilson chamber, had appeared to
establish very clearly the validity, for elementary particles of
electricity, of the classical laws of mechanics, amended in certain cases by relativity theory. This fact appeared fully to justify
the bold hypotheses of the founders of the atomic theories.
Nevertheless the discovery of the quantal phenomena and the
examination of the theoretical consequences of these discoveries
have since led, as we shall recall, to a complete revision of all
these conceptions.

Leaving now the realm of classical physics we are going to

study the attitude of contemporary physics in the face of the problem of chance and contingency.

One of the most curious consequences of the development of quantal theories has been to disclose to us that the elementary entities of matter are not entirely comparable with corpuscles conceived in the classical manner; to describe and predict the way in which they can manifest themselves to us it is necessary to invoke in turn the picture of waves and that of corpuscles, without either of these two pictures being sufficient to provide a complete description in itself. From this duality of the nature of the elementary entities, which we previously envisaged as simple point corpuscles, the present quantal theory deduces that their evolution cannot be regulated by a rigorous determinism, at least by a determinism which we could attain and state precisely; in our knowledge of them there always exist essential "uncertainties" which we have no means of eliminating. Nevertheless that is not to say that we could make no prediction for phenomena on the microscopic scale, but the only predictions that we are allowed are of a statistical nature and are expressed in the language of probability. Henceforth we can no longer say "at such an instant such an electron will be found in such a place", but only "at such an instant there will be such a probability that an electron will be found at such or such a place". It is only on the macroscopic scale, when we are dealing with heavy bodies (in comparison with elementary corpuscles) that the classical ideas of mechanics, such as position, speed, trajectory, motion, rigorously predictable in the course of time, will again become very approximately valid. The laws of mechanics thus cease to be applicable to elementary phenomena and must give way to statistical laws. It is only when we observe, with necessarily limited precision, phenomena on a large scale that we are able to entertain the illusion that there exist rigorous mechanical laws implying an absolute determinism.

There is here, therefore, a complete reversal of the old perspectives; it is no longer rigorous determinism and the precise laws of mechanics which, applied to the elementary entities, are at the basis of our physical explanations. This basis is now chance, probability, reigning over the kaleidoscopic world of corpuscles and quanta; the laws of mechanics,

with their apparent rigour, are nothing more than a macroscopic illusion due to the complexity of the objects on which our
direct experiences bear and to the lack of precision of our
measurements.

Faced with this complete overthrow of our traditional conceptions which appeared firmly established, a number
of physicists, especially amongst the most eminent of the older
generations, have declared that it seemed to them impossible
to abandon the principle of physical determinism. Indeed they
think that it is impossible in *practice* to follow the determinism of elementary phenomena without it being necessary
to reject its existence in order to do so. We shall have to explain
later the reasons for which this view seems to encounter somewhat grave difficulties. But we must note now that the idea
that it is necessary to maintain in principle the validity of
determinism and of causality, even on the elementary scale,
does not appear at all to appeal to many other physicists, in
particular amongst those of the younger generations. The
proof of this is to be found in the expositions—so profound—of
Johann von Neumann whose name I have already mentioned.

In a leading work which he published in 1932 in Berlin
before his departure for the United States, the eminent physico-
mathematician has, in particular, directed a severe indictment
against the extension—arbitrary in his view—of the apparent
determinism of the macroscopic phenomena to the phenomena
of the atomic scale, from which here are a few passages:

"One can sum up the state of the problem of causality*
in the physics of today as follows. In macroscopic physics no
experiment proves causality, for the apparent causal order of
the macroscopic world has no other origin than the law of
large numbers and that is altogether independent of whether
the elementary processes (which are the real physical
processes) follow causal laws or not. That objects macroscopically alike behave the same, is something which has
little to do with causality; these objects are not, in fact,

* In this account M. von Neumann uses the word causality where we would
more readily employ the word determinism. Indeed we think that quantal indeterminism permits a kind of feeble causality to exist.—See *Continu et discontinu en
Physique moderne*. Albin Michel (1941), page 64.

really identical, for the co-ordinates which define the state of their atoms scarcely ever coincide, and the phenomena macroscopically observable are the result of averages taken from these co-ordinates.

It is only on the atomic scale in the elementary processes themselves, that the question of causality can be really put to the test; but on this scale, in the present state of our knowledge, everything tells against it, for the only formal theory agreeing within a little with experiment and summarizing it, is quantal mechanics and it is in complete logical conflict with causality. . . . There exists today no reason which allows us to affirm the existence of causality in nature: no experiment can supply the proof of it, since macroscopic phenomena are, by their very nature, incapable of supplying it and because the only theory consistent with our knowledge of the elementary phenomena leads to its rejection."

Thus, for Neumann and for the greater number of quantal physicists of the present time, the determinism of macroscopic phenomena is an illusion due to the play of averages, a simple statistical appearance.

If we adopt this point of view, the conceptions of science on the important question of chance are thus completely modified. For scientists of previous generations chance was nothing but an appearance and every phenomenon was the inevitable consequence of its causes. If sometimes a phenomenon seemed governed by chance, it was, we were told, because its causes were so numerous and so complex that we were unable to analyse them all and take them into account exactly. The conception towards which contemporary quantal theory tends, seems to be entirely contrary. It leads us to think that the elementary phenomena are governed by pure chance, are "purely statistical" according to von Neumann's expression. Different eventualities can be produced at each instant and it is impossible to announce beforehand which one will be realized. The only thing that we can do is to attribute to these eventualities probabilities which can be calculated beforehand. It is the existence of these probabilities which permit, in the case of phenomena on the large scale where an enormous number of elementary processes intervene, a recovery of the appearance of rigorous laws and the illusion of determinism, by the play of averages and the law of great numbers.

But, it will be objected, can we not suppose that, if we are incapable of assigning rigorous laws to elementary processes, this simply proceeds from our inability to analyse them completely? If we succeeded in knowing all the factors which intervene in the elementary phenomena, should we not be able to re-establish determinism? Should we not, then, perceive that the indeterminism of the quantal physics of today is simply due, like the statistical character of certain laws of classical physics, to our ignorance of certain data? Similar circumstances had already been previously encountered. Some phenomena like the Brownian movement or the fluctuations of density in fluids, for example, are aleatory phenomena governed by the laws of chance; it could have been thought, also, that here was a question of pure chance, of a real contingency. Now, the adept of determinism will remind us, the kinetic theory of matter has taught us that the aleatory character of these phenomena is only apparent; according to it, they result from the non-co-ordinated movements of the material molecules which themselves, if we were able to follow them in detail, would appear to us as completely governed by the rigorous laws of mechanics. Unfortunately we cannot, in fact, follow the movement of molecules; their co-ordinates and their speeds are for us quantities for which we are unable to fix the instantaneous values; these are "hidden variables" and it is because the observable phenomena result from averages taken with respect to these hidden variables that they can have only an aleatory[1] character. Applying this argument to the quantal processes, one could claim with some degree of truth that, there also, there can be hidden variables and that the apparent indeterminism is an illusion from which, if it were humanly possible, the exact knowledge of the evolution of these variables would free us.

But—and here we touch on a capital point—it really seems that it is impossible to reconcile in this way, by the introduction of hidden variables, quantal indeterminism to an underlying determinism. It is this also which von Neumann has shown in his profound researches on the question. Indeed he has proved that the laws of probability expressed by the new wave and quantal mechanics for elementary phenomena, laws well verified by experiment, have not the form that they should have in order that we should be able to interpret them as due to our ignorance of the exact values of certain hidden variables. The way which appeared to remain open in this direction to restore determinism to the atomic scale, seems, therefore, to be closed before us. We perceive the scientific and philosophic importance of von Neumann's demonstration. Without being able to enter here into all the mathematical details of his argument, we would, nevertheless, like to explain its principle.

For this we shall start from very general considerations. Let us consider a system governed by classical determinism; at each instant all its elements must be characterized by quantities having perfectly determined values. Such would be the case of a gas conceived in accordance with the classical image of the kinetic theory for which we should know the positions and speeds of all the molecules.

In place of a single system, let us consider a great number N of systems of the same constitution. If all these systems are in the same state, that is, if each variable has the same value in all cases, von Neumann says that we have to deal with a "causal aggregate". In such an aggregate the mean value of the square of a quantity must obviously be equal to the square of the mean value of this quantity since both these quantities are equal to the well determined value—the same for all the systems—of the square of the quantity considered.

If a denotes any quantity whatever of the collection, we have $\bar{a}^2 = (\bar{a})^2$ and it can be easily shown that the validity of this relation for *every* quantity is the necessary and sufficient condition that the assemblage should be causal.

But, in a general way, if we consider an aggregate of N systems of the same constitution, each variable will have different values for the different systems. Thus the variable a will have a value a_1 in n_1 of the N systems, a value a_2 in n_2 of N systems, etc. . . . . Then, we will not have $\bar{a}^2 = (\bar{a})^2$ and the collection will not be causal. Nevertheless if n_1 systems are in the same state characterized by certain values of the variables, n_2 in a same other state characterized by other values of the variables, etc. . . . . the whole mass which is not causal will disintegrate into a certain number of collections, themselves indecomposable, which we shall call the "pure collections". We shall then say that the whole aggregate is a "mixture" of pure collections, the composition of the mixture being defined by the proportions n_1/N, n_2/N, etc. It is then easy to satisfy oneself—and this is an essential point—that if there exist hidden variables permitting the establishment of an exact determinism of phenomena, every collection which is non-causal for which $a^2 \neq (a)^2$ must be decomposable into a mixture of pure indecomposable collections of causal character for which $\bar{a}^2 = (a)^2$. Further, and this also is essential—every causal collection will have to be pure, that is, indecomposable into a mixture. This latter is actually the case which was always realized in the statistical theories with the deterministic base of classical physics, for example, in the kinetic theories of matter.

And now let us apply these general considerations to quantal physics. According to wave mechanics, the state of every system is defined by its wave function Ψ. Obviously we can imagine a collection of N systems of the same constitution of which n_1 would have a wave function Ψ_1, n_2 a wave function Ψ_2, etc.; we would thus obtain a whole aggregate which would not be causal and could be considered as a mixture of pure collections defined by the proportions n_1/N, n_2/N, etc. Up to here there is nothing new.

But let us concentrate our attention on one of the systems having, for example, the wave function Ψ or, what is statistically equivalent, on the assemblage of n_1 systems having this wave function. We shall be in the presence of an indecomposable collection, of a pure collection. Now it follows from the laws of wave mechanics, *laws well verified by experiment*, that for such a pure and indecomposable collection, all the quantities cannot simultaneously have a unique well determined value such that we do not generally have $\bar{a}^2 = (\bar{a})^2$.

Hence this important conclusion: "*In quantal physics a pure, indecomposable collection in a mixture has not the character of a causal collection.*" This conclusion renders it impossible to admit that, behind the indeterminism of the laws of present-day quantal physics there lies concealed underneath a determinism which would appear to us if we were able to understand the evolution of certain hidden variables. Indeed if it were so, the collections considered by quantal physics, which never have a causal character, should always be decomposable into a mixture, which is not the case of pure collections characterized by a unique wave function Ψ.

The reasoning—of a general scope—developed by von Neumann seems very convincing. It particularly strengthens the positions of those who regard elementary phenomena as having a "truly statistical" nature in von Neumann's sense. Pure probability, absolute contingency, would therefore rule for these phenomena. Nevertheless many of the best minds are still reluctant to adopt this point of view and to give the right of citizenship in science to the ideas of pure chance and radical contingency.* Certain scientists even consider such an attitude inadmissible because it seems to them in contradiction with the principle of sufficient reason. Perhaps this is after all nothing but the result of deep-rooted habits of thought, and in this respect it is somewhat curious to notice that young physicists, accustomed from the beginning of their studies to regard things in the manner of the new physics, seem to find there fewer difficulties than their elders.

However, even if one persisted in thinking (in spite of the arguments—nevertheless very substantial—of von Neumann) that the conception of pure chance is not yet inevitably imposed on atomic physics, the question of the existence of this pure chance has been raised and it deserves to attract the attention of philosophical minds. Its interest is not, moreover, limited to the realm of the physical sciences; it extends to sciences concerned with the study of life, of man and human societies, sciences where, the phenomena studied being always very complex, the laws have necessarily a statistical character. And this remark completes, we believe, our attempts to show the importance of a problem the new aspects of which we have sought to disentangle.

---

* To obviate all error of interpretation, it may be useful to point out precisely that pure chance, which is here in question, if it admits of a real indetermination breaking every rigorous causal chain, nevertheless does not imply that all possibilities are equally probable. Each "state" of a microscopic system admits certain "tendencies" which are expressed by the different probabilities of the various possibilities that it contains.

[1] Aleatory. This word occurs on several occasions and means that something is dependent on uncertain contingencies.

CHAPTER XI

THE GRANDEUR AND MORAL VALUE
OF SCIENCE

MAN experiences the desire and almost the need for knowledge. From the most distant origins of history we see him preoccupied with the study of the phenomena of the world which surrounds him, and with the endeavour to explain them. Assuredly these primitive explanations seem very naïve to us, all impregnated as they are with mythology and anthropocentrism. They are none the less the first signs of the curiosity and anxiety which lead the human mind to attempt to understand and co-ordinate the facts that he observes in nature; they are the first affirmations of that bold act of faith which leads us to bear witness to the existence of a certain correlation between the succession of natural phenomena on the one hand, and the pictures or reasonings which our mind is able to conceive on the other hand.

As our attainments were freed from the mists in which they were at first immersed, science took its modern form. Thus scientists have come to feel more and more keenly that there exists in nature an order, a harmony, which is at least partially accessible to our intelligence, and they have devoted all their efforts to discover each day more of the nature and the extent of this harmony. Thus was born what we often call "pure science", that is, that activity of our mind which has as its goal the knowledge of natural phenomena and of establishing amongst them rational relations, independently of all utilitarian preoccupation. At the same time, and as an addition, by teaching us more about the laws which govern phenomena, the development of science has progressively allowed for a great number of inventions and practical applications which have completely transformed, often for good and sometimes for evil, the living conditions of humanity. We shall for the moment leave aside the applications of science, to which we shall later return.

In the presence of the immense effort which humanity has exerted for generations past, and which it incessantly develops in our day, to succeed in extending and promoting disinterested knowledge of natural phenomena and of their co-ordination, one question is forced on our attention. What, in fact, is the *raison d'être* of this effort, what mysterious attraction acting on certain men urges them to dedicate their time and labours to works from which they themselves often hardly profit? How, for the unique pleasure of obtaining a momentary glimpse of some new aspect of truth, in the midst of the besetting preoccupations of daily life, in the midst of the conflict of interests of which it all consists, has pure science, single-mindedly turned towards the ideal, been able to find its way? Evidently this is one of the aspects of the dual nature of man, so often put into relief by thinkers and philosophers; restrained by our organic constitution and by our different emotions in the lower sphere of our daily occupations, we also feel ourselves urged on by the appeal of the ideal, by more or less precise aspiration towards spiritual values, and from those sentiments even the worst amongst us do not entirely escape. But this general explanation of high aspirations and disinterested efforts through man's moral nature, which are applied to so many different realms of human activity, is not in itself completely sufficient to account for the attraction which pure and disinterested science exerts on our mind. We must try to define still further the origin and nature of this attraction.

What, then, is the goal pursued, sometimes without being clearly aware of it, by the experimenter who works in his laboratory to determine the nature of the known phenomena or to observe new ones, and the theorist who, in his study, seeks to combine symbols and numbers to draw from them abstract constructions, establishing amongst the observable facts correlations or unsuspected resemblances? This goal, as we have seen, is, without doubt, to succeed in penetrating further into the knowledge of natural harmonies, to come to have a glimpse of a reflection of the order which rules in the universe, some portions of the deep and hidden realities which constitute it. Even the scientists or philosophers who, pragmatic in tendency, have reduced to a utilitarian role the value of scientific theories, as for example, the eminent physicist Pierre Duhem, have had to recognize that these theories establish between the phenomena a "natural classification", allowing us to sense the existence of an "ontological order" which is beyond us. All those who dedicate their efforts to pure science admit, whether they agree with it or not, the existence of such an order and it is to enable them to lift up for a moment, from one distant point to the next, a corner of the veil which conceals it from us that they expend their strength and their vigils. The great epoch-making discoveries in the history of science (think, for example, of that of universal gravitation) have been like sudden lightning flashes, making us perceive in one single glance a harmony up till then unsuspected, and it is to have, from time to time, the divine joy of discovering such harmonies that pure science works without sparing its toil or seeking for profit.

Assuredly the great discoveries are not accomplished in a day; it is necessary that they should be prepared for a long time by meticulous and austere labours. At times, immersed in the details of his absorbing work, the specialist, preparing his apparatus or developing his calculations, can very well lose sight of the far-off goal of his researches and be no longer greatly concerned with the harmony of the universe; and yet, what gives value to his efforts, what justifies its apparent uselessness, is that he thus supplies to the common task small contributions capable one day of facilitating the erection of some of those great syntheses which do honour to the human mind. Pure science untiringly pursues the search for this hidden order, these ultimate realities; each scientist conceives their existence and significance in his own way, according to the inclinations or philosophical convictions which influence him, but all scientists, when they are sincere, recognize that the search for truth is the real reason that justifies the efforts of pure science and constitutes its nobility. Moreover, on this important question of the goal of disinterested science, all true scientists, in spite of the differences of opinion which can separate them, are without doubt nearer to being in agreement than they themselves often imagine.

The great wonder in the progress of science is that it has revealed to us a certain agreement between our thought and things, a certain possibility of grasping, with the assistance of the resources of our intelligence and the rules of our reason, the profound relations existing between phenomena. We are not sufficiently astonished by the fact that any science may be possible, that is, that our reason should provide us with the means of understanding at least certain aspects of what happens around us in nature. Some thinkers, nevertheless, find this fact natural because, they say, humanity having had to endure during thousands of years the consequences of natural phenomena and to learn, in order to survive, to adapt itself to it, our mind has thus learned little by little to form its logic and its rules of reasoning under the pressure of the material world, and it must not, in consequence, be astonished to recover in the material world the logic and the rules of reasoning that it has extracted from it.

Personally, we do not find this argument very conclusive; in reality, in order that humanity should have been able to adapt itself to live in the world which surrounds us, it would undoubtedly be necessary that there should be already between this world and our mind some analogy in structure: if that had not been so, perhaps humanity would not have been able to survive. Well, it would have disappeared, that is all! Since it has survived, it is then, because it was capable of understanding certain of the rules which govern the succession of natural phenomena, in a way to adapt itself to these phenomena or even to utilize them to its advantage. This is why the pre-adaptation of our mind to the discovery of relations between phenomena and the order that is manifested in nature appears to us much more surprising than it is sometimes said to be.

What appears to us to show well that we can hardly explain this pre-adaptation by a secular experience dating from the origins of humanity, is as follows. In several cases, especially in the most recent science, the minute study of phenomena very delicate to observe, a study very different from the rough experiments that the cave man was able to make, has led us to discover in the depths of our own mind hitherto unsuspected resources, allowing us to interpret our new discoveries and to give to them an intelligible meaning. In saying this, we are thinking especially of the remarkable new theories of contemporary physics. Take for instance the theory of relativity;

starting from extremely delicate and precise experiments the results of which could not be foreseen by the older theories, it built up a new conception of space and time and of their reciprocal relations, a conception absolutely contrary to all the data of our usual intuition; it thus shows us that our mind can find in itself the necessary elements logically to constitute an interpretation of the ideas of space and time quite different from that which the experience of daily life suggests. By its successes, the theory of relativity therefore shows us how extensive is the parallelism which exists between the rules of our reasoning and the order which conceals itself behind the subtle phenomena which physics of today studies; it shows us that this parallelism infinitely surpasses all that the daily experience of the older generations was able to suggest to us.

More remarkable still is the example which can be drawn from physics of the atomic or microscopic scale, where the theory of quanta and of its extensions rules today. Here, still more so than in the case of the theory of relativity, we have had to appeal to conceptions very far removed from those which we have been accustomed to handle. To account for the phenomena of the atomic scale, we have been obliged, little by little, to abandon the idea that the movement of a corpuscle can be represented by a continuous succession of positions in space, by a trajectory progressively described with a certain specified speed. We have also had to abandon the traditional idea that phenomena, even elementary ones, are rigorously determined and exactly predictable, and to substitute for the rigid determinism of classical physics a more flexible conception, admitting that there exist at each instant in the evolution of elementary phenomena verifiable by us, different eventualities concerning which it is only possible to estimate the relative probabilities. We had, in addition, to abandon also all our intuitive and customary ideas on the individuality of corpuscles, on the role of the constituents in a complex system, etc. . . . . In an account like this it is not possible for us to dwell upon the detail of these difficult questions, but it seems to us essential to make the following remark.

In the development of these theories so daringly novel, which have been, let it be emphasized, imposed on us by the discovery of certain experimental facts, it has been possible to construct on the basis of these new conceptions a perfectly logical formalism, perfectly consistent with the rules of our reason, which allow of the assembling and connecting amongst themselves of all the ascertainable facts in the atomic scale. Here again we have found in our mind all the resources necessary to represent the order which rules in the atomic scale, although this order is stupendously different from what our imagination could conceive by starting from the usual perceptivity. And this fact seems to us sufficiently independent of the distant past of humanity.

In short, all these examples show us how remarkable is the harmony between the resources of which our mind disposes and the profound realities which conceal themselves behind natural appearances. To bring this harmony more completely into the light, to glimpse yet more the ontological order of which Duhem spoke, such appears to be the true mission of pure science. Removed from all utilitarian preoccupation, solely devoted to the search for truth, it appears to us as one of the noblest activities of which we are capable. By the wholly ideal nature of the goal it pursues, by the intensity and the disinterested character of the efforts that it demands, it possesses a moral value which cannot be denied.

Perhaps we may ask ourselves where this passionate quest for truth can lead us. Science advances with great strides; astonishing discoveries issue each day from its laboratories; by its bold theories it opens out for us wonderful new vistas on the mystery of things. Will it then soon lift the veil of Isis, make us definitely penetrate into the secrets of nature, give an assured answer to the great metaphysical problems which for so many centuries vex the soul of man? It does not seem that we are yet near the attainment of such a triumph of pure science. Mystery surrounds us; as Puvis of Chavannes has symbolically represented it in the vast fresco which adorns the great amphitheatre of the Sorbonne, we are placed as at the centre of a small clearing surrounded on all sides by an immense and gloomy, unexplored forest. No, it is not yet tomorrow that science will be able to give us the key to the enigmas of the universe; we are not yet near to the attainment of the end of an effort to which nothing permits us to fix the duration.

Nevertheless it is not impossible that the advances of science will bring new data capable, if not of solving, at least of clarifying certain great problems of philosophy. Already contemporary physics, by introducing its new ideas on space and time, on the impossibility of following the determinism of elementary phenomena, on the "complementary" character of certain pictures apparently contradictory, such as that of wave and of corpuscle, on the inability to discern elementary particles, already contemporary physics, I say, offers to the meditations of philosophical minds entirely new themes of which, at the present hour, we are far from having perceived all the consequences. The study of the nucleus of atoms, by making us penetrate to the extreme depths of matter, reserves many surprises for us and may bring us important revelations. Astronomy, by extending in an unheard of way the limits of the observable region of the stellar world, already brings to us data about the extent of the universe, its age, its evolution, calculated to orientate our cosmological conceptions. Still many other sciences furnish us each day with similar information concerning which the thoughts of the philosophers of the future will have to take account. But it is necessary to reserve a special place for biology; this is a science of capital importance because it is the science of life. Its advances are rapid, its discoveries, especially in genetics, are of captivating interest. Perhaps it will bring us, sooner or later, very important indications as to the role of the phenomena of life and the real place which it is suitable to attribute to them in the whole of nature.

Besides the advances in different sciences working on parallel lines, the discoveries of some are capable of hastening those of others or of facilitating their interpretation. Thus, certain scientists (in particular Bohr and Jordan) have recently expressed the view that the new conceptions of microphysics might be of such a nature as to throw light on the difficulties which are met with in the interpretation of biological phenomena. Without being able to discuss here the views which have been expressed on this subject, we shall, however, indicate the point of departure.

All the activity of living beings appears to be directed or controlled by a few extremely small centres; our organs of the senses, especially the eyes, are of such sensitivity that they succeed in describing to us phenomena of which the smallness is almost of the order of those of microphysics; the astonishing discoveries of contemporary genetics show us the whole of the developments of living beings, from the fertile egg up to the adult individual, as entirely orientated by the directive action of elements of an incredible minuteness (the genes) a minuteness which borders on that of molecular structures. All these facts and others besides can lead to the thought that a complete interpretation of biological phenomena must reveal the intervention of the laws and conceptions of microphysics and, as these laws and these conceptions are, as we have seen, of a very new nature, this remark seems capable, if we come some day to develop it, of leading to conclusions of great interest and of making us the better able to understand, if not the profound meaning of life, at least the difficulty which we experience in really understanding its nature.

Thus, therefore, science progresses; it marches on and will no doubt each day march further forward, on the road to a better comprehension of natural phenomena. From this point of view all hopes are permissible and the human mind will undoubtedly gather the fruits of its ceaseless secular efforts to discover new facets of the truth. The beauty and the moral grandeur of pure science, the progress that it achieves, the joy of knowing that it is deserving of the enthusiasm that it inspires in its adepts!

Nevertheless, as one should, in order to judge wisely, see the pros and cons in everything, it is important to add that, if the enthusiasm inspired in the scientist and the thinker by the feeling of increasing each day the number and scope of our attainments is quite legitimate, they must never pursue them to an excess of intellectual pride which would make them despise every other activity except their own. In the first place they must never lose sight of the ever limited character of our knowledge and the immensity of our ignorance; this feeling must inspire them with some humility in the face of the immense task which always remains to be accomplished. Neither must they forget that men of action whose employment is turned towards the practical side of life, that the humble who, ignoring science and its mysteries, carry out their daily task with devotion, also play an indispensable role in the grand advance of human societies and are in their way contributing to our progress. Nothing authorizes the thinking man, however exceptional he may be, to assert that intellectual superiority or the extent of one's attainments represents the only true values, and to ignore what is noble in all the devotion and in all the tasks conscientiously performed, or that which is useful in all fruitful activities.

We have just spoken about pure science. It is now also necessary to say some words about applied science. By the very fact that it reveals to us the existence of laws governing natural phenomena and the correlations existing between them, scientific knowledge furnishes us with the possibility of utilizing them to our advantage. Further, in proportion as science has developed, we have seen the number and variety of its applications multiply with an incessantly increasing speed. It would take much too long and also be quite useless to enumerate them; they have transformed the material life of civilized humanity and profoundly altered the conditions of our activities. We cannot, therefore, pass them by in silence and we must ask ourselves what is their value.

What we wish to examine first of all is to what extent does applied science—technics—participate in the greatness and intellectual value of pure science. Assuredly, as it does not pursue a purely ideal target but is above all preoccupied in satisfying the needs of daily life, as it is often obliged to take account of material contingencies and of financial or commercial conditions, applied science has not, from the purely intellectual point of view, as high a value as pure science. Nevertheless, it cannot be overlooked that in order to progress scientific technics needs to pursue studies the theoretical character of which is often of a high standard, and whereby it sometimes makes important contributions to pure science. To cite one example only amongst many others, the recent developments of electrotechnics have necessitated the use of methods of calculation and of modes of reasoning which are of great interest from the speculative point of view.

Technics also sets scientific research some very important problems which the latter has a great interest in studying and, if possible, in resolving, and the solution of which permits technics to make new advances. Thus is established between pure science and technics a fruitful exchange of views, the first providing for the second the informations which it needs to direct nature, and the second offering the first subjects for research and various suggestions. If we add that technics, in studying the difficult problems the resolution of which requires much work and ingenuity, imposes great efforts and protracted labours on those who make it progress, it will be understood, even if all sentimental consideration is set aside, that it, too, has its grandeur and that it must not be deprecated.

But, in order to judge the applications of science, one can regard it from another less strictly intellectual point of view. What indeed increases the moral value of applied science is that it is able to improve the conditions of human life, to diminish its difficulties, to alleviate its miseries and sufferings. The progress of mechanics, physics, and chemistry allows of the development of industries and inventions which increase the comfort of our material life, of the means of operation of which we dispose, and of the various possibilities offered to our employment. Natural and biological sciences lend their aid to agriculture and breeding; with their co-operation medicine and surgery combat diseases, mitigate suffering and contribute to prolong our existence. These are the great and fine works of applied science to which no one can fail to give his respect and admiration. They complete the nobility of the role of science, for in this way science works not only for the truth, it also works for the good.

Moreover, nothing allows us to say where the benefits which the applications of science can bring us will come to an end. The most recent advances make us glimpse the possibility, in a more or less near future, of new applications capable of having immense repercussions on our civilization. I shall give only two examples of this amongst many others which could be considered.

There is first of all the physics of the nucleus of the atom, a young science in full development; it reveals to us that enormous quantities of energy lie unused in the recesses of the deep-down structures of matter. Tomorrow it will, perhaps, teach us how to liberate them and to utilize them to our advantage and the face of the world will be changed thereby.*

Now look at genetics, a new branch of biology, which reveals to us the conditions of hereditary transmissions and throws strange lights on the development of living organisms; one day, perhaps, it will allow us to exercise an influence, at least to some extent, on the evolution of living beings in the course of generations and no one can foresee what would be the consequences of such a power which would truly make life the mistress of its own destinies. There is here a whole collection of perspectives capable of rousing the justified enthusiasm of those who place their hopes in the progress of human civilization, and of encouraging the eagerness for work of young people whom scientific research attracts and who, having the future before them, can hope to contribute towards making a part of the ambitious dreams of today pass into the reality of tomorrow.

Alas! Why is it necessary that there should be shadows cast over this bright picture? Why must it unfortunately be that the applications of science should not necessarily be beneficial? How could we forget it in an epoch when on all sides there sounds the tumult of arms and where there accumulate the ruins caused by the terrifying new means of destruction? If, through the progress of science, new possibilities for the amelioration of the lot of mankind are offered us, it is only too certain that at the very same time powerful new means for causing suffering, for killing and destroying, will be placed at our disposal. Shall we be wise enough not to make use of them, or, at least, not to abuse them? Here is a serious subject of preoccupation for the intellects of our time.

What renders this question particularly distressing is that, as we have just now said, nothing allows us to say what will be, even in the near future, the limits of the means of action with which we shall be provided by the development of scientific knowledge. Let us resume the two examples that I quoted a moment ago. Microphysics can make it possible perhaps shortly,† for us to liberate part of the vast quantities of energy which the nuclei of atoms conceal and then, without

*This was written before the invention of the atomic pile.
†Written prior to 1945.

doubt, we shall be able to manufacture explosives infinitely more powerful than those that we use today and capable of blowing up all or part of our planet. And, since we are giving free scope to our imagination, we can also suppose that, in a future more or less distant, the progress of genetics will permit us to call forth the appearance of new types of living beings who might be supermen, but also monsters; how, endowed with such power, would men make use of it? Would humanity be wise enough not to employ the new arms, which science would have provided, to perpetrate its own destruction?

At bottom these distressing questions raise above all a moral problem. Scientific discoveries and the applications of which they are capable are in themselves neither good nor bad; all depends on the use which we make of them. Tomorrow, as today, it will be, therefore, the will of mankind that is called upon to decide on the beneficial or evil character of these applications. To be able to survive the appropriate progress of his attainments, mankind of tomorrow will have to find in the development of his spiritual life and in the uplifting of his moral ideal, the wisdom not to abuse his increased forces. This is what Henri Bergson has splendidly expressed in one of his last works when saying: "Our enlarged body clamours for an addition to the spirit." Shall we be able to acquire this addition to the spirit as rapidly as the advances of science will develop? Undoubtedly on that depends the future destiny of humanity.

Chapter XII.—Un Glorieux Moment de la Pensée Scientifique Francaise—has been omitted by agreement with the Author.

HISTORY OF THE SCIENCES

THE FUTURE OF PHYSICS*

IT is assuredly easier to speak of the past than of the future. The past is crystallized, it has taken its definitive form. In so far as we can recover the documents and testimonies that it has left us, and where we are sufficiently skilled to make use of them, we can try to bring it to life again, we can seek to retrace the main lines of its structure and to extricate the lessons which evolve from it. Very different is every attempt to explore the future, for that is of necessity difficult and risky. All that we know for certain about it is that it will grow out of the present, and yet we do not even know (for philosophers are always arguing about it and now more than ever) whether it will be an inevitable consequence of the present, or if it will add some unforeseeable complement, something essentially new. Even in the hypothesis most favourable to speculation, that in which tomorrow is brought forth from today by the relentless play of a rigorous determinism, the forecasting of future facts in their innumerable multitude and their immense complexity would infinitely surpass all the efforts of which the human mind is capable and would only be possible to an intelligence infinitely superior to our own. That is why, even if an inexorable necessity bound it to the present, we could say of the future that it is the secret of God.

Thus to want to divine even the smallest part of what the morrow holds for us, is to plunge ourselves into a daring and perilous enterprise. In particular, try to imagine what will be the future advances of the sciences, or even more modestly, of a particular science; strain to foresee in what direction they will progress, with what new ideas they will provide us, and what new horizons in so doing they will reveal to us, what applications in the practical field they will be able to give us, and how they will thus have an influence on

---

* This account was written before the invention of the atomic bomb. I have not considered it necessary to modify the text, confining myself to the addition of some notes.

the material life of man and on his social organization. This is
a programme almost impossible to carry out without taking
the risk that the facts will afterwards come forward to bring
you cruel denials and demonstrate the emptiness of your
predictions. Some writers have, nevertheless, had the boldness to embark on such subjects. Men like Jules Verne or
Wells, for example, have allowed their imagination to run riot
and have tried to conceive of a future world transformed, as
they thought it would be, by the progress of science. They,
especially Jules Verne, chanced to be very accurate and to
imagine inventions which, after having appeared improbable
to their contemporaries, nevertheless, have been realized shortly
afterwards almost in the form in which they had been foreseen, and have then become of current use. On the whole,
these were novelists, who were not themselves scientists[1] and
who, for that reason, had nothing to prevent them from giving
free scope to their imagination. Other authors, from a
different point of view, have tried to sketch the future of
science by attaching more weight to the intellectual aspects of
these advances than to their practical applications. But it does
not seem, even judging by the most distinguished among them,
that their attempt has been very successful.

Nearly a century ago a young man did, indeed, venture to
take as the subject of one of his books this theme of the future
of science, brimful of the unknown. He was assigning himself a
formidable task! The author was, it is true, at the happy age
where one doubts of nothing and where the enthusiasm of
adolescence has not been blunted by the more balanced
reflection of mature age. When, at a much later date, he himself
came to publish his book[2] which, for a long time remained
unpublished, he was unable to conceal in his Preface the many
doubts he now experienced and the many reservations he now
expressed on the too decided opinions and the exaggerated
dogmatism of which his youthful work gave evidence. To tell
the truth, we find the reading of Renan's book today very
deceptive. Undoubtedly there are some fine pages in it, some
sublime and subtle thoughts truly worthy of the great mind of
this philosophic historian. There is also in it that sort of
mysticism which, according to himself, he owed to his upbring-
ing, which led him, in spite of the fervour of his negations, to

envisage all questions from an exalted and almost religious point of view; and this at times is not without charm, nor without beauty. But unfortunately, one also finds so many false ideas, exaggerations and naivetes in this book, written too quickly by a beginner too proud of youthful learning. Furthermore, this badly constructed work hardly fulfils the promise of its title.

Yielding to a natural inclination, Renan attaches a predominant importance to the restraints he had practised and for him science is reduced almost exclusively to philology and to the history of the origins of humanity, that is, precisely to those studies which, rightly or wrongly, would probably be placed outside the sciences, properly so-called, by those who cultivate them. This fact alone prevents Renan's book from corresponding to its title. With regard to the future of the exact sciences there is practically nothing to be learnt from it. On the whole, this work is not an attempt to sketch the possible future advances of the sciences and their consequences, it is much rather the exposition of a certain personal philosophy of science, or more exactly of a certain manner of regarding the value and significance of scientific researches in the realm of philology and history. This is why Ernest Renan's work cannot, even putting aside all differences of tendency and opinion, serve today as a model for one wishing to write on the future of science.

If I have insisted a little on the difficulties and dangers which exist in the wish to conjure up the future of science, if I have said that no attempt made in this way can, in my opinion, serve as a guide, it is in order to make it be understood why I regard it as impossible to approach this question in all its generality and why I have finally resolved not to deal with it except in some very particular points. First of all, in order to speak of the future of science with, I shall not say some certainty, but with some chance of not being greatly mistaken, it would be necessary to know all the sciences in their present state and to know them sufficiently well to be able to guess in what direction each one of them is going to take its next step. Not having any pretensions to this universality of knowledge, I shall restrict myself at first to the only part of the question which can come within my competence, I mean the future of physics. But, even after having thus restricted my subject, I shall in no wise attempt to treat it in all its aspects.

One of the most picturesque aspects of this question, one of these which would most keenly interest the general public, would obviously be to investigate the possible developments of the practical applications of physics and how the advances in this direction will react on our daily life. From the time of the discovery of the steam engine to that of the different methods of radio-communication, the applications of physics have been so important and have unsettled human civilization to such an extent that it would evidently be very interesting to guess in what direction and up to what point they will still be able to develop. But to approach this attempt at anticipation with some chance of success, one would have to be a physicist inclined to the practical applications of his science or an engineer well acquainted with the future possibilities of physics. In order that an invention should be carried out, it is not indeed enough that science should provide the principle of this invention, it is also necessary that the method of execution should be practicable; this is often the most difficult condition to fulfil and only a practician can pass judgement on it. A theorist like the author of the present exposition would, then, be poorly equipped to estimate what technical applications of physics will be effectively realized in the more or less near future. I shall, therefore, keep in general to physics considered as a pure science, independently of its applications. And, as the subject thus reduced seems to me still a thousand times too great to explore in a few pages, I shall limit myself to three questions relative to the future of physics which seem to me particularly interesting. To each of these I will devote a few reflections of varying length.

The first question that I wish to discuss is this; what are the future prospects at the present time opening up before the physics of the nucleus of the atom? How far will it be able to advance and what obstacles will it meet with in its way?

One of the most marvellous triumphs effected by physics during the last fifty years is its penetration into the mysterious realm of the atom. Incessantly refining its experimental methods and its theoretical conceptions, progressively adapting them to the study of more and more delicate scales, physics embarked on a vertiginous course towards the infinitely small. For quite a time the atom has ceased to be for the physicist the indivisible particle of the atomists of antiquity, or even the sort of elastic ball which the founders of the kinetic theory of gases imagined in about 1875. We know that it is a small world of a great complexity, a microcosm where numerous electrified particles move round a central nucleus, governed by mysterious laws which the importance assumed on so small a scale by Planck's quantum renders quite different from the laws which are valid on our scale.

Since the appearance of the celebrated work of Bohr we compare the atom to a small solar system where electron-planets revolve around a central nucleus which plays the role of the sun. Nevertheless, this planetary model of the atom, which so strikingly illustrates the splendid intuitions of Pascal on the infinitely small, must not, as we know today, be taken too literally, because the intervention of the quantum of action prevents the infinitely small from being truly a homothetic reduction of the infinitely great. Actually it is necessary to give up the too precise picture of point electrons describing orbits around the central nucleus just as the earth revolves around the sun. These things are not so simple in the microscopic world which no human eye will ever see. The electrons, those grains of electricity which on our scale show themselves as point particles, have no longer well-defined positions in the atom and appear to be everywhere present in a potential state. Their evolution in states so strangely opposed to our classical conceptions can only be described by a consideration of the waves of wave mechanics, or by other representations of a more abstract but mathematically equivalent appearance.

But let us lay aside these difficulties of representation which trouble the theorist, though they often leave the experimental physicist somewhat indifferent, and record what a wonderful harvest of new knowledge we have been able to reap in this intense study of the atom. Interpretation in all the details (and heaven knows they are complicated!) of all the optical spectra and of the spectra of X-rays, determination of the stationary states of the atoms by measurement of their powers of resonance or ionization, a more complete elucidation of the phenomena of the diffusion and dispersion of radiation with the discovery of the Raman and Compton effects, a definitely determined relation between the periodicity of the properties of chemical elements and the structure of their atoms, such are some of the remarkable advances which the exploration of the atomic realm has permitted. It is truly a new world dominated by the quantum of action which has thus been opened before astonished physicists and has revealed to them unsuspected treasures. The success has even been so complete that today the almost accomplished study of the outlying regions of the atom, where Bohr's electrons revolve, has lost a part of its interest. It is this which explains why the researches on the spectra of X-rays, so active about twenty years ago, have in these latter times been a little forsaken, or at least abandoned to somewhat rare specialists. What is properly meant by the atomic realm, that is, what is exterior in the atom to the central nucleus, seems pretty well known to us now; no doubt there is still much detailed research to be done on the subject, but rightly or wrongly, we no longer have the impression that it could again become the object of sensational discoveries. Already physicists have wished to go further and to penetrate the mysteries which are hidden in the interior of the atomic nucleus.

In the same way that the first atomic physicists regarded the atom as an indivisible element of which all analysis was impossible, the first promoters of the planetary model considered the central nucleus of the atom as a closed world before which all our means of action came to miscarry, and the structure of which we should perhaps have to resign ourselves never to know. Regulating the saraband of planetary electrons by its electric charge and by the Coulombian forces derived from it, the nucleus retains almost the whole of the atomic mass and, placed at the heart of the atom, it seemed the inaccessible fortress where the essential secrets of matter were concealed. No doubt the discovery of radioactive bodies had enabled us to understand that the atomic nuclei of these bodies are unstable and capable of being decomposed into lighter nuclei with the eventual liberation of electrons or of radiations, which proved, in spite of all, the complex nature of the nuclei. But the radioactive transmutations, insensible to all our means of action, went on in an inexorable rhythm without our ever being able to retard or accelerate them; if they revealed the complexity of the nuclei to us, they did not furnish us with any means for exploring this complexity.

A new era was opened in the history of microphysics on the day, when in 1919 Rutherford for the first time succeeded in artifically breaking the nuclei of atoms by bombarding them with the aid of other light nuclei in rapid motion (α-particles). From that moment, it became possible to submit to systematic investigations the question of the constitution of nuclei. A new branch of science was, at least in principle, founded; nuclear physics was born.

However, it was some years before the method created by Rutherford came to bear all its fruits. But in the interval the discovery of isotopes taught us that the number of distinct kinds of atomic nuclei is greater than we thought. Indeed, it is the electric charge of its nucleus which determines the chemical properties of the atom of a simple body. Nevertheless, different values of the mass may correspond to one determined nuclear charge, and in fact there exist atomic nuclei having the same charge but with masses a little different; these nuclei are called "isotopes". Atoms possessing isotope nuclei have the same chemical properties and differ only by their atomic weights. Simple bodies, as found in nature, are, in fact, formed of mixtures of isotope atoms in constant proportion. The enumeration of the different sorts of nuclei, taking the isotope into account, has been made possible notably by the splendid method of the mass spectra; it has led to the discovery of a great number of isotope nuclei which, if we wish to take the isotopes into account, involves considerable complications in the nomenclature of chemical combinations.

The discovery of the isotope had led us to extend the list of nuclei existing in nature, but it had furnished us with only very slight indications as to their structure. At that time the only elementary particles of matter that we knew were electrons and protons—nuclei of hydrogen with the same electric charge but with the opposite sign to that of the electron. It was naturally admitted that the nuclei must be formed of protons and electrons, for it had long been known that electrons emanate from radioactive nuclei at the time of their spontaneous transmutations under the form of β-rays, and the artificial transmutations obtained by the method of collisions also permitted the tearing off of protons from the nuclei shattered by the collisions. Nevertheless the hypothesis of nuclei formed solely of protons and electrons encountered certain objections. Soon after 1930, nuclear physics entered on a period of very rapid evolution. The discovery of deuterons and neutrons, the obtainment of artificial radioelements, and, more recently, the disclosure of the fission of uranium (the breaking of the nucleus of uranium into two nuclei having masses of the same order) and the discovery of heavy electrons, all these splendid advances which are due, some to the generalization of the methods of bombardment inaugurated by Rutherford, and others to the study of the mysterious cosmic rays, have considerably enlarged the field of our knowledge and have provided a daily increasing harvest of new results.

A whole chemistry of the nuclei, which employs transformation formulae entirely analogous to the combination formulae of classical chemistry, was established on the basis of these experimental results and forms a science already extensive and ramified; in it we recognize isotope nuclei, isobars or isomeres, we include artificial radioactivities according as they are accompanied by the emission of positive or negative electrons, and we establish the affiliations of newly discovered nuclei by basing them on the principle of the inertia of energy and by establishing delicate energetic schedules. Special chemical methods of great difficulty have had to be brought to perfection for us to succeed in isolating, and in characterizing, the new simple bodies obtained in extremely small quantities as the results of disintegration and of fission. This is indeed a whole new science which is a part both of physics and of chemistry and which is being rapidly built up.

Whilst our knowledge on atomic nuclei was developing on the solid basis of experimental results, bold theories sought to explain their structure, their stability, and their possible transformations. What considerably impedes the development of these theories is that we are here in a realm the scale of which is incommensurably smaller than that of our usual experience. Now, all the conceptions which we utilize in our theories being more or less directly drawn from our daily experience by the processes of generalization and abstraction, these conceptions must necessarily become more and more inadequate the further we depart from the scale of phenomena directly accessible to our senses. Already in the outlying regions of the atom, we have seen how the original simple idea of Bohr, in which the electrons revolve round the central nucleus like planets describing orbits, had to be replaced by much subtler conceptions, and much further removed from our usual intuitions. Already in this realm of the atom the dimensions of which are of the order of a hundred millionth of a centimetre, our habitual conceptions of space and time appear to be partially at fault.

The impossibility of localizing electrons at each instant, of attributing to them a speed and a trajectory, is sufficient to prove that the usual framework of space, a framework in which we are accustomed to be able, on our scale, to localize all phenomena, cannot be maintained with all its precision on such small scales.

In particular, the ordinary chemical actions, which are now attributed to certain properties of the outer electrons of the atom, introduce forces of a type altogether different from those of classical mechanics, called exchange forces, of which no representation is possible within the framework of our conceptions of space. If such difficulties already appear on the scale of the atoms, what insufficiencies of our former conceptions must we not expect to record in the realm, a hundred thousand times still smaller, of the nucleus of the atom? Nevertheless, extending as far as possible the theoretical ideas which had been successful for the atom, the theorists have succeeded in formulating the first ideas, certainly still insufficient but already very useful, of the structure of the nuclei.

It really seems that nuclei are formed, not by protons and electrons, but by protons and neutrons held bound to each other by these "exchange forces" of a new type which we mentioned before (see page 30). The positive and negative electrons which escape from the nuclei at the time by their disintegration would be created at that moment by the transformation of a proton into a neutron or of a neutron into a proton. Lastly, according to most recent theories, heavy electrons or mesons would also play an important role in this stability of the nuclei, for the exchange forces binding protons and neutrons in the nuclear structure would act through their intermediary. All these ideas are still in the melting pot and their development encounters many obstacles, but nevertheless they are of the greatest interest and promise to prove very fruitful.

Now, those who ask what future is in store for this nuclear physics, which so boldly and so brilliantly has pushed the exploration of the interior of matter to such an astonishing depth, are certainly justified in thinking that its future will be a most brilliant one. It is impossible to doubt that in multiplying research and in varying the means we discover for splitting atomic nuclei we shall arrive at remarkable results. We shall come, without doubt, to deepen more and more our knowledge of the nuclei; and since on the one hand this knowledge is in itself very important, and on the other all progress realized in a particular branch of physics has a very rapid effect today on this science in its entirety, we shall certainly have there an abundant source of enrichment for natural philosophy.

If up to the present the physics of the nucleus has only contributed to the progress of pure science, we must by no means assume that it will not fairly soon have important applications. In showing us the unity of matter and the possibility of transforming one simple body into another, nuclear physics has justified (in generalizing it to its extreme limits) the dominant idea which guided the alchemists of the middle ages when, intent on the mysteries of the great work, they sought to transform lead into gold, employing inadequate operations for the realization of a vision which nevertheless was profound. Who does not realize what new horizons the possibility of effecting a large-scale transmutation of elements would open to human industry? And since nuclear transformations set free enormous energies, when compared with those of chemical reactions, if we only knew how to produce them in as large a number as the molecular combinations of ordinary chemistry, we should be able to obtain tremendous practical results.

The difference in the intensity of the effects here arises from the fact that in ordinary chemistry, a reaction once unleashed at a point is, in general, propagated in the whole mass of the reacting bodies, whilst in nuclear chemistry the agent responsible for the transmutations (for example, a beam of particles employed in the bombardment of nuclei) promotes individual transmutations of isolated atoms, without there being a propagation of these transmutations throughout all the mass of matter present. The quantities of new bodies obtained by transmutation are, for this reason, so small that their obtainment offers no interest today for practical purposes, and the quantities of energy, the release of which accompanies their appearance, are also much too small to be utilized except as sources of data in research.

But that is, perhaps, nothing but a provisional situation attributable to the still embryonic state of our young science of the nucleus, and nothing forbids us to think that an increase in the return may one day completely transform the aspect of the question.* At the present moment it is impossible to foresee what would then be the repercussions of the processes of nuclear physics on industry, but it is certain that they would be immense.

What proves better than any other argument that it is not chimerical to envisage the eventuality of astonishing applications of nuclear physics is that one of them has already appeared to be nearly within the limits of actual possibilities. When a nucleus of uranium bombarded by neutrons undergoes the phenomenon of disintegration, its decomposition into lighter nuclei is accompanied by the emission of neutrons which, in principle, can in turn promote the disintegration of other neighbouring atoms of uranium. So we see that the phenomena of disintegration once unleashed at a point in a mass of uranium could be propagated and could promote an enormous liberation of energy capable of being utilized for different purposes. Some calculations have been made on this "propagation of the disintegration" in a mass of uranium and have shown that its realization was not *a priori* an impossibility.

*The hope expressed in this text has since been realized by the recent conquest of atomic energy which places at our disposal a part of the immense reserves of energy contained in the nuclei.

If no experiment up till now has come to confirm the effective possibility of unleashing such a propagation,* it is none the less true that already, it is clear, certain sensational applications of nuclear physics no longer seem very far from realization. And yet this young science has behind it scarcely ten years of intensive development. Who can say of what it will be capable in a few decades, if nothing comes to hinder its progress?

Since, however, it is always discreet to consider the pros and cons, we can also ask ourselves what obstacles nuclear physics risks encountering in the course of its forward march. They appear to be, possibly, of two totally different kinds, some arising from the fact that nuclear physics would grow to the limits of experimental possibilities, others because it would come up against the limits of our conceptual faculties. Let us examine these two categories of obstacles.

Nuclear physics attacks, as we have said earlier, the minute fortress where reside the individuality and stability of all forms of matter. To pursue its investigations it has need of extremely powerful means, for example, very high electric tensions. Perhaps it will be necessary to increase more and more the power of these means, if we wish to penetrate more and more deeply into the mysteries of the atomic nuclei. But then we may find ourselves in the presence of insurmountable difficulties with regard to their production. For example, to produce a high electric tension, the apparatus producing it will have to resist this tension so that it will not be annihilated by it; now all the machines which we can imagine are always constructed from material bodies and they have to be able to resist the tensions that they carry. We may come one day to be trapped in the following vicious circle; we should have to produce electric tensions capable of destroying matter and, to produce these tensions, would have to utilize apparatus itself formed of matter. Another obstacle of the same order would be the far too violent effects which might result from certain experiments of nuclear physics. Already, if we wished to realize the propagation of disintegrations in a mass of uranium, as mentioned above, the results might have a

*It is really by making use of this possibility that, since this text was written, the utilization of atomic energy under the form of an atomic bomb or a uranium pile has been realized.

terrifying destructive power. It is obviously desirable for experiments to take place to allow progress in nuclear physics to be made, but it is equally desirable that after the realization of these experiments, there should still remain some human beings to reap the fruits!

We have seen by a few examples the kind of practical obstacles which the developments of nuclear physics could encounter. Let us proceed to the second category of obstacles. Our theories of the atom have been somewhat difficult to establish because they have required a very extensive transformation of the conceptions up till then at the base of macroscopic physics; the necessary introduction of quanta on the atomic scale and the sacrifice which this introduction had forced us to make of certain ideas, which appeared to be of the clearest and most intuitive, have necessitated a considerable intellectual effort. The co-ordination of the knowledge of the realm of atoms, already so unimaginably small, has only been made possible at the cost of clarity in our picture. That is not very surprising since our representations are, on the whole, extracted from the data of our senses and these data have no longer any significance in the case of such small scales. In penetrating into the realm of the nucleus we must expect still further difficulties because of the even more abstract and more symbolic character of the theoretical pictures which we use.

All the intuitive representations which we might attempt to make would here have a fallacious character, much more so than in the atomic realm. Undoubtedly we shall still be able to progress by relying on the power of reason and on the synthesizing power of mathematical forms, but it does not follow that in an exploration, where little by little the support of intuition would entirely cease to fructify our theories, we should not end by being completely halted, quite lost in this new world where none of our modes of representation would any longer be applicable.

Undoubtedly it is a triumph for the human mind to have again been able to unravel laws and to establish theories for the phenomena of such a small scale, but can it be asserted that this success is bound to be maintained indefinitely? It is true that in case of a check, we would be able to continue to observe the facts without seeking their interpretation, to make pure experiments without troubling about theory, but it is very probable that such empirical research, deprived of every guide, would rapidly become sterile, for some theoretical picture is always necessary for a clear statement of the results of an experiment. Nuclear physics, in running up against the limits of resistance of matter, could, therefore, also run up against the limits of comprehension of our mind.

Very fortunately, even if such obstacles should really arise one day in the path of nuclear physics, we have not yet reached that stage. An immense harvest of experimental results, with the legitimate hope of still more remarkable results in a near future, some excellent theoretical attempts closely connected with the progress of quantal physics (such as the interpretation of nuclear interactions by mesonic fields), this is what the present state of nuclear physics offers to our attention. Everything predicts that this young science will bring invaluable contributions to the progress of our knowledge of the physical universe and that it will exert, sooner or later, an important, and perhaps decisive influence on the future development of human civilization.

The second question that I should like to put is the following: Are there still today some branches of physics that are totally unknown to us?

Well, this is quite certainly a question which, by its very nature, does not allow of any sure reply and can only give rise to conjectures. Let us first of all define its meaning. We know in nature different categories of phenomena (for example mechanics, gravifics, acoustics, optics, electrics, etc. . . .) which we fit into the framework of physics; similarly, on smaller scales we know molecular (atomic or nuclear) phenomena which we also fit into the framework of physics. Do there exist still other physical phenomena, at present unknown to us, which do not enter into any of the known categories and which, nevertheless, will have to find their place in the enlarged frameworks of the physics of tomorrow?

We have often, and sometimes rightly, reproached scientists belonging to what we a little derogatorily call official science, of having a certain tendency always to give a negative reply to every question of this kind. And yet it is quite certain that such a negative reply is very dangerous. Let us recall that it is scarcely sixty years since we knew neither Hertzian waves, nor X-rays, nor radioactivity, nor the whole collection of molecular, atomic and nuclear phenomena. Who can predict today what we will learn in future years? Perhaps there are even some facts which we now know and which one day will seem to belong to a class of phenomena of which we do not suspect the generality, of which we have not yet been able to recognize the generic character. Scientists of antiquity and of the Middle Ages knew the phenomena of electricity by friction, and the properties of permanent magnets of which Pierre de Maricourt gave a very learned description in the thirteenth century.

Nevertheless, who, in those far-off days, could have foreseen the development of this vast branch of modern science which we now call electromagnetism, and could have recognized in the few known properties of charged or magnetized bodies very particular examples (and moreover very complex ones) of an immense class of phenomena? For the scientist to believe that science is complete, is always as much of an illusion as it would be for the historian to believe that history was ended. The more our knowledge has developed, the more nature has appeared to us as possessing an almost boundless wealth in its different manifestations; even in the realm of a science already far advanced, such as physics, we have no reason to think that we have exhausted the treasures of nature or that we are near to having completed an inventory of it.

Much has been spoken, much is still spoken, about the possible existence of phenomena still little known and situated for the most part on the boundary of biology and physics. In writing these lines I have in mind the phenomena occurring in the art of divining, or in "metapsychic" researches, or again of those badly defined radiations the emission of which would be connected, according to certain statements, with the functioning of living organisms. At the risk of grieving many people of good faith, I must say that the existence of most of these phenomena does not seem to me scientifically established in a serious manner. No doubt, many sincere researchers, inspired with the sole desire of discovering new truths, have devoted themselves and still do so, to the study of what they sincerely consider constitutes real fact of an order still little known. Unfortunately, too often mixed with these are charlatans guided by interested motives, and this unhappy circumstance renders it particularly difficult to control the accuracy of the results obtained, the more so in that the researchers of good faith in like circumstances are often themselves victims of illusions or of autosuggestions. Further, a great number of those who write on these subjects give evidence of an insufficient general scientific education, confusing the most clearly expressed ideas and interpreting the theories of modern physics in the most fantastic manner. Very often we find some of them gravely issuing statements such as this: "It is well known today that each chemical substance possesses its ray", and phrases of this kind have no precise meaning for the serious physicist. From all these investigations, generally pursued in not sufficiently strict conditions by researchers who are often inadequately informed and sometimes not very scrupulous, it does not seem that up to the present we can draw any well-established conclusions. This does not, however, imply, that discoveries substantially confirmed may not some day make known to us, in those realms also, phenomena at present unknown, but nothing yet, it seems, gives us grounds to affirm this.

To come back from these rather shifting grounds on to the more solid rock of well-controlled scientific results, it is highly possible that the developments of biology, that science of such primordial interest to us, which today is soaring so rapidly ahead, may have certain repercussions on the development of physics, and reciprocally. It may be that certain physical phenomena could be exclusively linked to the functioning of living organisms; from another point of view it might also be that the original ideas introduced by recent physical theories, and especially by the quantal theories, could help us better to understand the origin of the difficulties raised by the interpretation of life and the so particular place that it occupies in the whole of nature. The curious attempts made in this way by certain physicists, notably by Bohr and Jordan, although assuredly somewhat premature and incomplete, give an idea of what one day could be the influence of the new ideas of physics on the development of biological theories.

Finally, it is possible that entire classes of purely physical phenomena still completely escape us, perhaps for lack of appropriate means for detecting them. Branches of physics of which we have no conception are perhaps still to be established (my readers will understand without difficulty that I cannot specify which!) and their conclusions, if we could know them in advance, would no doubt astonish us as much as the results of nuclear physics, for example, would have astonished the physicists of a century ago. On all that we are only able to utter baseless conjectures; but we can affirm, without great risk of being mistaken, that in physics as in all the other sciences, what we know is still but little beside what we do not know.

The last question that I should like to deal with concerns the influence which the progress of physics, and particularly of physical theories, is likely to exercise in the future on philosophic thought. Must we believe, for example, that these advances will furnish new results which will help the philosophers to apply unpublished solutions to the different problems put forward by the theory of knowledge or even by metaphysics? It is super-fluous to insist on the interest of this question.

The development of scientific research and that of philoso-phic speculation were for a long time effected on parallel lines. In antiquity and in the Middle Ages it was often the same men who cultivated both; the different branches of knowledge then hardly commenced to be differentiated in the heart of the yet confused mass where the data of science and the first systems of philosophy remained mingled. Nevertheless, already certain sciences such as geometry, astronomy or medicine had not delayed in making sufficient progress to acquire their autonomy, and starting from the sixteenth century, one saw the different schools of modern science detach themselves, one after another, from the original common trunk of philosophy and assert their independence. If in the seventeenth and eighteenth centuries there were few philosophers who were not themselves scientists, as the names of Descartes, Leibnitz or Kant alone are enough to prove, the nineteenth century, on the other hand, saw a certain divorce taking place between scientists and philosophers, the former regarding with a certain suspicion philosophical speculations which, it seemed to them, too often lacked adequate bases or posed in vain insoluble problems, whilst the latter often showed a tendency to be uninterested in the results of the different sciences, which, in their view, had no general significance.

But such a separation could only be prejudicial both to philosophy and to science. The *raison d'être* of philosophy is the attempt to sum up the totality of human knowledge in one supreme synthesis by submitting the methods employed in obtaining them to a comparative criticism, then to attempt to surpass this knowledge by building systems—general theories—structures which are rather fragile, but which respond to the anxieties and the aspirations of the human spirit. How could this arduous task be undertaken in a serious manner by men who did not know, at least in outline, the conclusions of science of their time? How can one compare and criticize the methods employed by the different scientific schools and appraise the value of their conclusions if one is not to some extent personally acquainted with these methods and has no sufficiently extensive knowledge of these conclusions? How can one attempt the ever-daring task of making general representations of the world if one has not first of all carefully studied the data on the world furnished by the accurate researches of science? If he ignores these data a philosopher cannot seriously approach his task. Conversely, it might appear that a scientist is not risking much in systematically ignoring philosophy, and it is quite true that a great many eminent scientists have been able to produce very fine work without ever having troubled themselves about philosophical interpretations. Nevertheless, for scientists, and in particular for the theorists, there is a certain danger in trying to ignore the effort of philosophers and especially·their work as critics; often, indeed, through not having sufficiently analysed the methods and concepts of which they make use, unconsciously and without discussion, they accept a certain philosophical system and then become so much the more dogmatic in that they refuse to submit their preconceived ideas to criticism. Thus many scientists of the present day, victims of an ingenuous realism, almost without perceiving it, have adopted a certain metaphysics of a materialistic and mechanistic character and have regarded it as the very expression of scientific truth. One of the great services that the recent evolution of physics has rendered contemporary thought, is that it has destroyed this simplified metaphysics, and with the same stroke has caused certain traditional philosophical problems to be considered in an entirely new light. Thereby the way has been prepared for a reconcilation between science and philosophy; for the development of science to continue, we must embark on, or at any rate touch upon, questions of philosophic import and sometimes consider their new and very original solutions; on the other hand the philosopher can no longer fail to take account of the new elements which are thus offered for his meditation by the work of physicists.

This contribution made to philosophy by theoretical physics has both its destructive and constructive side. Destructively, it has meant the criticism and rejection of a great number of ideas which had come to be considered as almost *a priori* evident, and which were accepted without discussion; in doing this, it has, in particular, removed the best arguments in support of that unconscious metaphysics which was tending to become a dogma in the minds of many scientists. We know the close criticism to which the theory of relativity has submitted the conceptions of space and time, one which has removed the *a priori* and intangible character long attributed to them. We know that by restoring, by the principle of the inertia of energy, the conception of mass to that of energy, it has, so to speak, dematerialized matter by removing its substantial aspects, by reducing it to nothing but a form of energy. Much deeper still have been the modifications brought about in our physical conceptions by the appearance of the quanta. Quantum physics has taught us that continuous reality, described by the theories of classical physics, was supported by a much more profound reality where the discontinuity expressed by the existence of Planck's quantum of action plays an essential part.

I shall not undertake to expound here in detail the surprises which the development of this new branch of physics which we call wave mechanics, or quantal mechanics, held in store for us. The impossibility of attributing to elementary physical corpuscles a well-defined position and movement at each instant in the framework of space and time; the necessity for duplicating the "corpuscular aspects" of these corpuscles by a "wave" aspect which alone allows us to follow their evolution; the necessity of replacing the rigorous determinism of the old mechanical or physical theories by a "probability", permitting no more than the affirmation of the possibility of certain eventualities and to attribute respective probabilities to them; the impossibility of constantly following in the course of time the individuality of several particles of the same nature; the existence amongst these particles of new interactions (exchange force and Pauli's exclusion) impossible of representation on our customary spatio-temporal scale, such are some of the astonishing conclusions of the new doctrines. In studying them, we have the impression of the complete insufficiency of our old and accustomed intuitions on time, on space and on motion, an insufficiency which is explained quantitatively as a function of Planck's constant by the famous Heisenberg uncertainties.

After having thus demolished some of our former, apparently most firmly established, physical conceptions, the quantal theories, in carrying out a constructive work, have introduced new conceptions of indisputable originality and depth; in doing this they have certainly brought important contributions to philosophic thought in its most general aspect.

One of these new ideas is that of "complementarity" introduced by Bohr. The double nature, corpuscular and undulatory, which we have been led to attribute to the elements of matter, leads us to think that a single reality can be presented to us under two aspects which, at first sight, appear incompatible, though actually never entering into direct conflict; when, indeed, one of these aspects asserts itself, the other disappears to an extent just sufficient always to avoid a flagrant contradiction. A "complementarity" of this kind, interpreted by Heisenberg's uncertainties, exists between the "wave" and the "corpuscle" aspects of the ultimate elements of matter; another seems to exist for a complex physical system between the whole aspect where it appears to us as an organized unit, and the aspect which makes us consider it as a collection of autonomous elements.

Bohr has not been afraid of stretching the application of the idea of complementarity even beyond the limits of physics, for example into the biological domain. For him the vital aspect and the physico-chemical aspect would be, in some way, complementary in a living being, the complete physico-chemical description of a living being requiring an analysis so extreme in its various parts that it would inevitably lead to the death of the subject studied, while the study of the vital functions would oblige one to ignore in a large measure the physico-chemical processes taking place in the depths of the tissues and of the cells; it would, therefore, be as impossible to describe life solely by the physico-chemical processes as it is impossible in atomic physics to describe the corpuscle solely by the wave or *vice versa*. Whatever may be the value that we should finally attribute to such extensions of the concept of complementarity, it remains none the less true that the concept is in itself of very great importance and appears capable of opening quite new horizons to philosophic reflection.

Another new idea is that it is impossible to attribute a rigorous determinism to the succession of phenomena, at least on the corpuscular scale. The apparent determinism in the macroscopic scales must, in small scales, give place to a probability which is content to calculate possible eventualities and their respective probabilities. In the present state of science, physicists are unable to go beyond this probability and recover the thread of a rigorous determinism in the phenomena of the microscopic scales. Will they be able to do so one day?

Although we must exercise great caution in making this kind of prediction we can, however, affirm that such a thing now appears rather improbable. Philosophers will have to discuss how far these results are consistent with the principle of causality, and see if they allow it to be maintained in its classic form or if they necessitate some small modification. As I tried to show in a communication to the Descartes Congress of 1937, there certainly exists in quantal physics a "weak" causality in the sense that every effect has always a cause and that the suppression of the cause always involves the disappearance of the effect; but no longer do we succeed in finding there the "strong" causality where the effect necessarily results from the cause and is connected with it by a rigorous determinism. Weak causality allows us to suppose that the same cause can produce one or other of several possible effects, with only a certain probability that such an effect will be produced and not such another. Physicists no longer succeed in finding anything except this weak causality on the very small scale; it is for the philosophers to examine whether they can be satisfied with it.

If I add that the most important phenomena of life appear to function in the interior of the cells or even of cellular nuclei on scales of the atomic order, the impossibility of establishing on this scale a rigorous determinism will no doubt appear as capable of playing an essential role in the evolution of our ideas on all that relates to life, and will perhaps even bring new elements to many of the traditional problems of philosophy.

Here is another question on which the development of contemporary physics has thrown new light; can we know physical reality in an objective manner, that is, in a manner independent of the processes we use to become acquainted with it? In other words, can we neglect, or at least render negligible, the perturbations which our methods of observation or of measurement may introduce in the state of the physical entities that we seek to describe?

To these questions the reply given by present-day physics is negative. As a result of the existence of the quantum of action, it is impossible indefinitely to diminish the reaction of our processes of observation on the very refined elements which we must observe to be able to describe the atomic world. We can see that, even in reducing this reaction to a minimum, it always results in the introduction of the uncertainties, foreseen by the Heisenberg relations, into our knowledge of the state of elementary physical entities. The impossibility of envisaging separately the object observed and the procedure of observation, leads, therefore, to the quantal indeterminism as defined above; it is intimately associated with Planck's constant and practically disappears on the macroscopic scale where the quantum becomes negligible. The partisans of "strong" causality may think that, if we succeeded in analysing in greater detail the interactions between the object observed and the means of observation, determinism would be re-established, the apparent indeterminism being then simply due to an insufficiency of our knowledge; but it seems that as a result of the existence of the quantum of action it is humanly impossible to make such an analysis. It seems, therefore, that determinism can no longer be proved by human science, and if we absolutely persist in maintaining its principle, this can only be done as a metaphysical postulate.

After all, in suggesting to us the complementarity of the ideas of element and system, in showing us the individual losing his personality in proportion as he dissolves into an organism which surrounds him, and finding it in proportion as he isolates himself, does not the new physics bring us suggestions of an extremely great originality and wealth of contents from which general philosophy and sociology could derive advantage? So to use them, it would undoubtedly be necessary to go far beyond the actual letter of the conclusions supplied, always presented in a precise and discrete form by such an exact science as physics. But has not the role of philosophers always been to attempt these bold extrapolations which, to the more positive mind of the scientist, are repugnant?

In this rapid survey I hope I have shown that physics in its present state has brought indisputably some new food for philosophical meditation. It certainly will not cease to do so. In bringing us each day more extensive information on the material world, it will necessarily furnish new points of departure to bold minds which are not afraid to construct general systems and to challenge metaphysical problems. Will true and lasting advances of philosophy result from it? We can at least hope so if we admit that there is an ultimate truth towards which, beyond our troubles and our vexations and in a form that we no doubt cannot foresee, the efforts of the enthusiasts of science and of the servants of the mind will one day converge.

---

[1] This remark does not apply to H. G. Wells who had a scientific training—more especially in biology—before he started on his literary career.

[2] *L'Avenir de la Science;* published in 1890.

CHAPTER XIII

HOW PURE SCIENCE AND TECHNICS HAVE BEEN OF MUTUAL ASSISTANCE TO EACH OTHER IN THE REALM OF ELECTRICITY

(This is a summary of Chapter XIV of the French edition.)

It is surprising today to think of the immense period in human history during which man had no knowledge of electricity, which is so fundamental throughout the whole of nature. Up to the eighteenth century all that was known of electricity and magnetism consisted of the results from experiments on electrifying some bodies by friction and of some of the properties of natural magnets. In the eighteenth century knowledge on the subjects progressed a little; two kinds of electricity were known and the electric nature of thunderstorms was established; it was even suggested that there might be some connexion between electricity and magnetism, but the physics of those days remained largely qualitative and experiments were frequently more of an amusing character than indicative of a real scientific research such as we understand it today. However, the end of the century saw the science of electricity and magnetism assume a more quantitative character, and scientists like Coulomb and Cavendish established exact expressions for electrostatic and magnetostatic attractions as functions of distances. Then the researches of Galvani on frogs' legs stimulated by electric currents pointed the way that was to lead to the conquest of electricity, while Volta and Davy studied the method of production and the properties of electric currents, leading to the discovery of the pile and of electrolysis. In 1819 Oersted observed the effect of an electric current on a magnet placed near it and thus established that a close connexion existed between electricity and magnetism.

Oersted's experiment was the spark that started the brilliant discoveries of Ampère who, in a few weeks in the autumn of 1820, bringing together theoretical calculations and experimental researches, created the science of electrodynamics.

With the assistance of Arago, Biot, Savart and Laplace, he formulated the laws for the production of magnetic fields by electric currents, and also for the action of magnetic fields on electric currents. He invented the principle of the solenoid and of the electro-magnet, thus foreseeing the possibility of the electric telegraph. He even came near to the discovery of the laws of induction—a discovery made by Faraday in 1831. Then between 1860 and 1875 Clerk Maxwell united all the known laws of electromagnetism in a vast synthesis which brought all luminous phenomena—the whole of optics—into the framework of electromagnetism. This wonderful fusion of two domains of physics, up till then quite independent, constitutes the perfection of an epoch which, in less than a century, led physicists to acquire the knowledge of all the laws of electricity and magnetism.

Up to the second half of the nineteenth century the progress of the science of electricity was chiefly effected in the domain of pure science where physicists were concerned with knowledge for its own sake without troubling themselves about its applications. But technical progress always follows fairly closely the real progress of pure science, and history provides many examples of this in different scientific realms, of which electricity and magnetism play a very prominent part. It is impossible to refer to all of these—their name is truly legion—but it was from the middle of the last century that these applications multiplied. It is only necessary to mention the electric telegraph, electric lighting, the telephone, electric arcs, dynamos, the transport of energy over great distances by high tension lines, etc., to realize what we owe to electromagnetic developments. It is scarcely necessary to say that the theorist is even now more required than ever and in some branches very abstruse mathematical calculations are essential for technical progress; in this connexion some reference may be made again to Maxwell's previously mentioned synthesis and the comparatively recent development in radioelectricity.

Maxwell saw that light, and more generally all radiations both visible and invisible, were of an electromagnetic nature. Some years later Hertz gave a direct experimental proof of this by his discovery of electromagnetic waves of wave-length very much greater than those of light and this discovery soon led to a practical application in wireless telegraphy which made rapid progress during the First World War, as pointed out on page 302 of the book. [After this several pages are devoted to a survey of the developments from the middle of the nineteenth century in the applications in various practical ways of the photoelectric effect, discovered by Hertz in 1887, of the discovery of the electrons, X-rays, etc., to which many references have been made in previous chapters, and it is emphasized that, while progress in these discoveries would have been impossible without the development of electric technique, on the other hand pure science lent its aid to developments in technique and there is a mutual dependence of each on the other.] [1]

For more than forty years physicists have devoted much time and energy to the study of atoms and their nuclei, and in this branch also is seen the dual characteristic just mentioned—the contemporary progress of physics rendered possible only by earlier developments in electrical technics, and, on the other hand, the contemporary discoveries of physics have promoted technical progress and undoubtedly will continue to promote it still more. This dual characteristic has many applications—a number of which will immediately occur to readers.

Reference had already been made to the electron microscope (see page 76 *et seq.*) which has rendered invaluable service where the ordinary microscope with a magnification restricted to about two to three thousand attains its limits. This microscope has been developed partly under the influence of wave mechanics and utilizes a beam of electrons which are made to converge by the action of an electric or magnetic field, and the object—magnified 10,000 to 50,000 times—is viewed on a fluorescent screen or recorded on a photographic plate. These very high magnifications are of immense value in various branches of science, but particularly in microbiological research. Here we have an example of electrical technique employing a kind of arrangement which would appear to have been reserved for a very different technique.

Methods for smashing the nuclei of atoms now depend on the use of electrified particles which have been accelerated by electric fields, and for this purpose very high potentials are required, such as were obtained from old electrostatic machines, which for many years have been mere curiosities. New forms of this old apparatus, of the Van de Graaf type, capable of attaining tensions of 1,200,000 volts, carrying 0·75 milliamps, have been designed, and here we find revived in a somewhat unexpected way one of the oldest branches of electrotechnique. To avoid the use of these rather inconvenient large machines and to obtain even greater energies for the accelerated particles, the cyclotron was planned, in the production of which much is due to Dr. E. O. Lawrence. The principle of this is now well known and we will not, therefore, enter upon a description of the cyclotron. Several powerful cyclotrons giving the particles very high energies of many millions of electron volts have been constructed in France and the United States of America and are rendering and will continue to render valuable assistance in the progress of nuclear physics.[2] Incidentally it may be remarked that in accordance with Einstein's relativity theory the mass of the electron starts increasing with its speed, with the result that the period of revolution of the electron on its circular trajectory in the cyclotron no longer remains invariable. The impulses received at each half turn by the electron are no longer concordant and the process of acceleration ceases. It is curious to find in this check to the use of the cyclotron an experimental proof of the relativity dynamics of the electron.

[Some remarks are made on the possibility of utilizing nuclear energy for industrial purposes.] The energy released by the fission of a gramme of uranium is the equivalent of that produced in the combustion of about ten tons of coal. It is true that the preparation of the substances to be used—uranium, plutonium and no doubt other substances in the future—is long, difficult and expensive, and also the disintegration products are dangerous to human beings so that many precautions are necessary. Yet, in spite of these difficulties, it seems probable that there will be established in the future, far from large towns and cities, electric-generating stations worked by atomic energy, and so perhaps the electricity industry will cease, at least in part, to pay tribute to coal and waterfalls.[3]

[In concluding this descriptive account of the mutual support of pure science and technics in accomplishing, in turn, new advances in the domain of electricity, de Broglie pays a tribute—a well-deserved tribute—to the honourable role played by French science. Nevertheless he admits that France has now no longer the place that she has had in the past and this is not surprising. Various ordeals, two homicidal and devastating wars, have enfeebled her; other nations, greater, richer and better equipped, are more favourably placed today to take the lead in scientific progress. "But France has always been the country of clear ideas, fruitful intuitions and ingenious discoveries. She can and she must remain in the front rank of the nations who assure the progress of science and of its technical applications."]

[1] Breaks in continuity in this and subsequent chapters are enclosed in square brackets.

[2] The Birmingham proton synchroton reaches more than 1,000 MeV and much more powerful nuclear machines now exist in America.

[3] Schemes of this kind are now in hand, and may be operating (e.g.) in England within a very few years.

CHAPTER XIV

A SKETCH OF THE HISTORY OF RADIOELECTRICITY

(Summary of Chapter XV of the French edition.)

In the previous chapter reference was made to the brilliant work of Maxwell in forming the synthesis between luminous and electromagnetic waves, and the subsequent work of Hertz on electromagnetic waves analogous to light-waves but of much longer wave-length. With the early oscillators utilized by Hertz and some of those who followed him, the lengths of the waves varied from a few metres to a few centimetres, and later apparatus used by Righi, Lodge, Lebedev and others was able to produce even shorter waves descending to the order of a few millimetres. These short waves were used by the earlier experimenters to guide them in their researches but they suffered from the disadvantage of being very weak. Towards 1900 the practical application of these waves commenced and Marconi, an Italian engineer, was the first to secure distant communication by means of the Hertzian waves, after which wireless telegraphy developed very rapidly. [It would serve no useful purpose in this summary to deal with the details of these developments which can be found in many works devoted to the various technical sides of the subject. One point, however, is worth mentioning because it had a most interesting—to say nothing of a ludicrous—sequel, and that is the developments in the lengths of the waves that were used. This is dealt with later in the chapter (see page 251).]

The antennæ forming the oscillator were gradually increased in length, thus increasing the wave-lengths until these attained hundreds or even thousands of metres; the antennæ of the military station of the Eiffel Tower which rises to nearly 300 metres above ground level gave a wave-length of 2,800 metres. At the same time less crude methods for reception were adopted, Galène's crystal, Ferrié's electrolytic detector or

Fleming's valve, and stronger waves were produced by Poulsen's arc, while the oscillator which interrupted the reception current at intervals of audible frequency came into use.

At the beginning of 1914, just before the outbreak of the First World War, the tendency was to make use of long wavelengths up to 10,000 metres or even more, and in most stations the waves emitted were weak. It is worth noticing that reliance was placed almost exclusively on the resources of electrotechnics and of physics on the large scale without appealing to the researches of physicists on the elementary particles of electricity. Theory seemed to indicate that the increase in the wave-length was desirable because only such could be effective at great distances owing to the rotundity of the earth—in other words, the surface of the earth would intercept short waves which could not, therefore, be used for long-distance transmission. The waves in view could only be obtained under somewhat difficult conditions and many serious technical problems remained to be solved. As for the reception, this required the use of an oscillator, an inconvenient apparatus which functioned irregularly. The apparatus then in use in wireless telegraphy was definitely based on electro-technics and was very cumbersome; powerful alternators, imposing batteries of condensers, great sparking-gaps in the form of disks or of crowns vigorously ventilated by jets of air by means of strong bellows, that is what one would have seen at stations like that at the Eiffel Tower in the beginning of 1914.

All this was changed by the appearance on the scene of bulbs with three electrodes which introduced a totally new technique into radio transmission soon after the commencement of the First World War. It is scarcely necessary to add that this development could not have taken place without the brilliant work of physicists during the last twenty years of the nineteenth century, especially on the granular structure and mobility of electrons and their amazing aptitude for assisting the passage of currents between the filament and the electrode. This thermionic effect was utilized by Fleming in the construction of his diode valves, and later on immensely improved by Lee de Forest's valve with three electrodes, referred to above. From these there followed great progress, including the use of very much less power in the transmitting stations and the development of radiotelephony, and in connexion with the latter there took place an extraordinary discovery with wide ramifications—the possibility of utilizing short waves.

It has already been mentioned that long wave-lengths were considered necessary for transmission over great distances owing to the view that short waves would be intercepted by the surface of the earth, and hence the former were reserved for official communications and the latter for mere amateurs. It may be remarked that the number of amateurs—certainly in the British Isles—was very great indeed, and while they were restricted to short waves, nevertheless the authorities, realizing that amateurs might materially assist in the development of the technics in wireless, encouraged them as far as possible. Science reaped a wonderful harvest by the work of amateurs who, in certain respects, had the laugh of the professionals.

Amongst these amateurs reference is made to Léon Deloy, an old colleague of the author, who had worked at the radio-station at the Eiffel Tower. He (and others) discovered that transmissions of very feeble power could be heard over long distances on the short wave-lengths—a discovery that caused considerable surprise amongst the professionals. The question arose, "How were these short waves, so badly adapted for turning round obstacles, capable of following the earth's curvature and reaching reception stations at great distances?" Of course it is now well known that this is effected by the partial reflection of these short waves by strongly ionized layers of rarefied gases in the upper regions of the atmosphere (the Heaviside layers). It is due to the presence of these layers whose existence has been placed beyond all doubt by the researches of Sir Edward Appleton, that the wireless waves emitted at the earth's surface are unable to escape completely from our atmosphere into space, but are partly reflected, and so are able to affect receptors in various parts of the world.

A very important lesson should be learned from this mishap suffered by the protagonists of long waves; we must beware of trusting completely to theoretical considerations in problems where we are not certain of having taken into consideration all the data (and one may well ask whether we are ever certain of knowing all the data).

"If theory has frequently guided scientific researchers and resulted in admirable discoveries, if it is necessary for the progress of science, it has also at times been able to delay these advances when we have relied too blindly on certain of its conclusions which are always subject to revision" (page 330 in French edition).

Towards the end of this chapter something is said about the various advantages of a directed beam, such as the economy in the energy that is used, the possibility of secrecy of communication, the reflection of the waves (comparatively little enfeebled, owing to the concentration) from obstacles whose presence can thus be detected, etc. The use of these very short waves has led to some wonderful results and amongst these must be included the services which radar has rendered to the army, navy and air force during the last war, and since then in various other ways, such as detecting the presence of icebergs or sea coasts, sounding the atmosphere for meteorological purposes, determining the topography of a region from aeroplanes, and even for measuring the distance of the moon by the time required for a beam to reach its surface and return after reflection to the earth.

Most readers will endorse the sentiments expressed in the last sentence of this chapter: "In our troubled time, in the presence of an uncertain future, it is comforting to evoke the different stages of one of the most beautiful successes of the human genius."

CHAPTER XV

LINK BETWEEN PURE SCIENCE
AND ITS APPLICATIONS

(Summary of Chapter XVI of the French edition.)

[THIS chapter commences with a quotation from Montaigne's *Essais*: "Science is a great ornament and it is an implement of wonderful use."] This phrase is frequently quoted because it forcibly puts into relief the two aspects under which science can be envisaged, according to whether we place ourselves at the purely intellectual point of view or, on the contrary, at the point of view of its practical applications. These two orientations of science, the one directed towards the disinterested search of truth and the other towards the practical application of our knowledge, although complementary, have, nevertheless, a certain tendency to oppose each other. This opposition is nothing but a particular aspect of the conflict which tends to manifest itself in all domains between thought and action. We see this exemplified in many ways; for example, in the difference in outlook between the scientist engaged in research in his laboratory or in his study, and the technician in his industrial laboratory or at his writing desk. The multiplicity and complexity of many branches of science and technics have necessitated a more and more marked specialization in all domains, with the result that there is a tendency for activities which were once united to disintegrate and to isolate certain classes of research workers who had collaborated both for a long time and fruitfully.

This raises the important question whether some efforts must not be made to maintain pure and applied science in close relation and to prevent a separation which would be as disastrous for the one as for the other. [A considerable portion of the chapter is devoted to a consideration of the reasons for opposing such a separation and of the means for doing so.]

No one will seriously dispute the fact that the great attainments of modern industry have originated in the researches of scientists who, in most cases, devoted themselves to disinterested investigations and had no thought, at least immediately, of their practical applications. History abounds with examples. The science of motion—mechanics—was established in the seventeenth and eighteenth centuries through the efforts of men of genius such as Galileo, Descartes, Newton, d'Alembert, Lagrange, etc., and it was no mere chance that at the end of this period there appeared the first industrial machines and the first factories. Further, how could these machines have been perfected or new ones invented if the laws of motion had not been known? In the last chapter something was said about the pioneer work of those who were responsible for the enormous advance in modern electrotechnics, and the names of such men as Carnot, Mayer, Clapeyron, Joule, Clausius, Lord Kelvin and many others, are familiar to everyone interested in science, especially in connexion with the laws of thermodynamics. Examples might be multiplied in other realms of physics and of chemistry and other sciences, but this is unnecessary. It is beyond doubt that the development of the different branches of Mechanics, Physics and Chemistry has preceded and promoted the development of the great technical applications which have changed the face of the modern world, and we shall now proceed to deal with an objection which, no doubt, will be in the minds of many who read this chapter.

It must be admitted that some great discoveries have been made partly by chance or as the result of merely groping and feeling one's way, scientific theories playing absolutely no part in the discoveries. As an instance of this, there is the case of Zénobe Gramme, a simple Belgian workman without education, who invented the first continuous current generator capable of real use industrially, and that with hardly knowing anything about the laws of electricity. In the last chapter we mentioned the work of amateurs in connexion with developments in short-wave transmission over great distances, which professionals had pronounced to be impossible. Examples might be multiplied but in spite of this it still remains true, generally speaking, that progress in industry has had its source in scientific research which has led to the establishment of the great branches of physico-chemistry.

It must not, however, be assumed that those well-established industries no longer require the assistance of men devoted to pure scientific research for its own sake; every day discoveries made by scientists who work without any practical goal in view are used for unforeseen applications. Thus, the use of X-rays allows one to explore the deep or superficial structures of all kinds of bodies, including metals and alloys and fats, which have been so thoroughly studied by Trillat, and much information has been derived which was useful from the point of view of their application. In another sphere we find the same kind of thing; the diffraction of electrons by crystalline structures in the superficial layers of bodies, now used for industrial purposes, owes its success to de Broglie's own work more than twenty years ago on wave mechanics, during which he attributed undulatory properties to electrons, thus enabling him to foresee their diffraction by crystals, and here he was guided only by theoretical principles.

We have thus been given a few examples of the applications which the researches of pure science, today as in the past, can have in the practical field. A close collaboration of science and technique is highly desirable. The progress of industry is likely to be considerably retarded or even stopped if pure science did not continually contribute to it the results of its research. But the advantage is reciprocal and pure science can derive great advantage by contact with the practical applications of its research. Indeed one great danger confronting pure and disinterested science is that of being too much wrapped up in itself, theorists thus running the risk of being absorbed in abstract discussions which are often sterile, and experimenters being obsessed with the study of detailed issues of secondary importance. Thus, each side can safeguard its autonomy and employ different methods, knowing that if they are able to combine their efforts they can render each other great services and their collaboration can be very fruitful.

Having decided that collaboration is very desirable, the question arises how such collaboration between pure science and its industrial application can be carried out under good conditions. It is suggested that between the two categories of different activities there should be a sort of frontier zone, where certain researchers and certain laboratories would be chiefly employed in maintaining the liaison between pure science and technique, endeavouring to make technique benefit by the progress of pure science and at the same time maintaining pure science fully informed of the needs of technique. To carry out this scheme the personnel must be partly recruited amongst young people in the great schools or establishments of higher education, who would bring the assistance of their solid theoretical foundation to the solution of practical problems, and partly amongst the engineers from technical schools, who had already taken part in the life of industrial establishments and who would bring to the examination of new scientific problems their technical abilities and their sense of concrete reality. Naturally this double recruitment would raise a number of problems which, de Broglie admits, he does not feel competent to discuss in detail, but the brief outline of certain difficulties and dangers to be avoided—and probably others unforeseen would arise—gives every hope that, with good will on all sides, such a scheme could be carried out with mutual advantage to pure science and industry.

It may, however, be pointed out that owing to the different educational systems prevailing in different countries, no universal scheme for the co-operation between the two aspects of science could be formulated, though it would be possible to lay down general principles as a guide in all cases. [Some space is devoted to the details, chiefly for French educational and industrial institutes, and no doubt important developments will follow more or less on the lines suggested. It is admitted that the role of industrial laboratories in scientific research is much more important in some countries than it has been in France, and the United States of America is specially mentioned in this connexion, reference being made to the discovery by Davisson and Germer in the Bell Laboratory, New York, in 1927, of the phenomena of the diffraction of electrons, already referred to (see page 71). Amongst the institutes in France which, he thinks, could contribute most efficaciously to the recruitment of personnel, is the National Centre of Scientific Research which has already played an extremely fruitful and successful role in the development of researches in pure science, and which also seems able to contribute very efficiently to the establishment of desirable interconnexions between science and industry.]

To the objection that the present time, with all the unrest and strained relations, and even with wars being waged in some parts of the world, is not opportune for undertaking the task outlined in this chapter, there is the reminder that it is perhaps, precisely in difficult times such as exist today, that great efforts for co-ordination and reorganization must be attempted. In the midst of accumulated ruins the moment is then propitious to open new paths, to try to raise new edifices and to make plans for the future. "The efforts accomplished during these dark and grievous periods are often the seeds from which there will emerge glorious tomorrows" (page 349). Following the peace of 1815, after the Battle of Waterloo, France soon regained eminence amongst the nations in pure science and in industrial developments. [The names of many eminent men of science in different branches are given and should be examples to inspire others, at the present time of difficulties in France, to prepare for the springtime of science and industry in the France of tomorrow.]

CHAPTER XVI

AT THE DAWN OF THE ATOMIC ERA*
(Summary of Chapter XVII of the French Edition.)

IN the last chapter of his great work, *The Two Sources of Morality and Religion*, Henri Bergson, having reached almost the end of his book, showed to us a humanity in the formidable grip of mechanism, and as if succumbing under the weight of the discoveries and inventions which the creative activity of its mind had been able to realize. Doubtless it was as though inscribed in the destinies of man, of *homo sapiens*, of *homo faber*, some day to use the forces of nature for his advantage, but Bergson rightly said:

". . . machines which move on petrol, on coal, on hydro-electric power and which convert into motion the potential energies accumulated during millions of years, have given to our organism so vast an extension and so formidable a power, so disproportionate to its dimensions and strength, that surely it had never been foreseen in the plan of the structure of our species."

And wishing to make us appreciate the essential point and the disquieting side of the problem, he added: "Now, in this excessively enlarged body, the spirit remains what it was, too small now to fill it, too feeble to direct it", and further on, "Let us add that this increased body awaits a supplement of the soul and that the mechanism demands a mysticism". Finally, the work finishes on these words, pregnant with meaning: "Humanity groans half-crushed under the weight of the advances that it has made. It does not know sufficiently that its future depends on itself. It is for it, above all, to make up its mind if it wishes to continue to live. . . ."

Today, on the morrow of the discovery of the atom bomb which has shown that, henceforth, man can at will utilize

* Discourse given to the society, 'Les amis de Bergson', 29th November, 1945.

those formidable reserves of energy which are concealed in the very heart of matter—the nuclei of atoms—we understand much better the terrifying extent of the anxieties which the distinguished author of *Creative Evolution* expressed some twenty years ago. We shall realize to what extent this new source of energy is superior to all those which we previously were able to utilize, if I recall that, in the phenomena of the fission of uranium, a single gramme of uranium can furnish us with as much energy as more than ten tons of coal, and it is not out of order to think that in the utilization of atomic energy we shall attain still greater returns. Thereby we shall acquire a new power of which it is almost impossible to fix the limits. But it must be stated with some sorrow that it was in order to produce an engine of formidable power of destruction that men for the first time made use of this fundamentally admirable discovery of modern physics; and this fact in itself is somewhat disquieting.

Without doubt atomic energy will very probably be capable of beneficent applications. It will allow us to economize our reserves of coal and petrol, make our factories function, turn our motors; transformed, for example, into electric energy, it will supply us in almost unlimited quantity with motive power, heat and light. The era of atomic energy can be an era of admirable progress, an era of a better and easier life. But it can also be an era of inexpiable strife, surpassing in extent and horror all the wars of the past where, with the aid of terrifying means of destruction, humanity runs the risk of completely destroying itself. It would serve no purpose if we deceived ourselves by misleading illusions on the possibility of such catastrophes for, alas! human passions have remained the same, and the terrible events which in these last years have stained all parts of the world with blood scarcely allow us to hope that, in the future, the wisdom and love of his fellow man will necessarily always prevail in the heart of men.

And so the drama presents itself in the sense that Bergson had foreseen. With our power of action suddenly and enormously increased, will our enfeebled spirit, nevertheless, be sufficiently strong to put it to good use? It is on our will and our will alone that there is going to depend the good or the evil use of the unheard of forces which science has handed over to our control. We perceive the almost tragic magnitude of the moral problem which is here raised. "Humanity does not know sufficiently that its future depends on itself. It is for it to see first if it wishes to continue to live," said Bergson. How precise and profound a meaning these words hold today on the threshold of the unknown, and perhaps formidable future which opens before us!

So long as the means available to man, which enabled him to act on his surroundings, were limited, the consequences of his evil actions were themselves also limited, and the damage which resulted from them for human societies was able to be expunged more or less rapidly. In proportion as the means of action and consequently of destruction, placed at our disposal by the progress of the sciences and of technics, were developed, the ravage that they were capable of producing has become more and more extended and the wounds thus produced, because they were deeper, have taken longer to heal. The evolution of wars in modern times offers a tragic example of this. They have involved more and more extensive regions of the earth, casting into the furnace of battle a larger and larger number of combatants, each day exposing more of the civilian populations to the same dangers as the soldiers. With the use of atomic energy, the wars of tomorrow can assume an infernal character, the whole horror of which it is difficult to imagine.

But it is not only wars that could have terrible consequences in the future. We can easily imagine other catastrophes which show still better the nature of the danger. Fifty years ago some heated people, whom we then called anarchists, threw bombs in different public places, into cafés, churches and even into the Chamber of Deputies. These attempts caused the death of a certain number of people and justly roused public indignation. The number of victims and of material destruction was, however, limited. How much greater would it be if tomorrow new anarchists succeeded in utilizing, in their criminal attempts, atomic bombs capable of destroying entire cities! Here we really grasp the true nature of the drama; the will of one man only can become sufficient to unleash a pheno-menon of a formidable power. By this enormous increase in our power the responsibility of man is augmented in a like proportion, and the consequences of a moral weakening can become incalculable. Hence the moral problem acquires a significance much greater than in the past. It seems, to use Bergson's language, that our souls have not grown in proportion to our bodies, and therefore humanity will not have any excess of the spiritual forces on which morale can lean without too much peril in following the dangerous roads ahead.

From many points of view we can envisage the problems raised by the discovery of the utilization of atomic energy. Certain of these problems are of a political order and concern international relations; others bear on the development and transformation of industries and touch upon the new technique which the use of atomic energy will perhaps render possible. We are not here concerned with these problems in spite of their importance, but I should like to draw attention to two aspects of the question which more particularly interest the scientist, one being of moral order, the other of material order.

Up to the present the research worker devoted to tasks of pure science had no need to be in the least preoccupied with the consequences which his eventual discoveries might have for mankind. Dominated by the attraction which the search for truth exercises on the mind of man, enraptured by the joy procured by the sensation of having divined the secrets of nature and solved a few of the enigmas which she poses to us, the scientist was able, with an easy conscience, to dedicate himself to pure science; with Henri Poincaré he was able to adopt the formula, "Science for the sake of science", or to proclaim without any misgivings as I did myself a few years ago at the end of the Preface of one of my books: "It is necessary to love science because it is a great work of the mind."

Assuredly science for a long time has had applications in the practical domain, and by this its advances have had repercussions on human life. No one ignored this nor the fact that certain scientific discoveries, those of explosives for example, were not at times without certain grievous consequences for the security of men. Nevertheless, the scientist calmed the fears which this reflection might suggest to him by telling himself that on the whole the advantages of science greatly surpassed its ills, and forty years ago at the epoch when the successive discoveries of lighting by gas, railways, telegraph, telephone, electric lighting, the utilization and distant transport of electric energy, automobiles, etc., had considerably improved the conditions of human life, public opinion, in agreement with the scientists, considered that the work of science, taken as a whole, was incontestably beneficial.

Things were somewhat perceptibly modified from this point of view at the time of the First World War. The use of aeroplanes for bombing, the military use of toxic gases, the invention of tanks, etc., created a certain uneasiness in opinion and even amongst scientists, many of whom began to ask themselves whether they had, from the moral point of view, the right to be indifferent concerning the material consequences of their discoveries.

The discovery and use of atomic bombs, for reasons which I have already recalled to mind, cannot but increase still more this feeling which, little by little, the scientist has about his responsibilities and, by reason of the consequences which could result from them, they are able to startle public opinion and to lead it to ask itself whether the esteem and the admiration which it devoted to science were really justified. Here is a new frame of mind the consequences of which it is important to study.

It has often been said that one should love "Art for Art's sake", but it has justly been objected that art can sometimes be immoral and that this immorality can have grievous repercussions. However grave may be these repercussions, they are, nevertheless, nothing compared with those which a bad use of atomic energy could have, so that the formula "Science for the sake of Science" can in its turn be attacked. Are scientists who have devoted their efforts to make atomic physics progress, who have cheerfully seen the gates of a new world open up before them, who have felt the unspeakable joy of seeing the human mind sufficiently strong to understand what takes place on scales so removed from our usual experience—these scientists who have had faith in the value of science—going to be overcome by scruples, to doubt the moral scope and the material consequences of their work? Each time that they will undertake a piece of work, are they going to ask themselves if they have the right, in the face of their moral conscience, face to face with public opinion, face to face with the whole of humanity, to pursue researches from which can ensue in a more or less distant future unheard of catastrophes? And does not that new frame of mind which can extend from physics to other sciences, to biology, for example, run the risk of paralysing the activity of the scientist, of preventing him from making new useful discoveries and of pursuing the work of science in what it has that is elevated and glorious for the human mind? We only create if we have freedom of mind and tranquility of conscience; if, in consequence of honourable scruples, both come to fail him, will not the scientist be partly or completely hindered in his efforts? Such are some of the questions that are now presented to us and on which it is good that we should reflect.

But there is yet another matter. States cannot remain uninterested in the utilization of atomic energy; as much from the military point of view as from the industrial point of view, it is going to be of capital importance to them.

To remain masters of certain secrets, to control the developments of certain techniques, they are no doubt going to be led to interest themselves more than in the past in scientific research and they will be tempted to submit it to regulations, to inspections to which it had not been accustomed. Is it not said that even in the United States the scientists who know the secret of the atomic bomb have no longer all their freedom of movement? It is no longer only the scruples which may arise in the hearts of scientists, it is the decisions of public authority, the supervisions that it exercises, which are capable of impeding the activity of men of science. Here we risk finding that antinomy which exists in so many other domains and which is at the root of so many social or political struggles; individual liberty and initiative are necessary for great creations whilst organization and discipline are necessary to prevent individual initiatives from taking a direction contrary to general and national interests. To reconcile what is indispensable in the liberty of men with that which is necessary in the social order, is a question of balance always difficult to resolve in practice.

But if this problem in many domains has presented itself for a long time past with more or less acuteness, scientific research did not appear to raise it, and the scientist boldly demanded absolute right of orienting as he wished the effort of his mind and the meaning of his experiments. It is henceforth to be otherwise? And, if scientific research undergoes external constraints, will it not thereby be vitally injured? May not the life of the mind itself suffer thereby? Here are new problems which I permit myself to submit to your reflections.

I have just set forth several somewhat engrossing aspects of the present evolution of scientific progress. Nevertheless it is not necessary to lose all faith in the future. Humanity has already passed through many difficult situations and it has always succeeded in emerging to its advantage. Often the feeling of the imminence of a danger gives birth in the heart of men to sentiments or mysticisms which can serve to avoid it. It is necessary that we should thoroughly realize the peril that the bad use of atomic energy would constitute for our species in order to promote in us the reactions which can preserve us from danger. It is somewhat comforting from this point of view to aver that in the war which has just ended, though so terrible in so many respects, none of the adversaries dared to make use of toxic gases. It may be due to a feeling of moral responsibility or fear of reprisals, perhaps both, but the fact is there; toxic gases were not used.

Confronted by the dangers with which the advances of science can, if employed for evil, face him, man has need of a "supplement of soul" and he must force himself to acquire it promptly before it is too late. It is the duty of those who have the mission of being the spiritual or intellectual guides of humanity to labour to awaken in it this supplement of the soul.

CHAPTER XVII

THE GREAT ADVENTURE

IT is very often said that the rapid development of modern science and of its applications constituted a great adventure for humanity, and indeed it is one of which neither future developments nor the final consequences can be measured today.

The effort of scientific research is developing, we know, on two parallel but very distinct planes. On the one hand it tends to increase our knowledge of natural phenomena without preoccupying itself with deriving any profit from it; it seeks to state precisely the laws of these phenomena and to disentangle their profound relations by welding them into vast theoretical syntheses; it also seeks to predict new ones from them and to verify the exactness of these predictions. Such is the aim that pure and disinterested science proposes, and no one can deny its grandeur and nobility. It is to the credit of the human mind that it has untiringly pursued, through the vicissitudes of the history of peoples and of individual existences, this passionate search for the different aspects of truth. But, on the other hand, scientific research also develops on another plane—that of practical applications. Becoming more and more conscious of the laws which governed phenomena, having learned each day to discover new ones, thanks to the improvements in experimental technique and to the refinement of theoretical conceptions, man has found himself to be more and more the master in his dealings with nature. Paraphrasing a celebrated proverb, we can say that having discovered the laws of nature, by conforming to them man has become capable of directing her.

To be sure this application of acquired knowledge to obtain certain results has far-off origins; the discovery of fire and its application, the art of utilizing metals for the purpose of making instruments or arms go far back in the past. But it is chiefly in the last three centuries that, the progress of science having become accelerated, the number of its applications has increased in a prodigious fashion. Mechanics—sister of Astronomy—Physics, which has been incessantly branching off under the form of entirely new sciences such as Electricity and Heat, Chemistry, the first real advances in which scarcely go back to the end of the eighteenth century, have made possible innumerable applications; inventions which have changed the conditions of human life, industries which have undergone immense developments, have found their origins in them. And the movement thus unleashed keeps on accelerating; the progress of the sciences and of their utilization develops with an ever increasing rhythm, as the snowball descending the mountain slopes grows larger with an increasing speed. Realms up till now forbidden suddenly open up before us. Here is the physics of the atom which allows us to penetrate to the core of matter and which unveils to us how, deep down in the atomic structures, at the heart of the elementary particles and of the nuclei of atoms, prodigious quantities of energy are concealed; it has just taught us how to liberate and use them at our will; all our industries will be transformed by them, our power of action will through them be madly increased, once more the face of the world is going to be changed. Here is biology which, intent on the mystery of life, begins to catch a glimpse of the conditions which govern the development of living beings and the transmission, through generations, of hereditary characters; tomorrow, perhaps, it will allow us to influence the development of embryos, to regulate, at least to a certain extent, the play of heredity, and then we shall truly be able to say that life has become mistress of its own destinies.

These are prospects which can legitimately raise the enthusiasm of young research workers and give optimistic minds a glimpse of a marvellous future. But does not this incessantly accrued power of man over nature admit of dangers? Having opened Pandora's box, shall we be able to allow the emergence of only beneficient inventions and praiseworthy applications? But how avoid these questions in the times in which we are now living? Every increase of our power of action necessarily increases our power of doing harm. The more means we have for giving help and relief, the more means we have for spreading suffering and destruction. Chemistry has enabled us to develop useful industries and furnished pharmacy with beneficial remedies; but it also permits the manufacture of poisons which kill and explosives which pulverize. Tomorrow in disposing of intra-atomic energies, according to our inclination, we shall no doubt be able to increase in unheard of proportions the well-being of men, but we shall also be able to destroy at one stroke entire portions of our planet. If later on we are able to work on the transmission of life, we shall be able, perhaps, to produce admirable supermen, but all the imagination of a Wells would be necessary to describe the harm that we might also possibly do.

But of what avail are vain fears! We have been launched into the great adventure and like the snowball that rolls on the sloping descent it is no longer possible for us to stop. We must run the risk, since risk is the condition of every success. We must have confidence in ourselves and hope that, masters of the secrets that permit the unleashing of natural forces, we shall be sufficiently reasonable to use the increase in our power for beneficial ends. In the work of science man has been able to show the force of his intelligence; if he wishes to survive his own successes, it is necessary that he should now show the wisdom of his will.

ON STATISTICS OF THE PURE CASES IN WAVE MECHANICS AND THE INTERFERENCE OF PROBABILITIES

IN this Appendix I should like to explain clearly certain points relative to the statistical formulation of wave mechanics. This indeed runs the risk of being badly understood by minds accustomed to the usual formalism of mathematical statistics. The reason for this is that the usual mathematical statistics is based on postulates which cease to be exact in wave mechanics in such a way that, to make the formalism of wave mechanics enter into the general picture of the Calculus of Probabilities, it is necessary to construct a mathematical statistical theory more comprehensive than that of which use is generally made—by abandoning certain too restricted postulates. We think that, in the present state of physical theories, it is very important that specialists in the Calculus of Probabilities should ponder these questions which we shall now try to explain in the simplest possible way.

When we attempt to explain the principles of the Calculus of Probabilities by citing simple examples, we always assume, and generally without saying so explicitly because it seems self-evident, that statistics deal with events possessing objective characteristics, independent of the manner in which they are established. Thus it is usual to draw deductions from coin-tossing (a game of heads or tails) from dice, playing cards, etc., and each of these objects, which are objects on our scale relevant to macroscopic physics and directly perceptible by our senses, has characteristics which are not modified by the fact that we ascertain them. Let us consider a playing card; it has its colour (heart, spade, etc.), and what I shall call its "rank" (ace, king, etc.), and it seems obvious that the fact of ascertaining the colour of the card cannot change its rank, or inversely. To take another example, if in a group of conscripts we measure the height and the circumference of the chest of each of them, can we imagine that the fact of measuring the height could exercise any influence on the value of the circumference of the chest or inversely?

The very important postulate which is thus surreptitiously introduced at the origin of the arguments on probabilities can truly be named "postulate of objectivity". It is that, indeed, which permits the consideration of a dice, a playing card, etc., as having objective properties independent of the manner in which they are established; thus in a game of cards a certain card will be a "king of hearts" because, whatever may be the process used to establish its colour and its rank, whether these confirmations be simultaneous or successive, it will always be found that it is a heart and that it is a king.

It is also necessary to insist on another consequence of the postulate of objectivity. It implies that the different verifications which can be made on the object can be effected in any order whatever, that they can be, in particular, simultaneous or successive.

Admitting the postulate of objectivity and its consequences, we are then led to lay down a certain number of principles which we shall recall by dealing with the case of discontinuous probabilities, the generalization in the case of continuous probabilities being very easily made afterwards. We shall confine ourselves to the case when the events to which our statistics are relevant present only two objective characteristics which interest us; we shall represent these characteristics by two aleatory variables U and V capable of taking respectively two series of discontinuous values $u_1, u_2 \ldots$ and $v_1, v_2. \ldots$ We can then define the probabilities P_i and P_k of the values $U = u_i$, and $V = v_k$. If amongst the N objects on which the statistics are based, n_i have the value u_i of the characteristic U, we put $P_i = n_i / N$, and if there are n_k of them which have the value v_k of the characteristic V, we put $P_k = n_k / N$. But the objects having by hypothesis characteristics independent of the verifications and of the order of the verifications, there will be a certain number n_{ik} of N objects for which we shall have at the time $U = u_i$ and $V = v_k$, and we shall put $P_{ik} = n_{ik} / N$, P_{ik} being by definition the probability of having at the time the values $U = u_i$ and $V = v_k$ of U and V.

We shall easily be able to define also "joint probabilities".

Thus, the probability of obtaining $V = v_k$ when we know that $U = u_i$ will be $P_k^{(i)} = n_{ik}/n_i$ and the probability of obtaining $U = u_i$ when we know that $V = v_k$ will be $P_i^{(k)} = n_{ik}/n_k$, and immediately we shall verify the fundamental relations

$$P_i P_k^{(i)} = P_k P_i^{(k)} = P_{ik} \qquad (1)$$

But obviously we have

$$P_i = \underset{k}{\Sigma} P_{ik}, \qquad P_k = \underset{i}{\Sigma} P_{ik} \qquad (2)$$

since $n_i = \underset{k}{\Sigma} n_{ik}$ and $n_k = \underset{i}{\Sigma} n_{ik}$.

From (1) and (2) it therefore follows that

$$P_i = \underset{k}{\Sigma} P_k P_i^{(k)}, \quad P_k = \underset{i}{\Sigma} P_i P_k^{(i)} \qquad (3)$$

For example in a 32-card game, if U corresponds to the colour and V to the rank, we have

$$P_i = 8/32, \quad P_k = 4/32, \quad P_{ik} = 1/32, \quad P_k^{(i)} = 1/8, \quad P_i^{(k)} = 1/4$$

and the verification of the relations (1), (2) and (3) is immediate.*

The general results known under the name of "theorem of total probabilities" and "theorem of compound probabilities" are contained in formulae (1), (2) and (3). As is well known, we must, in enunciating the theorem of compound probabilities, insist on the fact that the probabilities $P_k^{(i)}$ and $P_i^{(k)}$ must be evaluated by taking into account what is supposed to be known from a previous determination of the value of U or of V. An often-cited example of this is that the probability of drawing two kings in succession from a 32-card pack is $\dfrac{4}{32} \times \dfrac{3}{31}$, for after the removal of the first king, there remain in the pack 31 cards of which 3 are kings.

It is, moveover, easy, in the general scheme, to introduce the problem of the successive drawing of two cards, when we

---

* Needless to say, all the probabilities P_i, P_k . . . obey such relations $\underset{i}{\Sigma} P_i = 1$.

are interested, as in the last example, only in their rank. It is sufficient to denote by U the rank of the first card and by V that of the second; we ought then to put

$$P_i = P_k = 4/32, \ P_{ik} = 16/31 \cdot 32 \text{ if } i \neq k, \ P_{ik} = 12/31 \cdot 32 \text{ if } i = k,$$

as is easily seen. Formulae (1) then give

$$P_k^{'(i)} = P_i^{'(k)} = 4/31 \text{ if } i \neq k; \ P_k^{'(i)} \neq P_i^{'(k)} = 3/31, \text{ if } i = k,$$

and the relations (2) and (3) are easily verified.

It is easy to modify the preceding formulation to the case of continuous probabilities, when we can define the probability densities. Always considering two aleatory variables U and V, we shall denote by $\rho(u)du$ the probability that U should be found to have a value included in the range du and by $\rho(v)dv$ the probability that V should be found to have a value in the range dv. We shall assume the existence of a density $\rho(u, v)$ such that $\rho(u, v) \, du \, dv$ is the probability for which, at the time, U is found to have a value in du and V a value in dv. This also proceeds from the postulate of objectivity and its consequences. It is, then, easy to transpose formulae (1), (2) and (3) from the discontinuous to the continuous case. The probabilities $P_k^{(i)}$ and $P_i^{(k)}$ will be respectively replaced by the continuous functions $P(u|v)$ and $P(v|u)$, defined as the probability of V given U and the probability of U given V. We then obtain the following relations which replace, respectively, the relations (1), (2) and (3)

$$\rho(u, v) = P(v|u)\rho(v) = P(u|v)\rho(u) \tag{1'}$$

$$\rho(u) = \int_{-\infty}^{+\infty} \rho(u, v) dv; \ \rho(v) = \int_{-}^{+\infty} \rho(u, v) du \tag{2'}$$

$$\rho(u) = \int_{-\infty}^{\infty} \rho(v) \ P(v|u) dv; \ \rho(v) = \int_{-\infty}^{\infty} \rho(u) \ P(u|v) du \tag{3'}$$

formulae which still contain the theorem of total probabilities and that of compound probabilities.*

* Of course all the probability densities $\rho(u)$ obey relations such as
$$\int_{-\infty}^{+\infty} \rho(u) \, du = 1.$$

All the formulation that we have now explained is well known and we have recalled it only by way of recapitulation. But here is a new and essential point; the general formulation does not apply to the statistics which we meet in wave mechanics, at least when the aleatory qualities U and V are canonically conjugate quantities, such as a co-ordinate q and Lagrange's conjugate moment p (associated quantities in non-commutative operations).

To understand the question it is necessary first of all to recall the principles of wave mechanics. I shall summarize these without entering into details which can be found in other expositions.

Given a microphysical system, let A and B be two quantities measurable relative to this system; to these quantities correspond linear and closed operators A and B of which the appropriate values and the appropriate functions are respectively a_i and ϕ_i, β_k and χ_k. Any measure of A can supply as a value only one of the a_i; any measure of B can supply as a value only one of the β_k. The appropriate functions ϕ_i of A forming a complete system of orthonormal functions, the function of the wave of the system will be able to develop according to the ϕ_i. Let us suppose that the wave function Ψ of the system is exactly known (a clear case in von Neumann's sense) and that we have

$$\Psi = \underset{i}{\Sigma} c_i\, \phi_i; \qquad (4)$$

then, in accordance with the principles of wave mechanics, $|c_i|^2$ will give the probabilities of the different possible values a_i of A. This is the general principle of spectral decomposition.

If A and B are non-commutative operators $(AB \neq BA)$, which occurs when the quantities A and B are canonically conjugate, then the system of the ϕ_i does not coincide with the system of the χ_k and we have

$$\phi_j = \underset{k}{\Sigma} a_{jk}\, \chi_k, \quad \chi_k = \underset{j}{\Sigma} a_{kj}^{-1}\, \phi_j \qquad (5)$$

the a_{jk} and a_{kj}^{-1} not reducing to Kronecker's symbols δ_{jk}. The matrix of which the a_{jk} are the elements is a unitary matrix (complex orthogonal), that is (the asterisk indicates the complex conjugate quantity): $a_{jk}^* = a_{kj}^{-1}$.

We have, then,

$$\Psi = \sum_j c_j \ \phi_j = \sum_{jk} c_j \ a_{jk} \ \chi_k$$

and the principle of the spectral decomposition applied to the quantity B shows us that the probability of finding for B the value β_k is $|\sum_j c_j \ a_{jk}|^2$. In the pure state represented by the function Ψ, we have then

$$P_i = |c_i|^2 \qquad P_k = |\sum_j c_j \ a_{jk}|^2. \qquad (6)$$

The wave function Ψ being always normalized, these formulae give us the probabilities in absolute value.

But now suppose that we measure first A, then B. If the measure of A gives the value a_i, the function Ψ representing the state of the system after this measure will be $\Psi = \phi_i$ and formula (5) then shows that the probability of finding a second measure $B = \beta_k$ is $|a_{ik}|^2$. In the same way, if we have B first, then A, we would find for the probability of finding $A = a_i$ after having found $B = \beta_k$ the value $|a_{ki}^{-1}|^2 = |a_{ik}|^2$. Finally we can put

$$P_k^{(i)} = P_i^{(k)} = |a_{ik}|^2. \qquad (7)$$

We have then been able to define here, as in the usual statistics, the probabilities P_i, P_k, $P_k^{(i)}$ and $P_i^{(k)}$, but the essential point is that these quantities do not, in general, satisfy the relations (3) any longer. For example, we have in general

$$|\sum_j c_j \ a_{jk}|^2 \neq \sum_j |c_j|^2 |a_{jk}|^2 \qquad (8)$$

for the second member depends only on the moduli of the complex quantities c_j and a_{jk}, while the first member depends in general on the difference of their arguments (difference of phase). Physically, this signifies that the probability of the measure $B = \beta_k$ is not the same if we measure B directly on the initial state, or if we first measure A, then B. Mathematically, the reason why the relations (3) are not satisfied proceeds from the fact that in wave mechanics probabilities are expressed by the square of the moduli of the complex quantities.

It is easy to see that the relations (1) can no longer be satisfied because the quantities $P_i P_k^{(i)}$ and $P_k P_i^{(k)}$ are not equal; they would not be so, in fact, unless we had

$$|c_i|^2 = |\underset{j}{\Sigma}\, c_j\, a_{ji}|^2,$$

which cannot take place because the a_{ji}'s do not reduce to Kronecker's δ_{ji}'s. From this there follows the impossibility of defining the probabilities P_{ik} in the sense of the usual general scheme; even if we should come to find the P_{ik} satisfying the relations (2) the relations (1) would not be satisfied.

It is therefore impossible to introduce into quantal mechanics the probability P_{ik} of having at the same time $A = a_i$ and $B = \beta_k$. This is obviously connected with the impossibility postulated by the new mechanics of measuring simultaneously two non-commutative quantities, as are by hypothesis the quantities A and B. We can measure successively the two quantities, which permits us to define P_i, P_k, $P_k^{(i)}$ and $P_i^{(k)}$, but each measure of one of these quantities has an influence on the value of the other, which completely excludes the possibility of simultaneous measures and of defining the P_{ik}. As the classical formulation which permits the possibility of defining the P_{ik} and which includes the validity of the relations (1), (2) and (3), proceeds from the postulate of objectivity, as we have previously seen, it seems that wave mechanics abandons this postulate. We shall return later to this point.

Does the non-validity of equations (1), (2) and (3) imply that the theorem of compound probabilities is no longer exact in wave mechanics? The answer is in the negative, if at least we take care to express this theorem correctly. The impossibility of defining a quantity P_{ik} satisfying equation (1) does not indeed prevent the definition of a quantity $P_{i,k}$ which is the probability of obtaining by successive measures $A = a_i$ and $B = \beta_k$, at the same time as a quantity $P_{k,i}$ which is the probability of obtaining by successive measures $B = \beta_k$ and $A = a_i$. But as the measure of one quantity can influence the values of the other, we shall no longer have, in general, $P_{i,k} = P_{k,i}$ and we can no longer define $P_{i,k}$ as equal to the common value of $P_{i,k}$ and $P_{k,i}$. This will not prevent us setting down the formulae

$$P_{i,\,k} = P_i\, P_k^{(i)}, \qquad P_{k,\,i} = P_k\, P_i^{(k)} \qquad (9)$$

which express the theorem of compound probabilities. But

here, even more than in the classical formulation, it is necessary to insist on the fact that $P_i^{(k)}$, for example, is the probability of the value $B = \beta_k$ *when we know that* $A = a_i$, because to know that $A = a_i$ it is necessary to have made a measure of A and every measure of A can influence the value of B.

We are, besides, still able here to define the probability $P_k^{(A)}$ of finding $B = \beta_k$ after having found for A any one of the values a_i as well as the probability $P_i^{(B)}$ of finding $A = a_i$ after having found for B any one of the values β_k. In conformity with the theorem of total probabilities, we shall write

$$P_k^{(A)} = \sum_i P_{i,\,k} = \sum_i P_i\, P_k^{(i)}, \qquad P_i^{(B)} = \sum_k P_{k,\,i} = \sum_k P_k\, P_i^{(k)}$$

formulae which replace formulae (3) and in which it must be noted that in general we have neither $P_k^{(A)} = P_k$ nor $P_i^{(B)} = P_i$.

The non-validity of equations (3) resulting from the inequality (8) is due to the intervention of the arguments or phases of the complex quantities. We say that (8) expresses the "interference of probabilities" and this is one of the most fundamental results of wave mechanics. In fact, it is this interference of probabilities which is explained physically by the existence of the phenomena of interference for light and for corpuscles (diffraction of electrons, for example); we shall show this further on in studying the experiment of Wiener's fringes. But let us note henceforth that the interference of probabilities is demonstrated in an unexceptionable manner by numerous and precise verifications of the theory of interferences in physical optics and in wave mechanics of particles.

We have explained the statistical formulation of wave mechanics in the example of discontinuous probabilities. It is easy to extend the formulation to continuous probabilities by introducing the probability densities. Let us show this by the very simple example of a corpuscle constrained to be displaced, in the absence of any field, in a straight line taken as axis of q. Here we have to consider two canonically conjugate aleatory variables; the variable $U = q$ and the variable $V = p$, p being the momentum along the axis of q. The operator $P = -h/2\pi i \dfrac{\delta}{\delta q}$ admits as appropriate values every real value of p and to any given real value of p there corresponds as an appropriate function the plane wave $e - \dfrac{2\pi i}{h} pq$ which, suitably normalized, will be denoted by $a(p, q)$. It can be easily shown that

$$\int_{-\infty}^{+\infty} \phi(p, q) \, \phi(p, q_0) \, dp = \delta(q - q_0) \qquad (10)$$

$\delta(q - q_0)$ being Dirac's singular function which generalizes in the case of the continuum Kronecker's discontinuous symbol δ_{ik} (equal to 0 if $i \neq k$ and to 1 if $i = k$). On the other hand, the operator Q = multiplication by q, admits as appropriate values every real value $Q = q_0$, and to q_0 corresponds as an appropriate function exactly Dirac's singular function $\delta(q - q_0)$.

If $\Psi(q)$ is the function of the wave of the corpuscle supposed well known (the clear case in von Neumann's sense), we shall be able to develop it in the forms

$$\Psi(q) = \int_{-\infty}^{+\infty} c(p) \, \phi(p, q) \, dp = \int_{-\infty}^{+\infty} \Psi(q_0) \, \delta(q - q_0) \, dq_0$$

the first expression being a Fourier integral and the second resulting immediately from the properties of Dirac's singular function. In accordance with the fundamental principles of wave mechanics the probability densities relative to the aleatory variables Q and P when the corpuscle is in the state described by $\Psi(q)$ are then

$$\rho(u) = \rho(q) = |\Psi(q)|^2 \qquad \rho(v) = \rho(p) = |c(p)|^2 \qquad (11)$$

We can, as in the classical scheme, introduce the joint probabilities $P(u|v) = P(q|p)$ and $P(v|u) = P(p|q)$; formula (11) and the obvious formula

$$\phi(p, q) = \int_{-\infty}^{+\infty} \phi(p, q_0) \, \delta(q - q_0) \, dq_0$$

easily show that

$$P(q|p) = P(p|q) = |\phi(p, q)|^2 = C. \qquad (12)$$

But the quantities $\rho(q)$, $\rho(p)$, $P(p|q)$ and $P(q|p)$ defined by (11) and (12) do not satisfy the relations (3') of the classical scheme. The two quantities

$$\rho^{(P)}(q) = \int_{-\infty}^{+\infty} \rho(p) \, P(p|q) \, dp = C \int_{-\infty}^{+\infty} |c(p)|^2 \, dp = C$$

$$\rho^{(Q)}(p) = \int_{-\infty}^{+\infty} \rho(q) \, P(q|p) \, dq = C \int_{-\infty}^{+\infty} |\Psi(q)|^2 \, dq = C$$

are constants and equal to each other, but they are not equal to $\rho(q)$ and $\rho(p)$ respectively as the classical scheme would require.

Further, the expressions $\rho(q) P(q|p) = C |\Psi(q)|^2$ and $\rho(p) \, P(p|q) = C |\Psi(p)|^2$ not having the same value, equations (1) do not allow us to define a density $\rho(q, p)$.

We can, however, see if there does not exist a function $\rho(q, p)$ satisfying equations (2′). In fact this function exists. Bass, recapitulating a result of Wigner, has given it the following form:

$$\rho(q, p) = \frac{2}{h} \int_{-\infty}^{+\infty} e^{-\frac{4\pi i}{h} z} \Psi(q-z) \Psi^*(q+z) \, dz \quad (13)$$

This function satisfies the relations (2′) with the forms (11) of $\rho(q)$ and of $\rho(p)$. But, if we introduce the definition (13) into the formulae (1′), we should find for $P(q|p)$ and $P(p|q)$ the following values:

$$P(p|q) = \frac{\rho(q, p)}{|c(p)|^2} \qquad P(q|p) = \frac{\rho(q, p)}{|\Psi(q)|^2}$$

which differ from each other and do not coincide with the values (12) which the principles of wave mechanics impose. It is, therefore, impossible to find a density $\rho(q, p)$ satisfying the whole of the conditions (1′), (2′) and (3′) of the classical scheme and this non-existence of the density $\rho(q, p)$ corresponds to the impossibility of measuring simultaneously the non-commutative quantities q and p.

As we have recalled at the beginning of this study, the general formulae (1), (2), (3) or (1′), (2′), (3′) of mathematical statistics are based on the more or less clearly explicit postulate, that the physical entities on which statistics rests possess objective characteristics independent of the operations effected in establishing them. It is because this postulate is not valid for corpuscles or systems of microphysics that the concepts and the formulae of the usual statistics are not applicable to them. It is amusing and instructive to imagine the nature of a pack of cards of which the pack was endowed with statistical properties analogous to those which we meet in microphysics.

Let us consider for this latter a 32-card pack. To each card is attached the value of two aleatory variables; the colour U being able to assume the values heart (1), spade (2), club (3) and diamond (4), and the rank V being able to take the values ace (1), king (2), queen (3). . . . We shall suppose that, to establish the colour and rank of a card, two distinct operations which can never be carried out simultaneously are necessary. We shall also suppose that, as for an ordinary 32-card game the probabilities P_i and P_k of the values u_i and v_k are respectively equal to $1/4$ and $1/8$. But the most characteristic property that we shall attribute to our pack of cards and which will render it analogous to a system of microphysics will be the following; the fact of establishing the colour of a card can influence its rank and inversely. Such a hypothesis would obviously be absurd for a pack of ordinary cards because ordinary cards are macroscopic objects endowed with objective properties, but the corpuscles of the atomic scale behave almost as do the playing cards which we imagine.

For our paradoxical pack of cards we can define the P_i's, the P_k's and even the $P_k^{(i)}$'s and the $P_i^{(k)}$'s, but the P_{ik}'s will not exist and in general we shall not have $P_i P_k^{(i)} = P_k P_i^{(k)}$. To be more precise let us suppose for example that the fact of verifying that a card is "hearts" automatically implies that the subsequent verification of the rank gives the value "king" with probability $1/4$ or the value "queen" with probability $3/4$, and let us further suppose that the fact of verifying that the card is a king automatically implies that the subsequent verification of the colour gives the value "spades" with the probability $1/3$ and the value "clubs" with the probability $2/3$. We then postulate that $P_k^{(i)}$ is equal to $1/4$ for $k=2$, to $3/4$ for $k=3$ and to 0 for the other values of k, and that $P_i^{(k)}$ is equal to $1/3$

for $i=2$, to $2/3$ for $i=3$ and to 0 for $i=1$ and 4. The other $P_i^{(k)}$'s and $P_k^{(i)}$'s have values which we do not know. Then the probability of finding hearts and king in noting first the colour, then the rank, will be $\frac{1}{4} \cdot \frac{1}{4} = \frac{1}{16}$, whilst the probability of finding king and heart in verifying first the rank then the colour will be $\frac{1}{8} \cdot 0 = 0$. Moreover, the probability of verifying "king" after having verified "hearts" will not be equal to the probability of directly verifying "king" which we suppose always equal to $\frac{1}{8}$. The relations (1) and (3) therefore, are not satisfied.

Let us further remark that if, after having made the second verification, we should wish to repeat the first, we should not in general obtain the same result. Thus, in the example developed earlier, after having successively verified that the card is a heart and a king, we should not be able to say that it is a king of hearts since a new verification of the colour would give "spades" or "clubs". This circumstance is again entirely analogous to those which we meet in microphysics.

It is interesting to note carefully the fact that, in the pack of cards with the strange properties which we have imagined, the cards lose, at least partially, the characteristics of objectivity which they possess in the usual packs. In these latter the cards have well-defined objective characteristics; one of these, for example, being that king and hearts is a king of hearts. It is this which permits us to define the probabilities and to write down the relations (1), (2), (3). On the contrary, in our pack of "microphysics" cards the cards have no longer objective characteristics; none of them is *a priori* a king of hearts and even, if we have successively verified one of them as "hearts" and "king", we cannot say that this would be a king of hearts. This is why the $P_{(ik)}$'s no longer exist here, and if we can still define the P_i's, P_k's $P_i^{(k)}$'s and $P_k^{(i)}$'s and use the theorem of compound probabilities, we can no longer write down the relations (1) and (3). And yet our playing cards, although deprived of objective characteristics, nevertheless *exist*.

It is the same in microphysics. The corpuscles of the atomic scale exist, the physicists admit this and from this point of view remain realistic in the philosophical sense of the term; but these corpuscles have no objective characteristics, which we can attribute to them at certain times depending on the operations which we perform to verify them (measurements) and on the order in which they are effected.

The example of the "microphysics" pack of cards is instructive, but it does not offer a complete analogy with the case of systems of microphysics. Indeed, for these the probabilities are expressed by the square of the modulus of a complex quantity, and it is this which gives rise to the intervention of the interference of probabilities. This essential characteristic of the probabilities of the quantal theory does not appear explicitly in the example of the pack of cards.

To conclude, we shall show by a simple physical example how the interference of probabilities explains the existence of what is called, in experimental physics, the phenomena of interference. We shall consider the experiment of Wiener's fringes which are produced in the neighbourhood of a mirror and we shall imagine that the incident wave falls normally on the mirror, the case of oblique incidence not involving any essential complication.

The incident wave of the form $ae^{2\pi i v t} e^{-2\pi i x/\lambda}$ is totally reflected by the mirror, and the reflected wave of the form $ae^{2\pi i v t} e^{2\pi i x/\lambda}$ is superposed on the incident wave. The formulae are applicable to the reflection of light by a mirror as well as to the reflection of a beam of corpuscles (electrons). The only difference is that the relation between λ and v is not the same in the two cases, but this is of little consequence here.

If we denote by V the total volume occupied by the incident wave and the superposed reflected wave, the first will be represented by the function of the *normalized* wave

$$\Psi_1 = \frac{1}{\sqrt{V}} e^{2\pi i v t} e^{-2\pi i x/\lambda}$$

and the second by the function of the normal wave

$$\Psi_2 = \frac{1}{\sqrt{V}} e^{2\pi i v t} e^{2\pi i x/\lambda}$$

which will be the two appropriate functions of the operator

$p_x = -\dfrac{h}{2\pi i} \dfrac{\partial}{\partial \chi}$ corresponding to the particular values $\pm\dfrac{h}{\lambda}$. In the vicinity of the mirror the total wave Ψ formed by the super-position of Ψ_1 and Ψ_2 will be*

$$\Psi = c_1\Psi_1 + c_2\Psi_2 = \sqrt{\frac{1}{2}}\left[\frac{1}{\sqrt{V}}\ e^{2\pi i v t}\ e^{-2\pi i x/\lambda} + \frac{e^{i\phi}}{\sqrt{V}}\ e^{2\pi i v t}\ e^{2\pi i x/\lambda}\right]$$

the factor $\dfrac{1}{\sqrt{2}}$ being a factor of normalization such that the integral of $|\Psi|^2$ in the volume V will be equal to 1.

Let us consider the two aleatory variables $U=x$ and $V=p_x$ giving the position and the component x of the momentum associated with the wave Ψ. The quantity V can take only the two values $\pm\dfrac{h}{\lambda}$, while U can take all the values x_k corresponding to all the positions of the corpuscles on the left of the mirror. The principles of wave mechanics immediately give

$$P_i = |c_i|^2 = \tfrac{1}{2} \quad \text{for} \quad i=1, 2$$

$$P_k = |\Psi|^2 = \frac{1}{V}\ \left[1 + \cos\left(4\,\pi x_k/\lambda + \phi\right)\right]$$

The first expression signifies that if we make an experiment allowing us to attribute a momentum to a corpuscle, we would have an equal probability of finding it directed towards the mirror or directed in the reverse sense.

Concerning the expression of P_k, it shows the existence in the vicinity of the mirror of a periodic variation of the probability of the presence of a corpuscle, this being zero for the abscissae x_k such that the cosine is equal to -1, and maximum for the abscissae x_k such that the cosine is equal to 1. This variation, which is a consequence of the difference of the phases between the incident and the reflected wave, results from the interference of probabilities and is physically explained by Wiener's fringes in the vicinity of the mirror.

If the two beams in the sense of inverse propagation which are superposed at the left of the mirror were unconnected, the probability of the presence of a corpuscle in this region would be

---

* ϕ is the difference of phase introduced by reflection on the mirror.

$|\Psi_1|^2+|\Psi_2|^2$ instead of $|\Psi_1+\Psi_2|^2$ and we would find $P_k=\mathrm{I}/V$; there would then be no interferences of probabilities, nor in consequence Wiener's fringes.

We shall conclude by drawing the attention of specialists in the Calculus of Probabilities to the necessity of basing this science on postulates sufficiently wide for it to be able to contain the statistical laws of microphysics, statistical laws which we can regard as resting on very assured experimental bases.

INDEX

283